MENSA

PRESENTS

MIGHTY MINDBENDERS

THIS IS A CARLTON BOOK

Specially produced in 1998 for
The Book People Ltd, Hall Wood Avenue, Haydock St Helens WA11 9UL
in association with Carlton Books Ltd,
20 St Anne's Court, Wardour Street, London W1V 3AW

A CIP catalogue for this book is available from the British Library

ISBN 1-85613-397-4

Printed and bound in Great Britain

MENSA
PRESENTS
MIGHTY MINDBENDERS

John Bremner & Carolyn Skitt

TED SMART

CONTENTS

FOREWORD

Most people are content to go through life with their brain ticking over at a mere fraction of its true capacity. This book is not for them. Our intention is to present a mind workout that will bend, stretch, and squeeze your mental powers to the very limit.

We start with some I.Q. development tests. Everyone has some level of intelligence. It is formed very early in life and then becomes fixed so that you will never exceed that level. However, just as you can develop your muscles with exercise, you can make the most of your mental powers by using them to perform increasingly difficult tasks. The puzzles in this section start off easy but rapidly become more challenging.

The second section of the book is concerned with quite another type of intelligence. Solving the mind-bending mazes we have created will take quite different skills, and will help to develop a whole area of mental power you did not know you possessed. We have taken traditional patterns from all over the world and turned them into labyrinths of fiendish complexity. If you can figure these out, you need never get lost in a strange town again!

If you like puzzles or are curious about your real I.Q., why not contact Mensa? We can arrange a proper test which will tell you your true I.Q. score. Mensa is an international high I.Q. society with over 100,000 members world-wide. The biggest national Mensa societies are to be found in the US and Great Britain. It is a society where people from every walk of life, every race, every creed, and every political viewpoint can meet in friendship.

Whatever your score in these tests it is a good idea to find out your true I.Q. After all, we measure our bodies, so why not our minds? To contact Mensa, write to American Mensa Limited, 2626 E 14th Street, Brooklyn, New York 11235-3992.

R. P. Allen

Robert Allen,
Editorial Director, Mensa Publications (UK).

INTRODUCTION

These I.Q. tests are supposed to be fun as well as a challenge. They begin on an easy plane but gradually rise to a more difficult one. The tests measure speed and accuracy of thought, and should be regarded as a form of mental jogging. Many people take physical exercise but not so many mental exercise. Now is your chance.

TO THE I.Q. TESTS

We have put together this series of puzzles for your amusement. In each of the tests the correct answer is to be found in one of the shapes. Proceed through each test as quickly as possible and first answer those questions you find easiest. Then return to the more difficult ones. Check your answers, when the time is up, total the correct answers and then find your fun I.Q. score from the table.

TEST 1

1 Which of the numbers should replace the question mark?

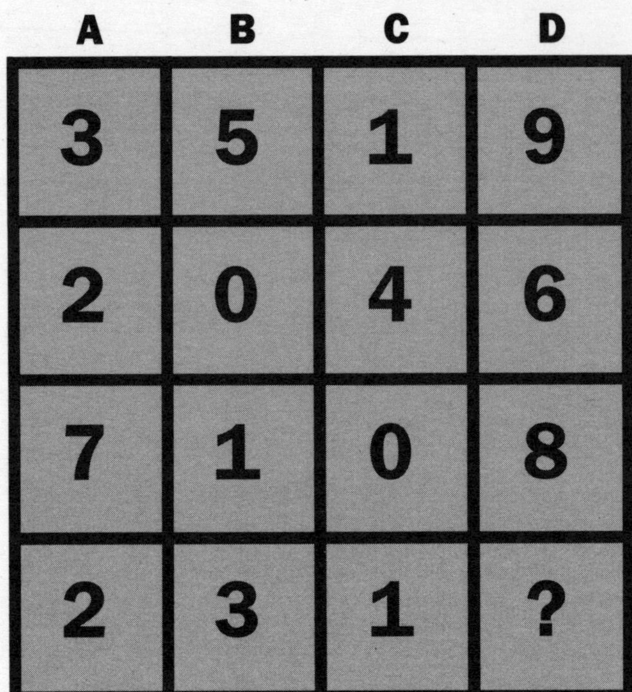

A	B	C	D
3	5	1	9
2	0	4	6
7	1	0	8
2	3	1	?

8 A　2 B

9 C　1 D

4 E　6 F

2 Each same symbol has a value. Work out the logic and discover what should replace the question mark.

Z	Z	Ψ	Ω	?
Ξ	Ξ	Ξ	Ξ	8
Ψ	Z	Ψ	Ω	16
Ψ	Z	Ψ	Ξ	13
13	11	14	14	

6 A　12 B　7 C

15 D　10 E　9 F

TEST 1 time limit 20 minutes

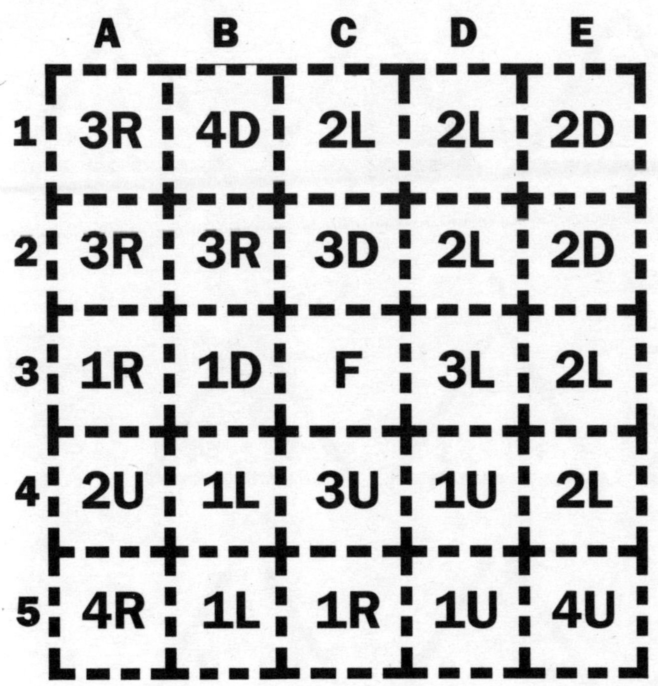

3 Here is an unusual safe. Each of the buttons must be pressed only once in the correct order to open it. The last button is marked F. The number of moves and the direction is marked on each button. Thus 1U would mean one move up, while 1L would mean one move to the left. Using the grid reference, which button is the first you must press?

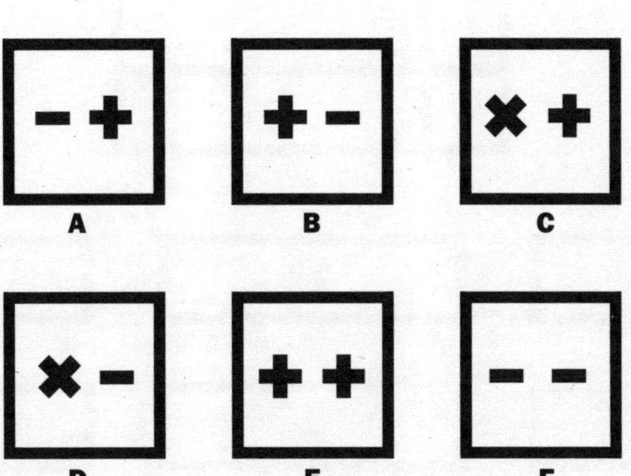

4 Insert the correct mathematical signs between each number in order to resolve the equation. What are the signs?

TEST 1 time limit 20 minutes

TEST 1

5 Which triangle continues this series?

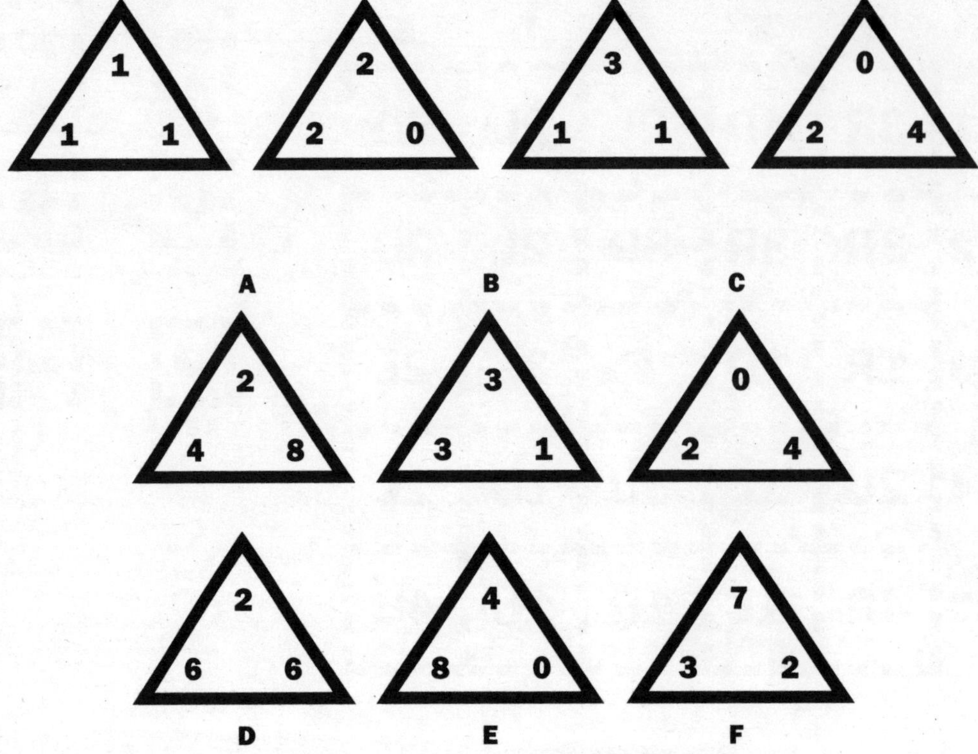

6 Discover the connection between the letters and the numbers. Which number should replace the question mark?

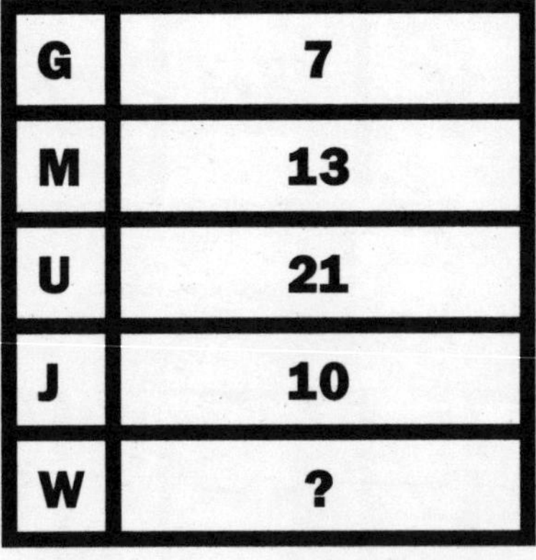

G	7
M	13
U	21
J	10
W	?

14	23	9
A	B	C
26	**2**	**11**
D	E	F

TEST 1 time limit 20 minutes

7 Which of the constructed boxes cannot be made from the pattern?

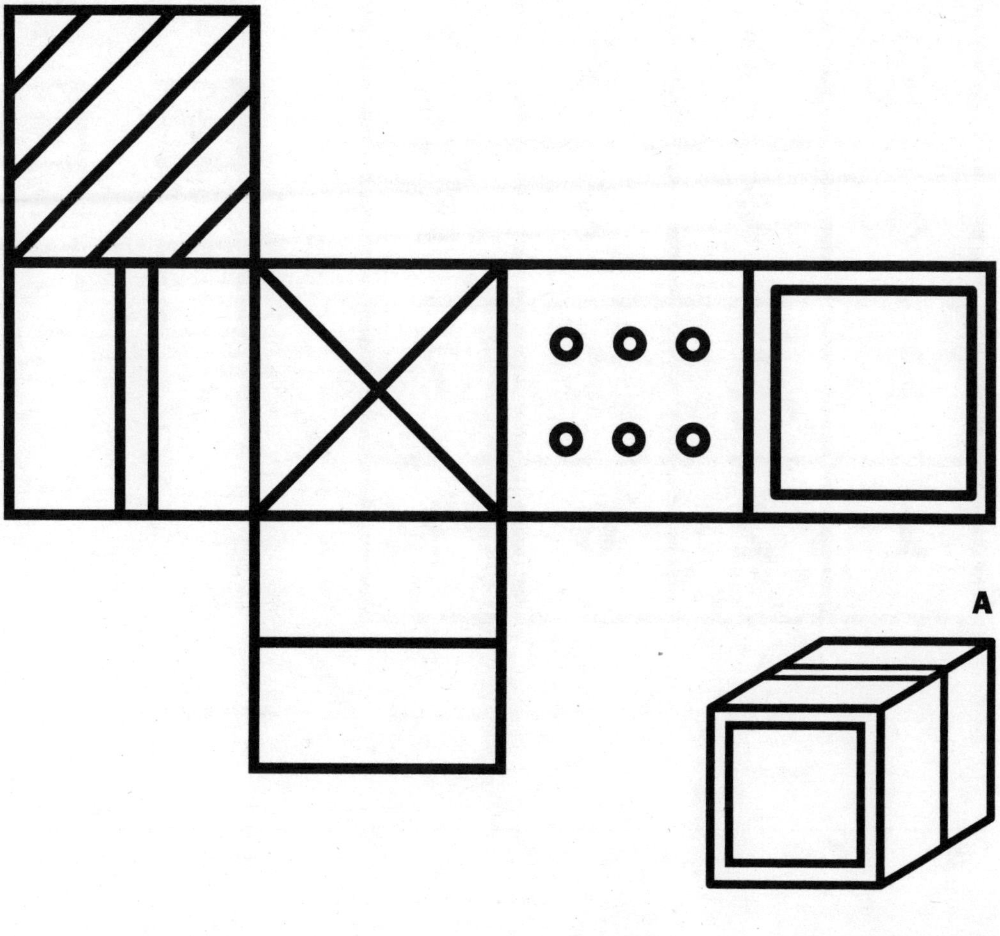

A

B

C

D

E

F

15

TEST 1 time limit 20 minutes

TEST 1

8 Which of the numbers should replace the question mark?

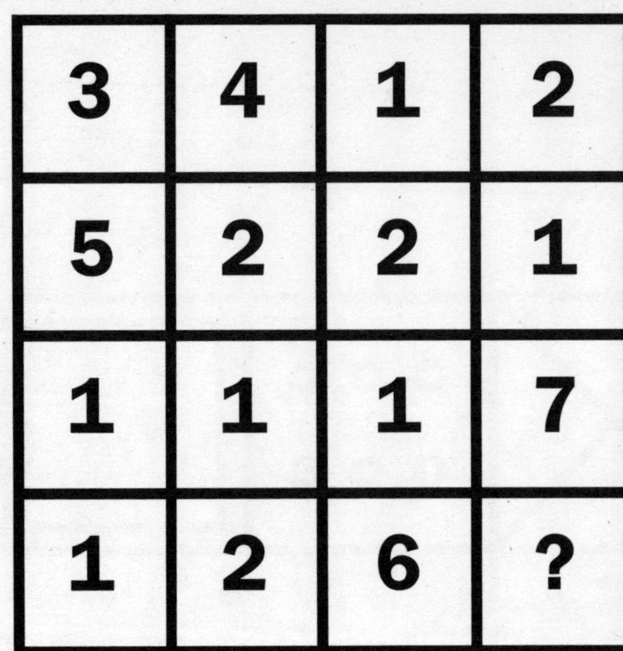

3	4	1	2
5	2	2	1
1	1	1	7
1	2	6	?

A 3　B 5
C 1　D 6
E 2　F 4

9 Which of the clocks continues this series?

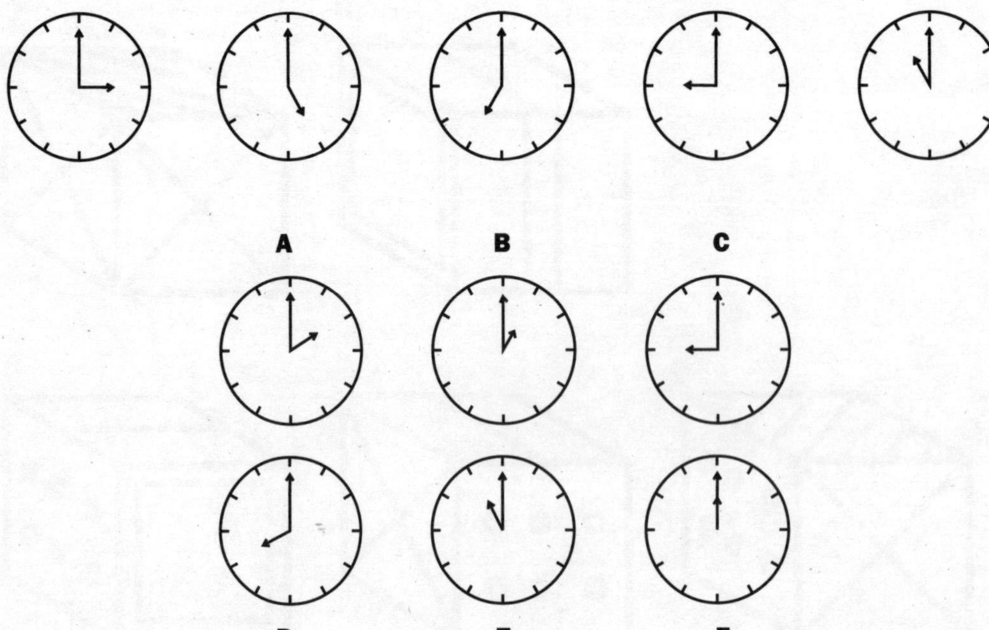

TEST 1 time limit 20 minutes

A	B
2	5

C	D
7	6

E	F
4	9

10 When rearranged the shapes will give a number. Which of the numbers is it?

4	2	4	2	4
2	4	4	4	2
4	4	2	2	4
2	4	2	4	2
2	4	2	2	2

A	B	C	D	E	F
36	16	18	45	29	32

11 Move from ring to touching ring, starting from the bottom left corner and finishing in the top right corner. Collect nine numbers and total them. Which is the highest possible total?

TEST 1 time limit 20 minutes

TEST 1

12 This square follows a logical pattern. Which of the tiles should be used to complete the square?

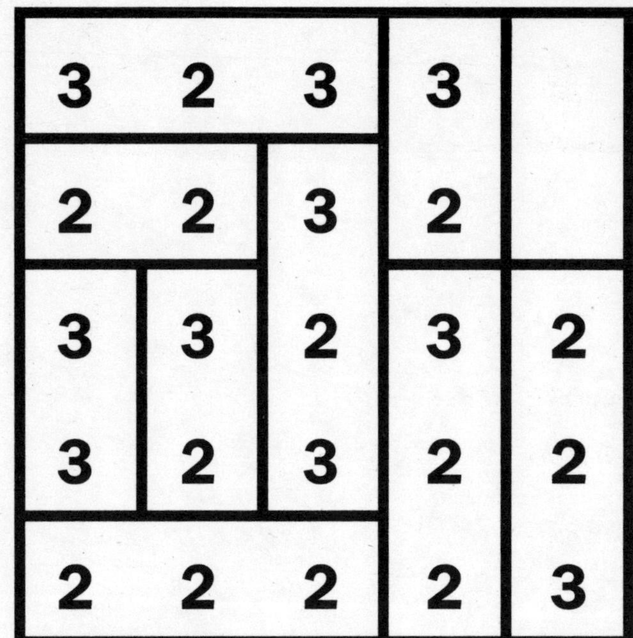

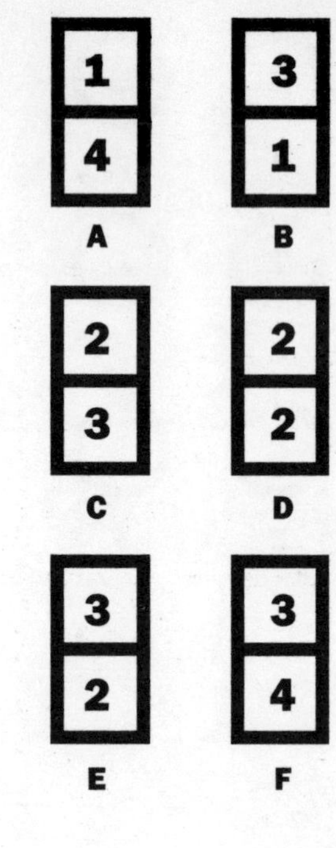

13 Which of the slices should be used to complete the cake?

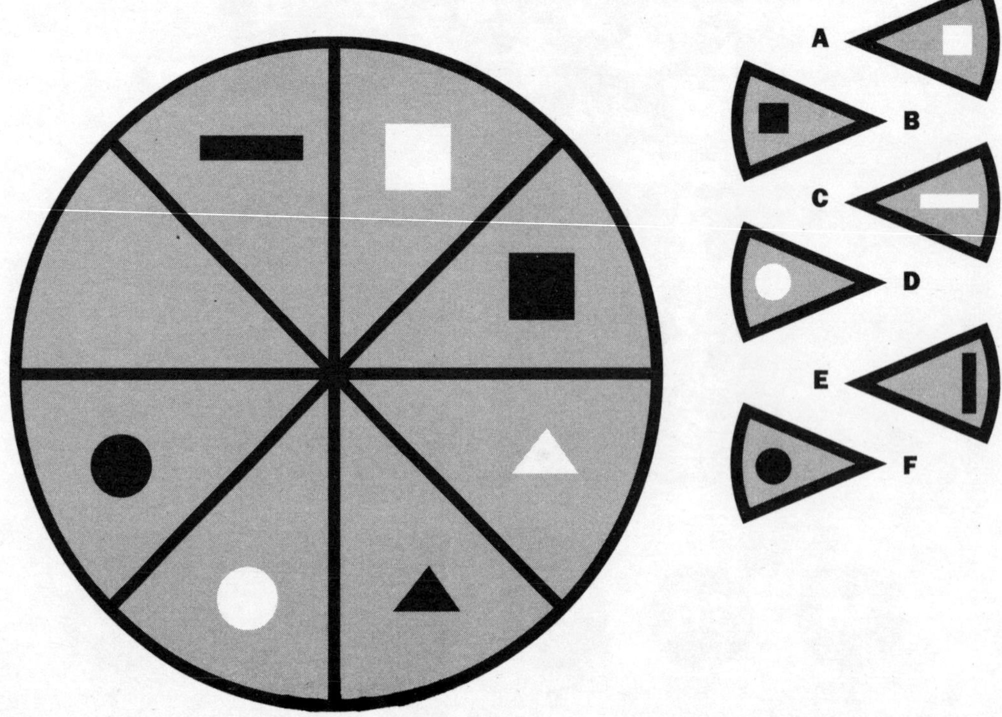

TEST 1 time limit 20 minutes

5	2		2	5
1		?		1
5	8	4		3
	2	2	2	8
3	2	2	10	3

A	B	C	D	E	F
4	1	3	6	5	2

14 Each straight line of five numbers should total 20. Which of the numbers will replace the question mark?

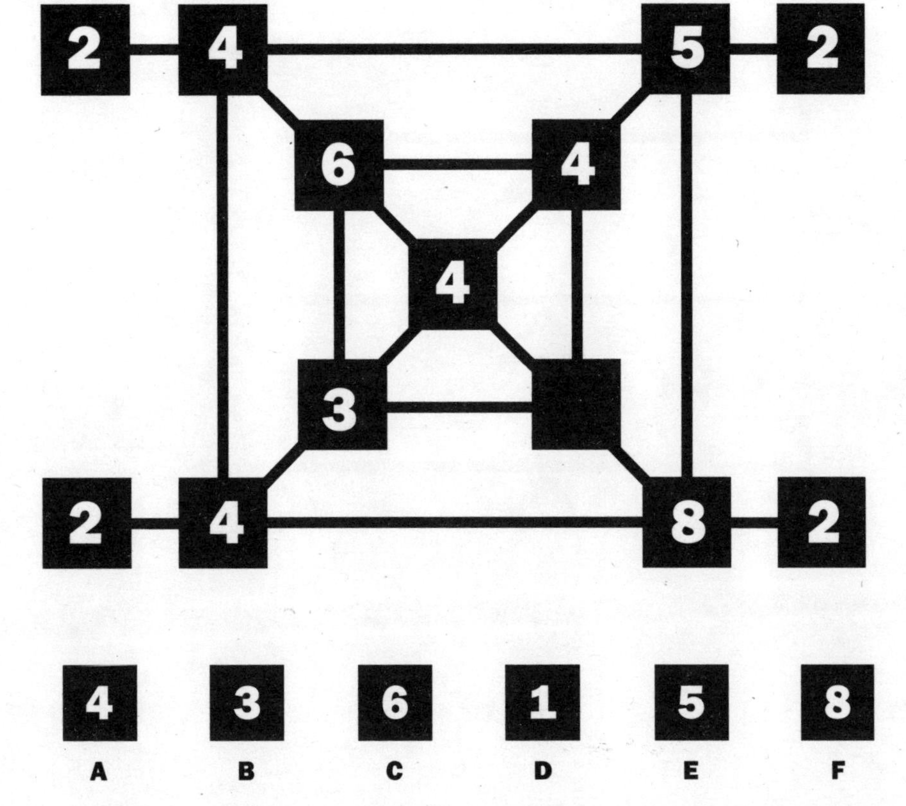

15 Start at any corner and follow the lines. Collect another four numbers and total the five. One of the numbers in the squares below can be used to complete the diagram. If the correct one has been chosen, one of the routes involving it will give a total of 28. Which one is it?

TEST 1 time limit 20 minutes

TEST 2

1 Which of the boxes should be used to replace the question mark?

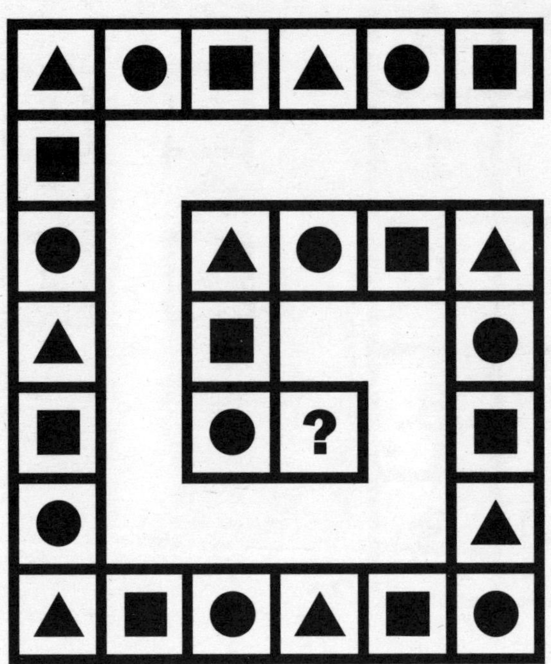

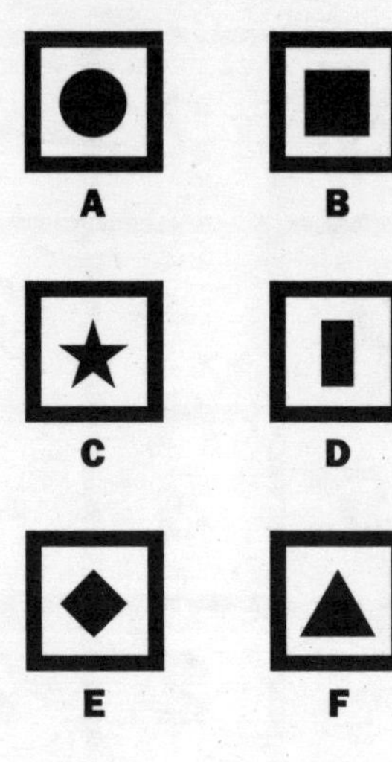

2 Scales one and two are in perfect balance. Which of these pans should replace the empty one?

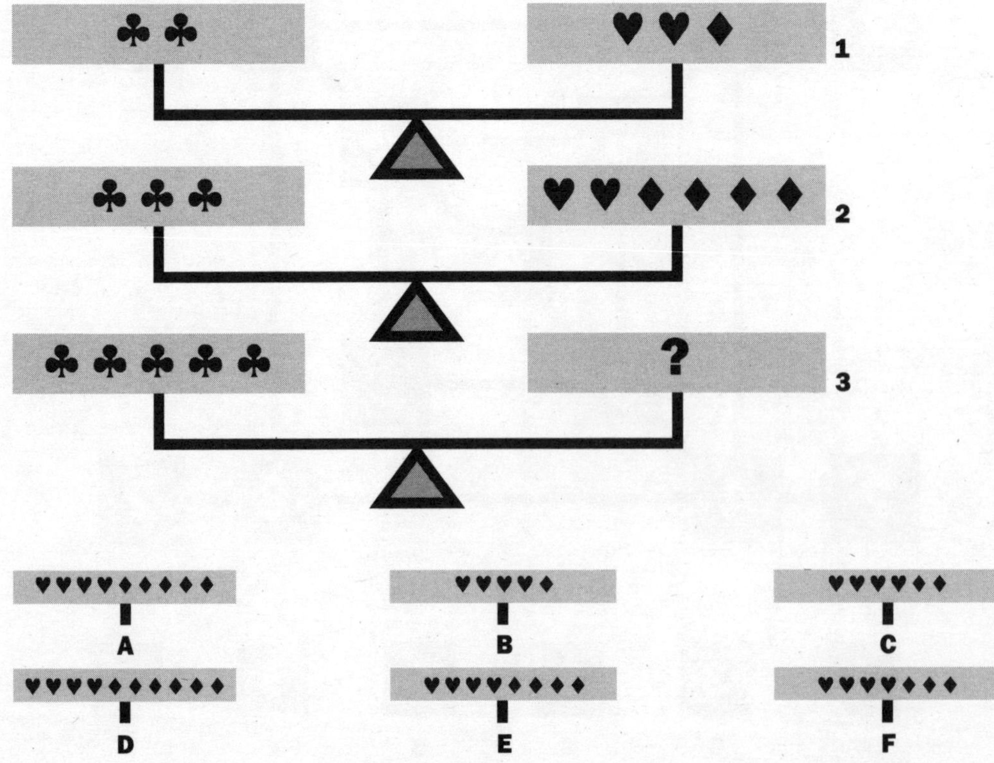

TEST 2 time limit 20 minutes

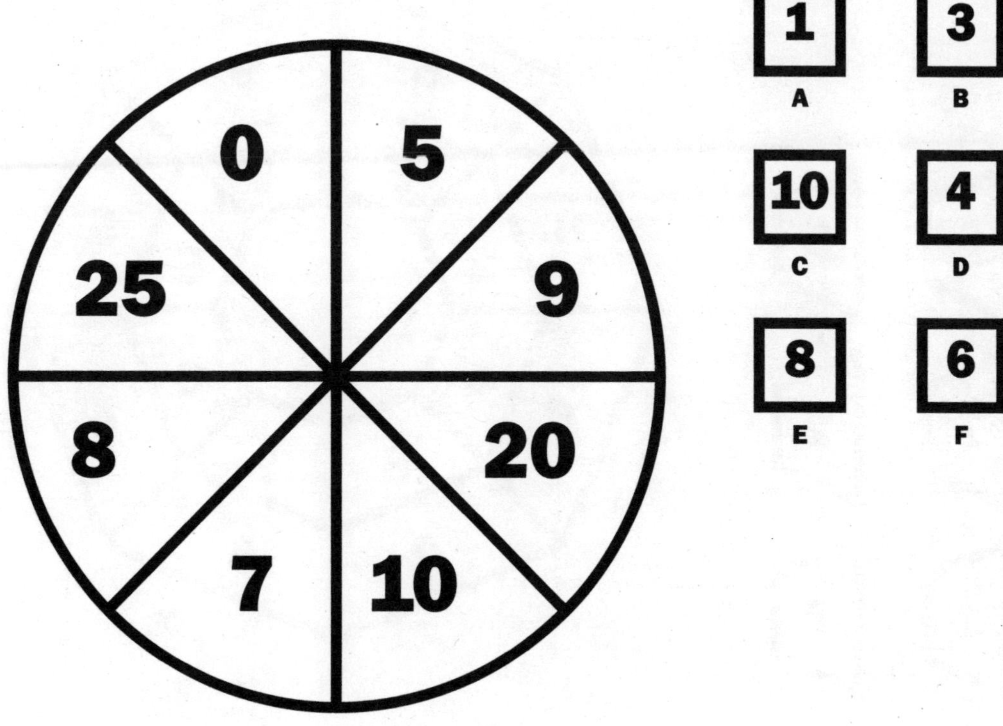

3 How many ways are there to score 25 on this dartboard using three darts only? Each dart always lands in a sector and no dart falls to the floor.

	A	B	C	D
1	A A B	A B C	D D D	D C A
2	B A D	A A A	C C D	B B B
3	B C C	B B A	C C C	A B D
4	C D D	A C D	D C B	B B C

A3 A	B2 B
D4 C	C2 D
B4 E	A1 F

4 Which square's contents matches D1?

TEST 2 time limit 20 minutes

TEST 2

5 Which of the numbers should logically replace the question mark in the octagon?

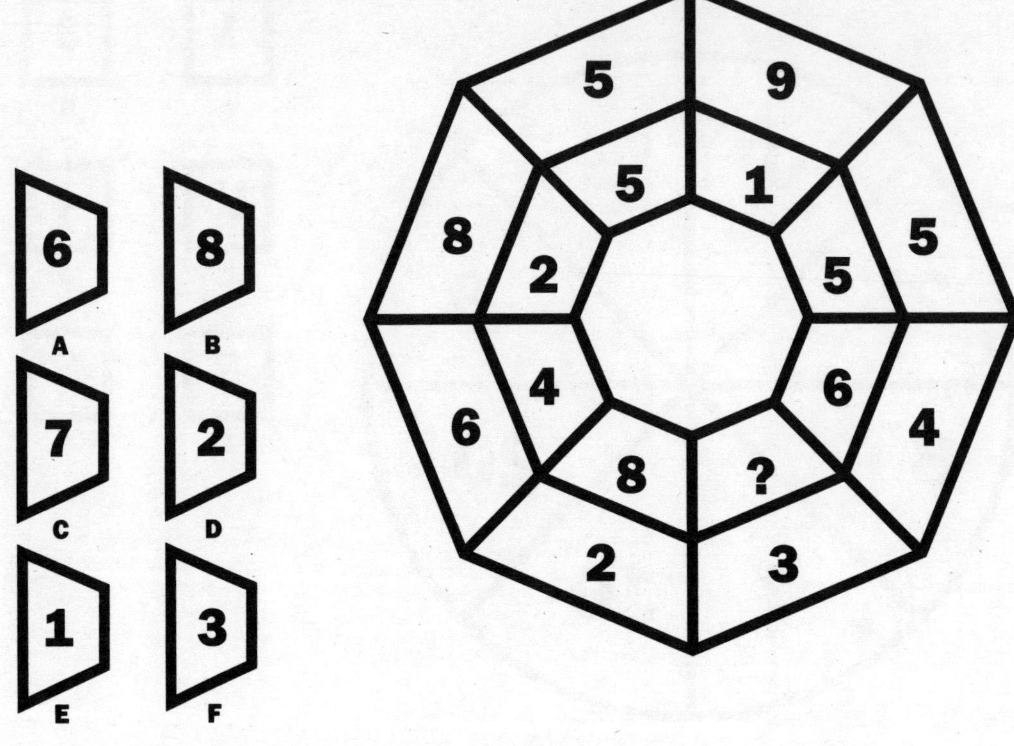

6 Which number is missing from this series?

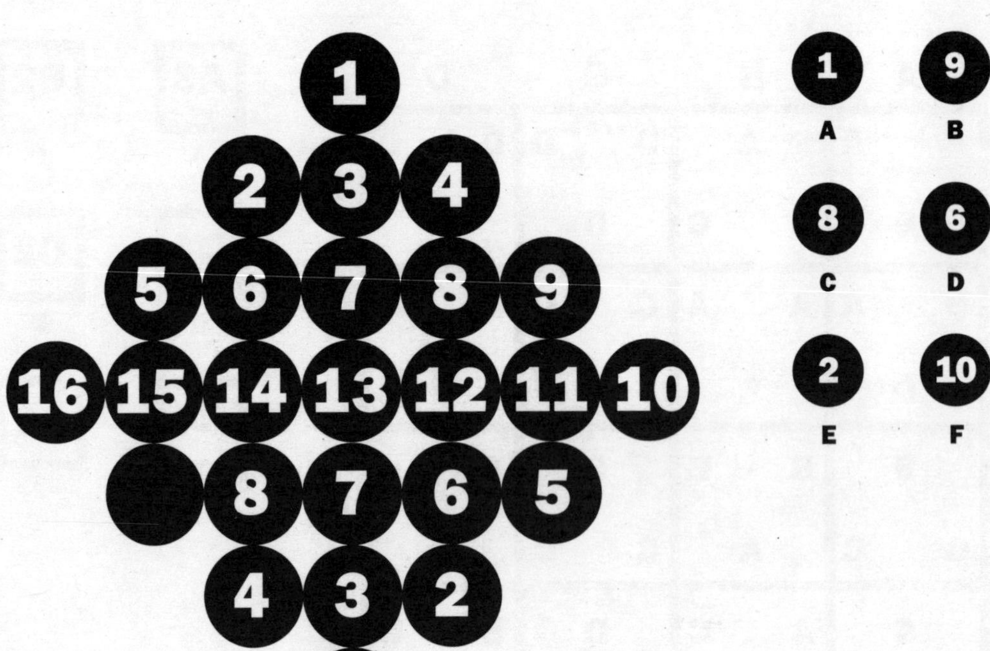

TEST 2 time limit 20 minutes

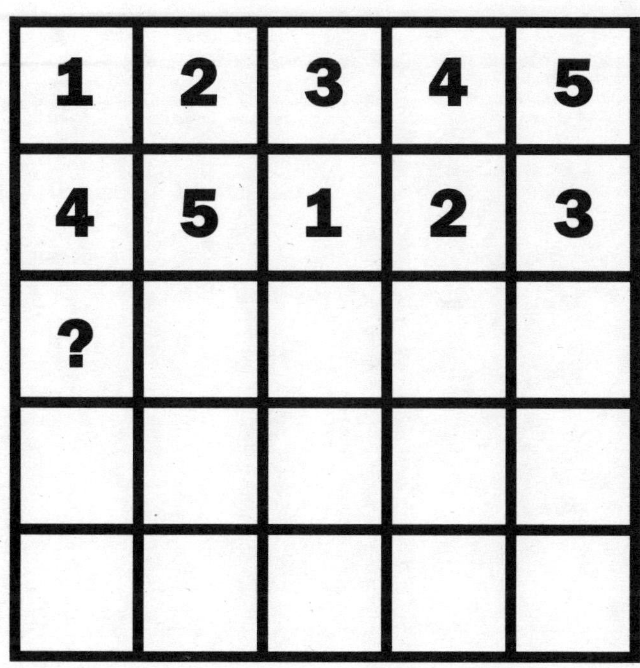

1	2	3	4	5
4	5	1	2	3
?				

A: 1 B: 5

C: 2 D: 3

E: 4

7 Complete the square using the five numbers shown. When completed no row, column or diagonal line will use the same number more than once. What should replace the question mark?

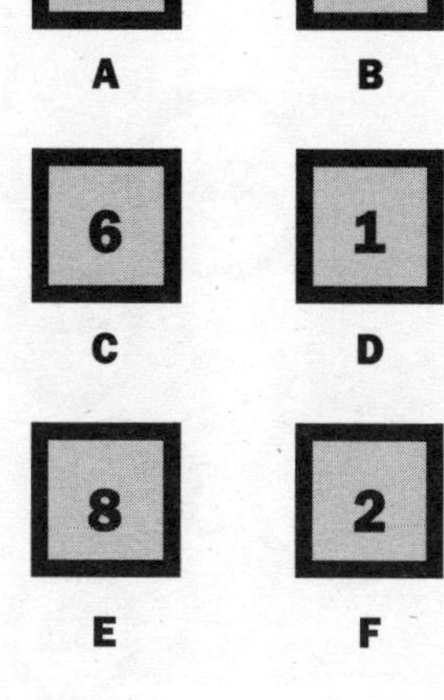

6	3	1	4	9
5	1	0	2	8
1	2	1	2	?

8 Which of the numbers should replace the question mark?

TEST 2 time limit 20 minutes

TEST 2

9 Start at 1 and move from circle to touching circle. Collect four numbers each time. How many different routes are there to collect 11? A reversed route counts twice.

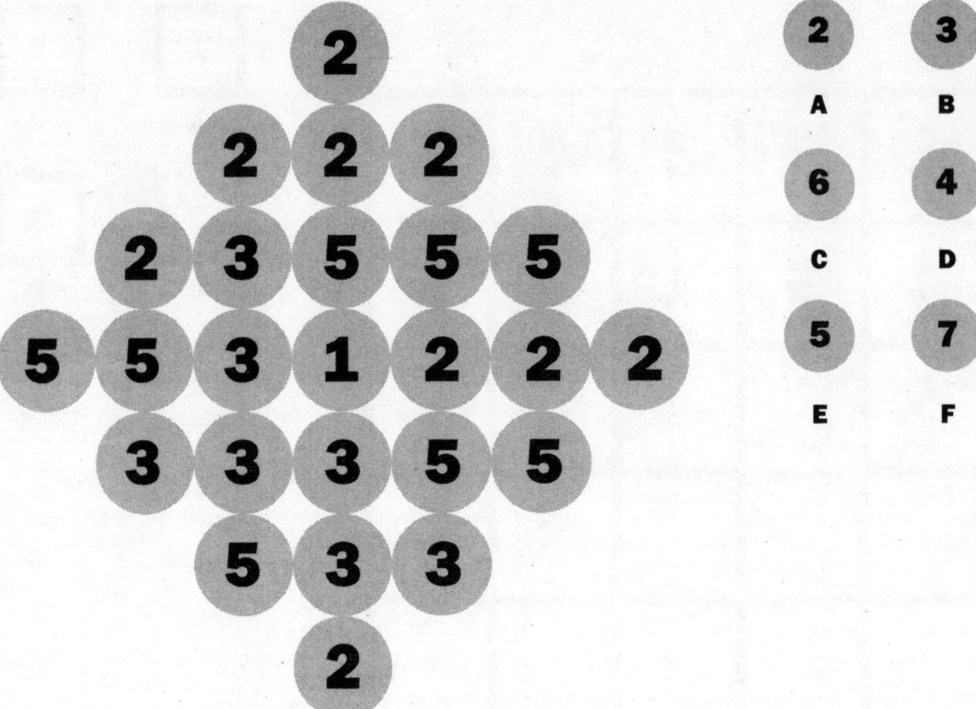

10 Here is an unusual safe. Each of the buttons must be pressed only once in the correct order to open it. The last button is marked F. The number of moves and the direction is marked on each button. Thus 1i would mean one move in, whilst 1o would mean one move out. 1c would mean one move clockwise and 1a would mean one move anti-clockwise. Which button is the first you must press?

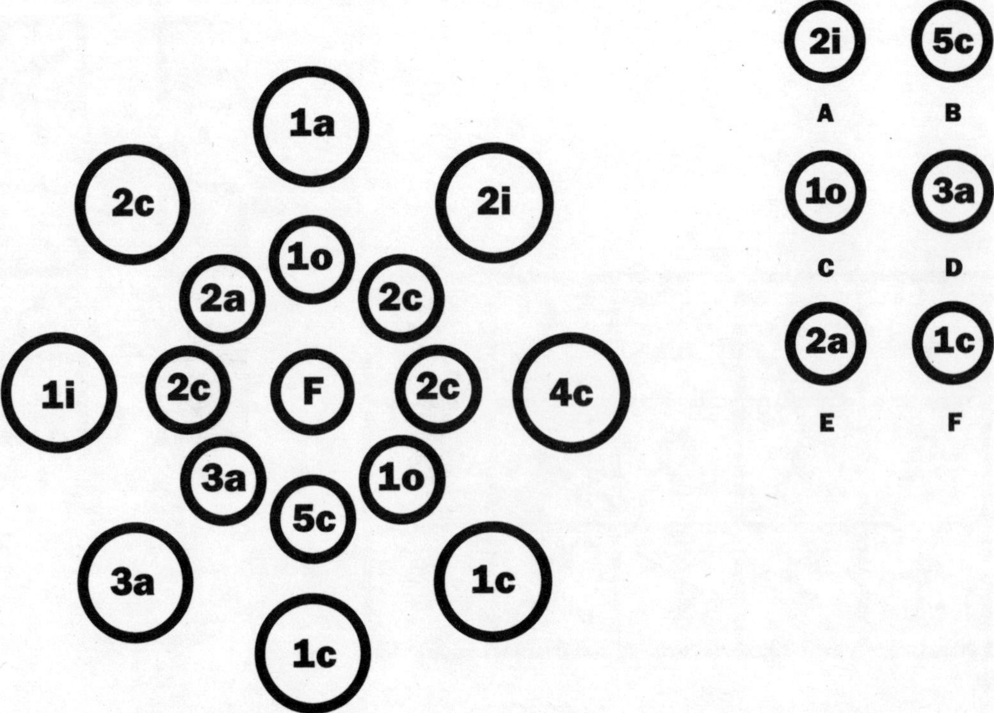

TEST 2 time limit 20 minutes

TEST 2

11 Which of the numbers should replace the question mark?

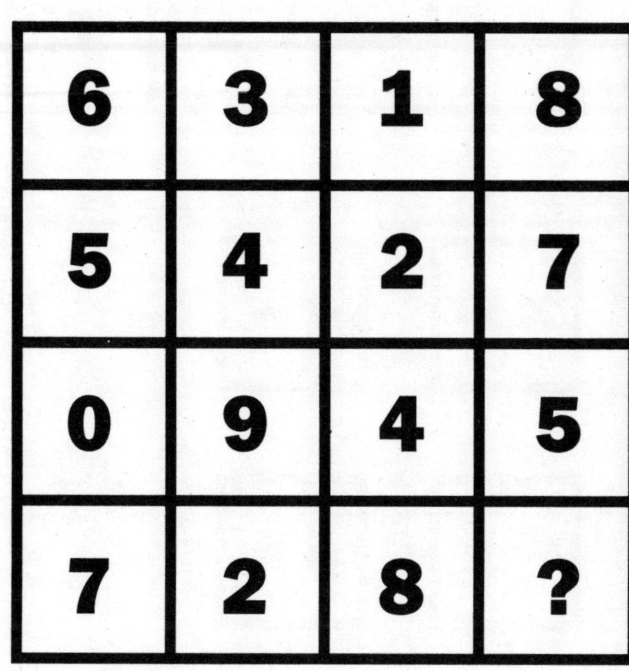

6	3
A	B
2	4
C	D
1	5
E	F

12 Which triangle continues this series?

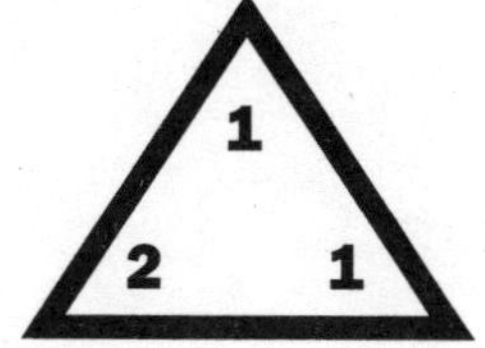

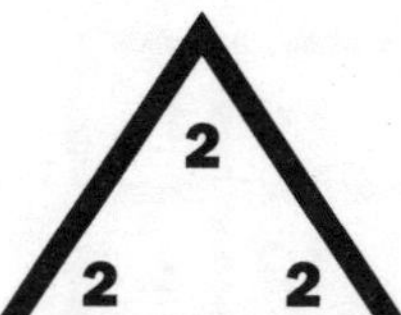

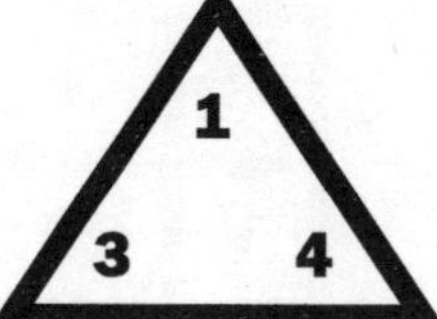

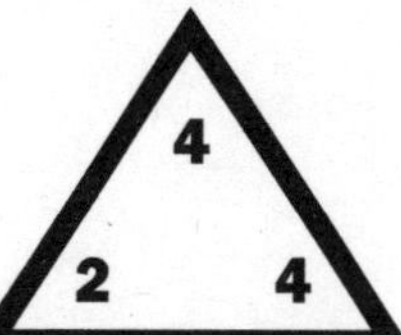

A

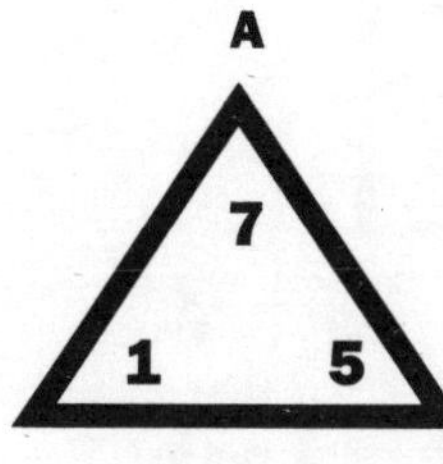

B

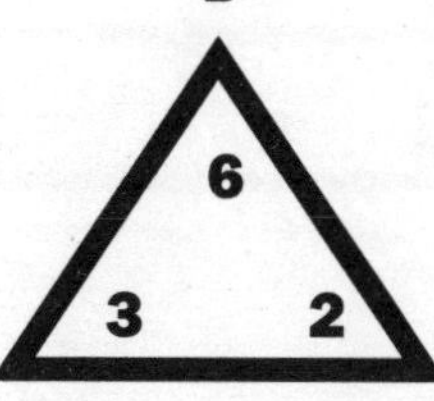

C

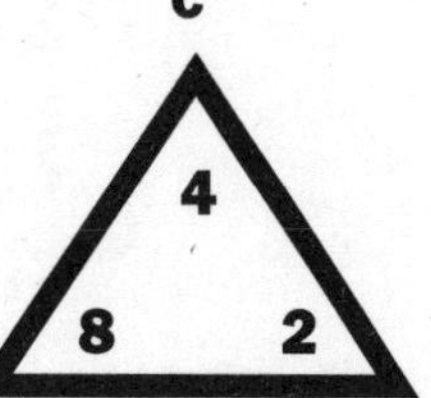

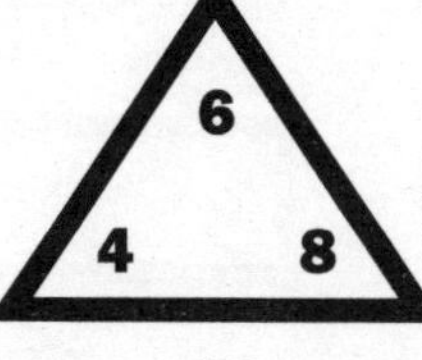

D

E

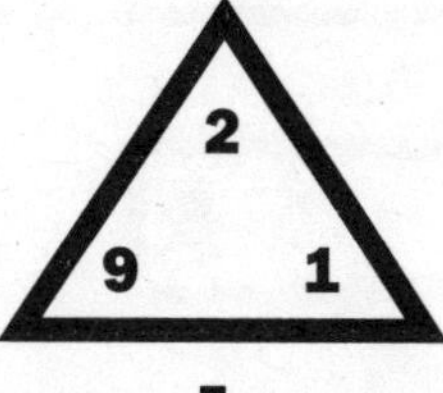

F

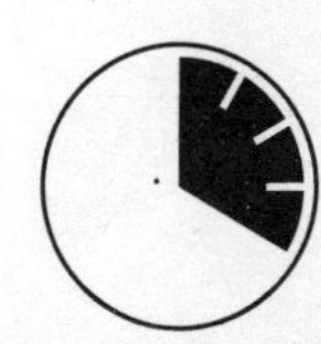

TEST 2 time limit 20 minutes

TEST 2

13 Insert the correct mathematical signs between each number in order to resolve the equation. What are the signs?

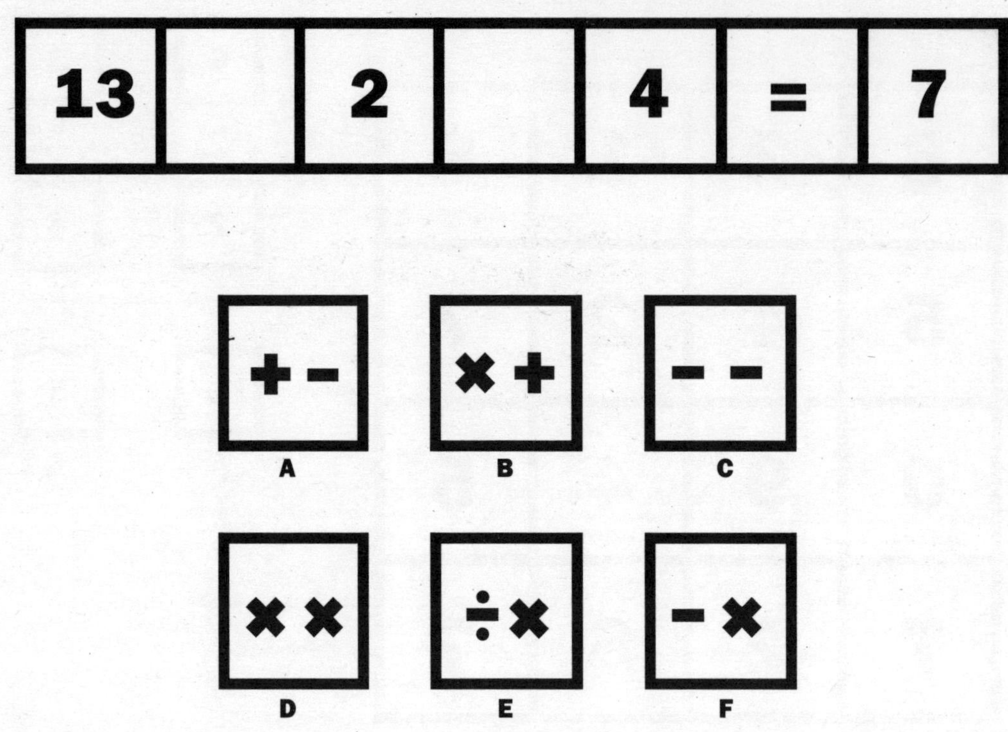

14 Discover the connection between the letters and the numbers. Which number should replace the question mark?

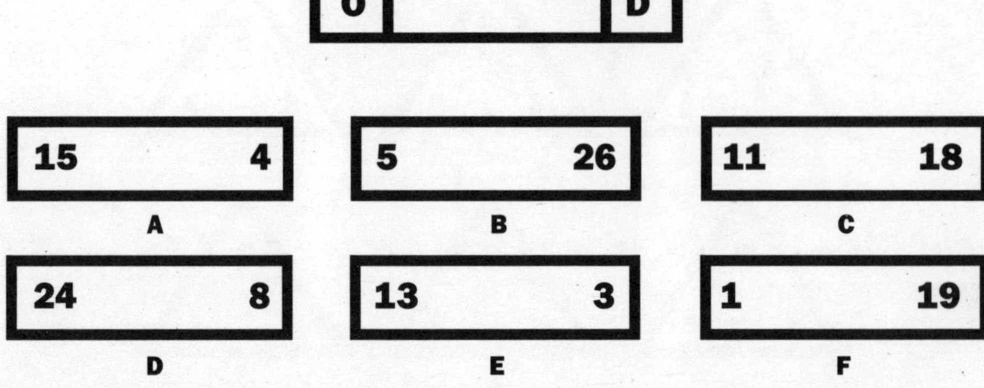

TEST 2 time limit 20 minutes

15 Which of the constructed boxes can be made from the pattern?

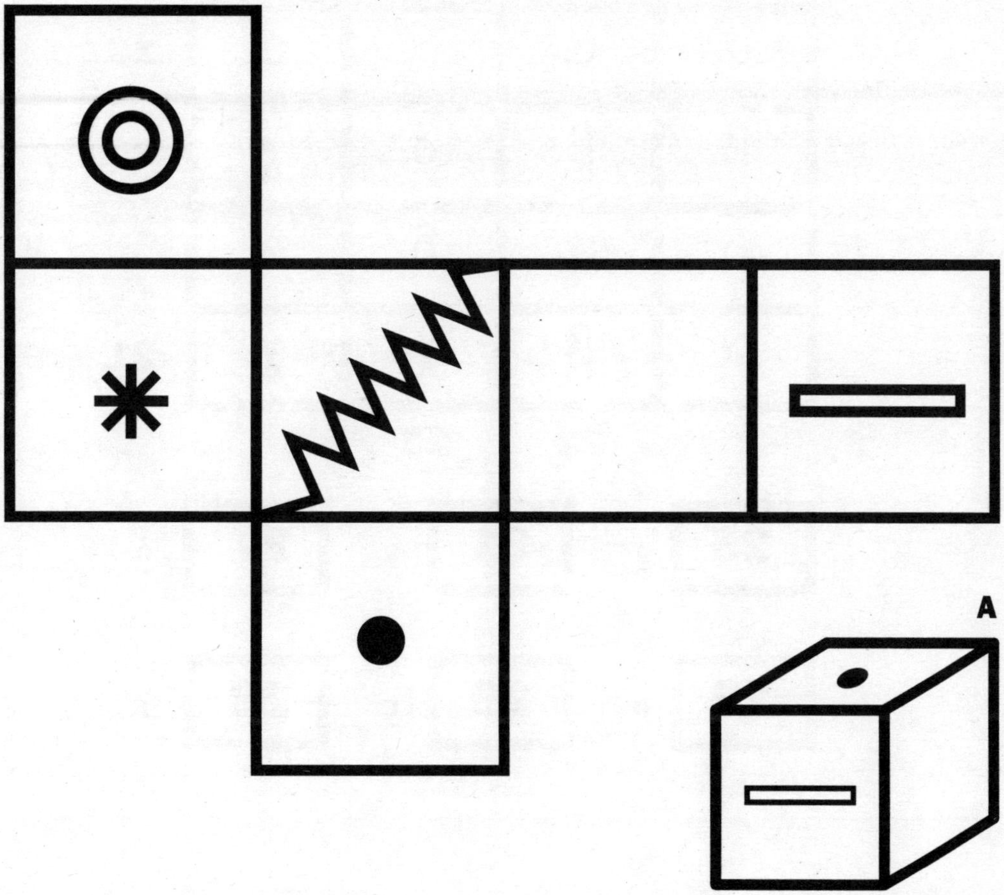

A

B

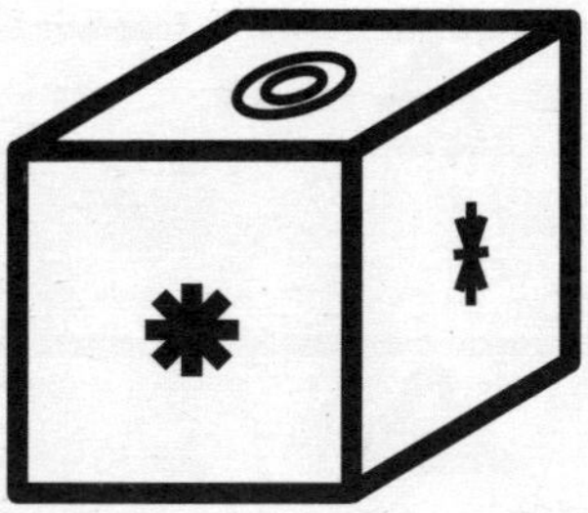

C

D

E

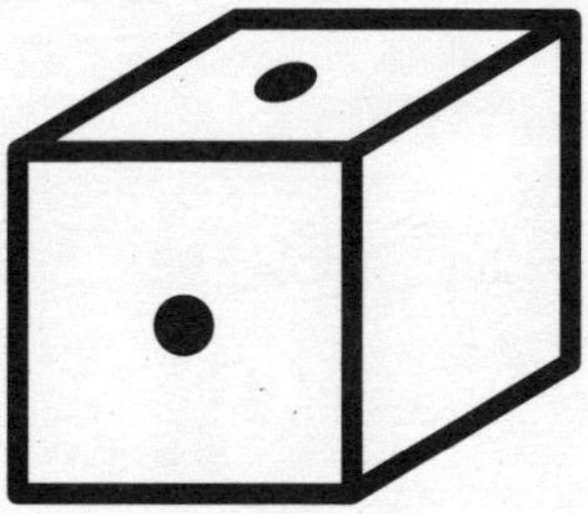

F

TEST 2 time limit 20 minutes

TEST 3

1 Each same symbol has a value. Work out the logic and discover what should replace the question mark.

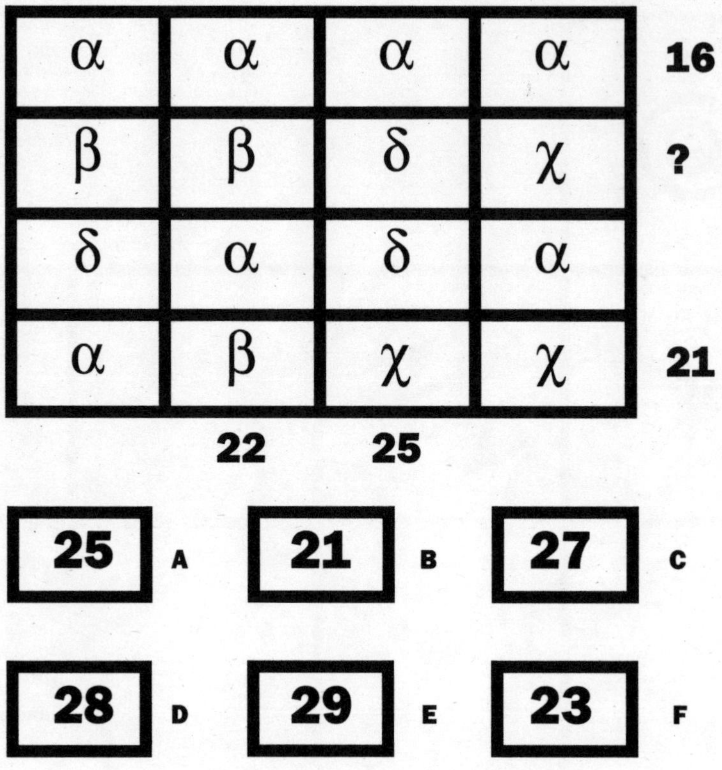

2 Scales one and two are in perfect balance. Which of these pans should replace the empty one?

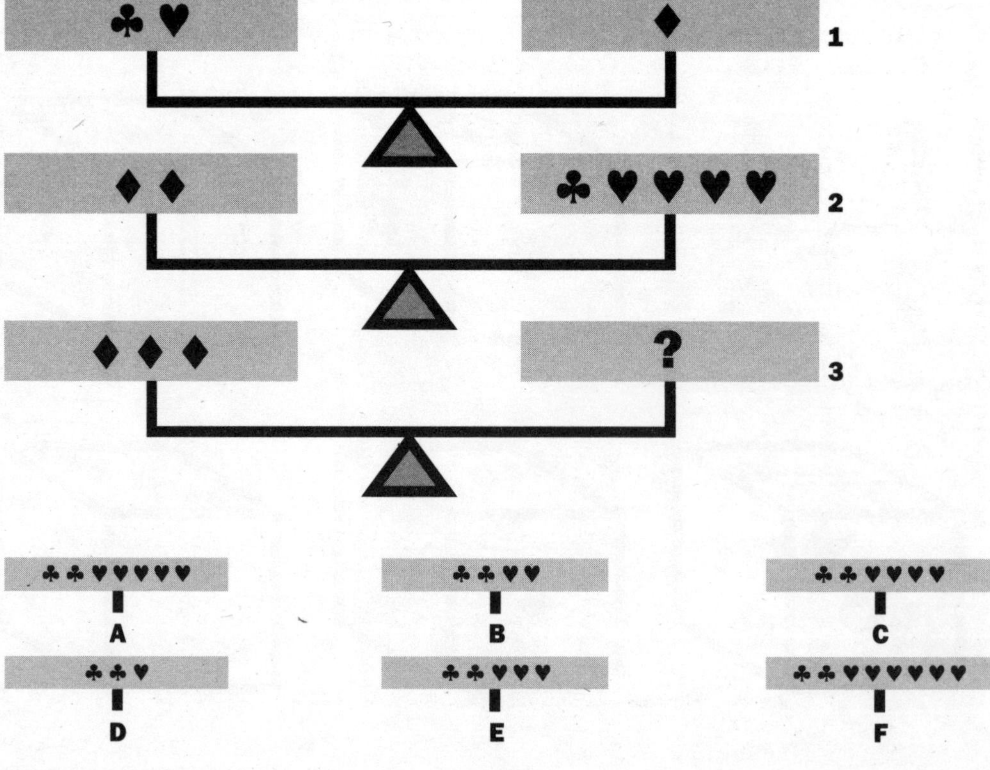

TEST 3 time limit 25 minutes

TEST 3

3 When rearranged the shapes will give a number. Which of the numbers is it?

6	1	7	3
2	5	2	8
3	5	5	1
4	4	1	?

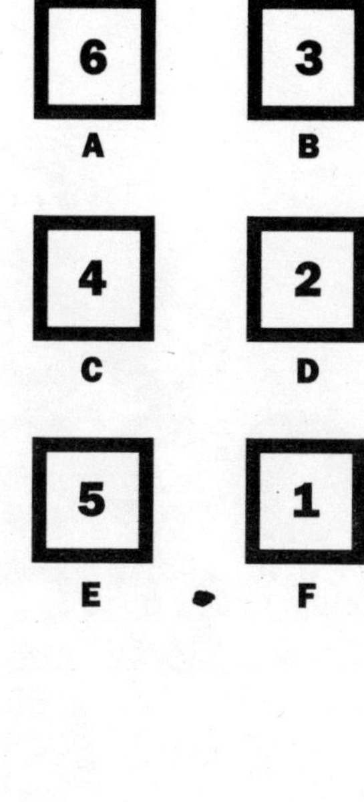

4 Which of the numbers should replace the question mark?

TEST 3 time limit 25 minutes

TEST 3

5 Here is an unusual safe. Each of the buttons must be pressed only once in the correct order to open it. The last button is marked F. The number of moves and the direction is marked on each button. Thus 1i would mean one move in, whilst 1o would mean one move out. 1c would mean one move clockwise and 1a would mean one move anti-clockwise. Which button is the first you must press?

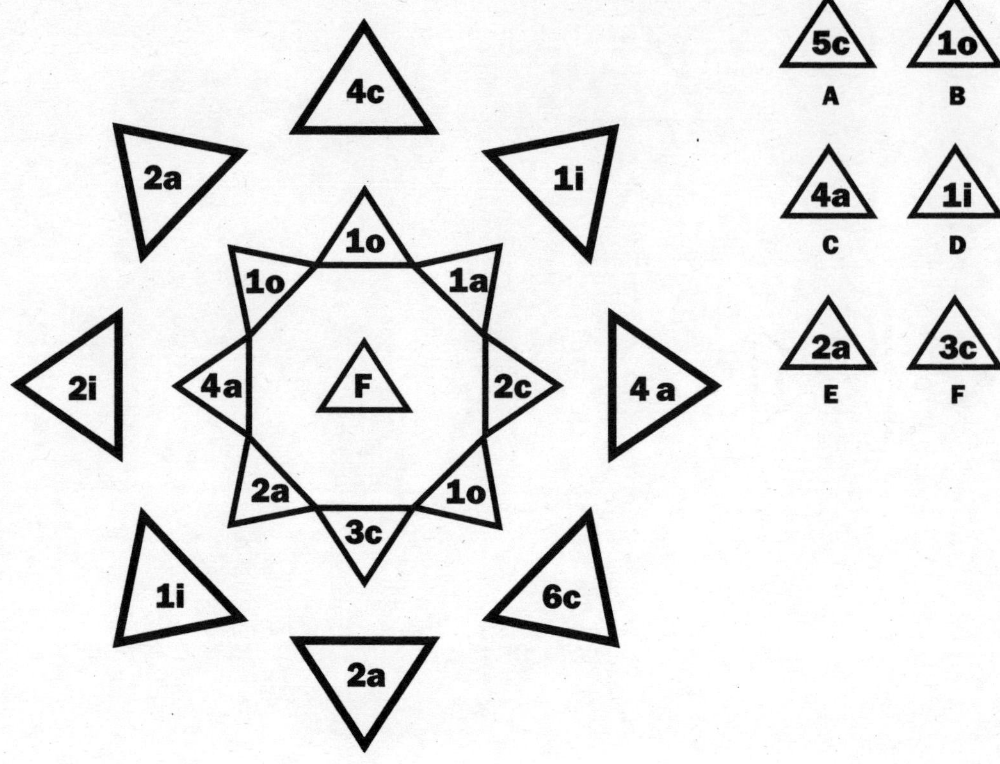

6 Which number is missing from this series?

TEST 3 time limit 25 minutes

TEST 3

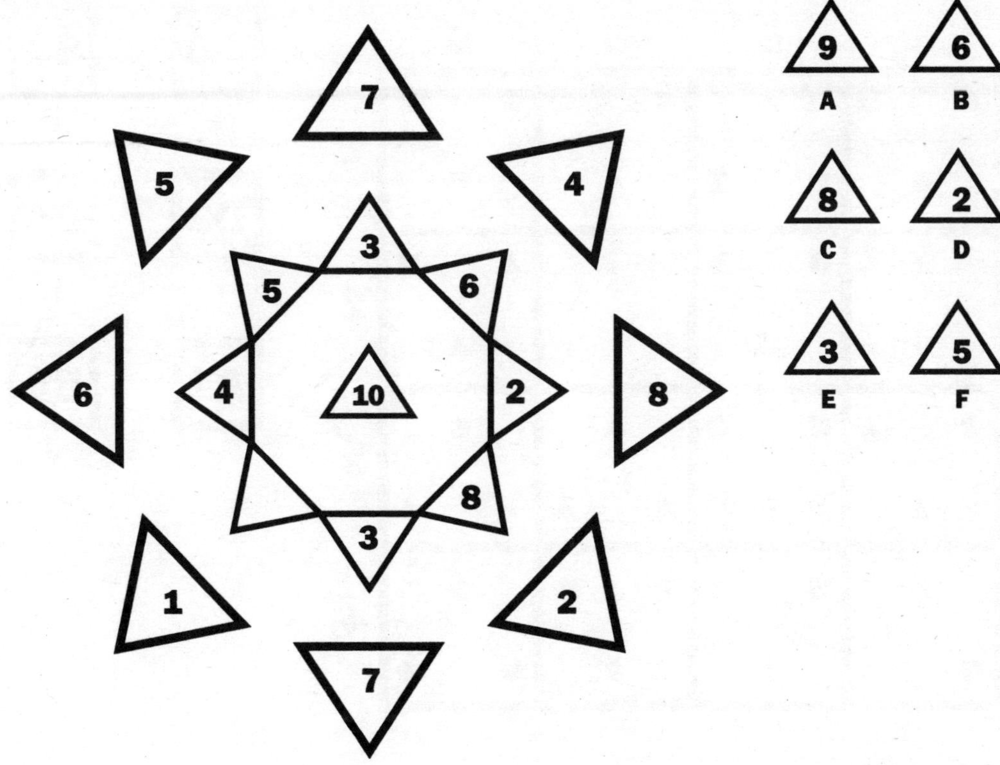

7 Which triangle should replace the empty one?

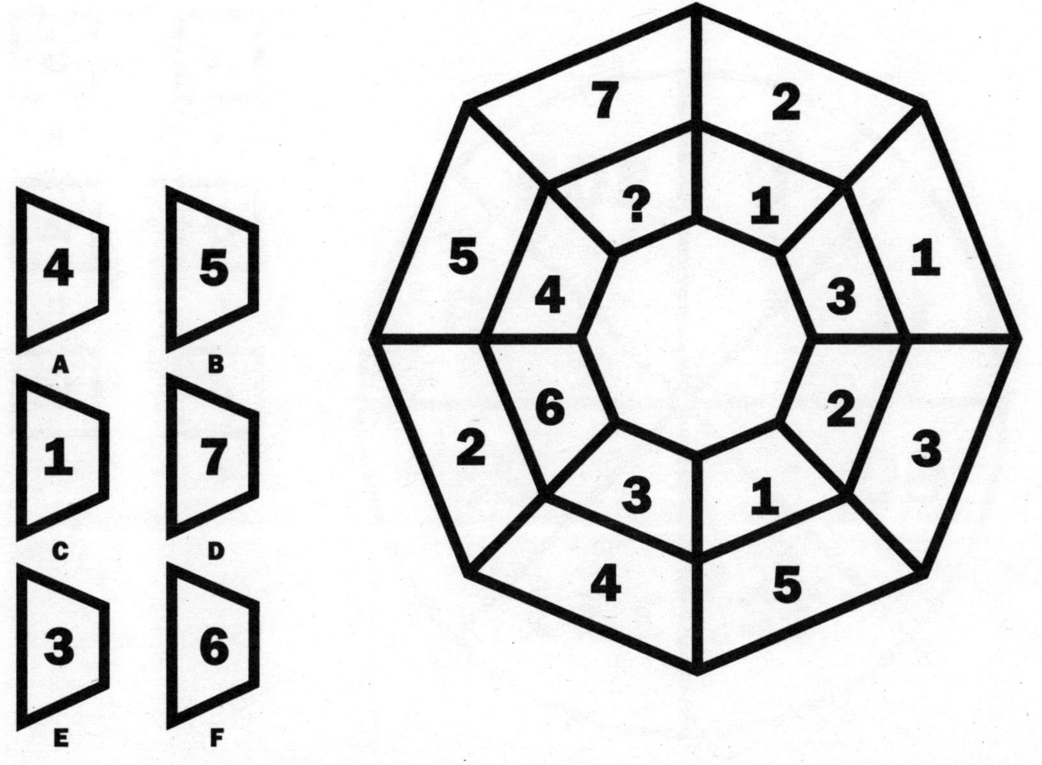

8 Which of the numbers should logically replace the question mark in the octagon?

TEST 3 time limit 25 minutes

TEST 3

9 Which square's contents matches C4?

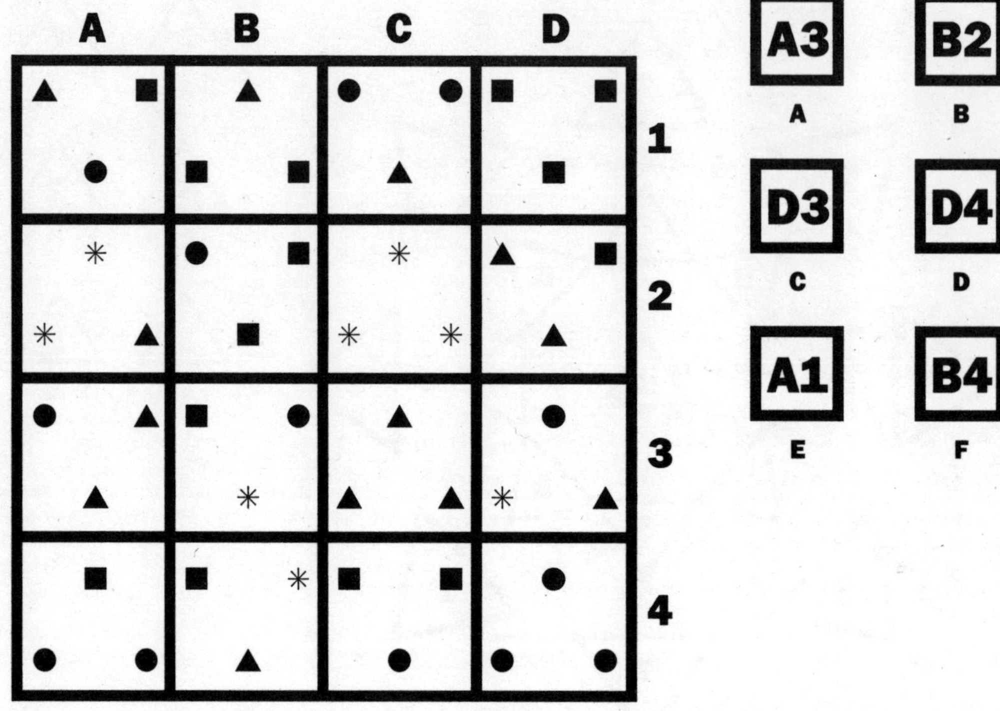

10 How many ways are there to score 123 on this dartboard using three darts only? Each dart always lands in a sector and no dart falls to the floor. Any sector can be used more than once in any set of throws, but the same set of numbers can be used in one order only.

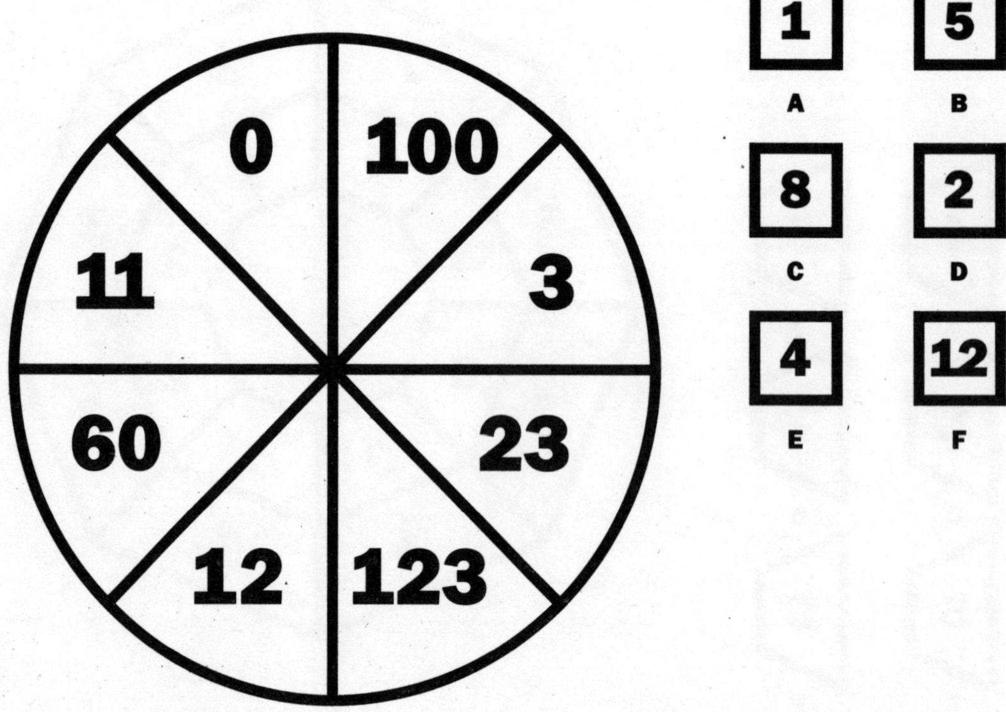

TEST 3 time limit 25 minutes

TEST 3

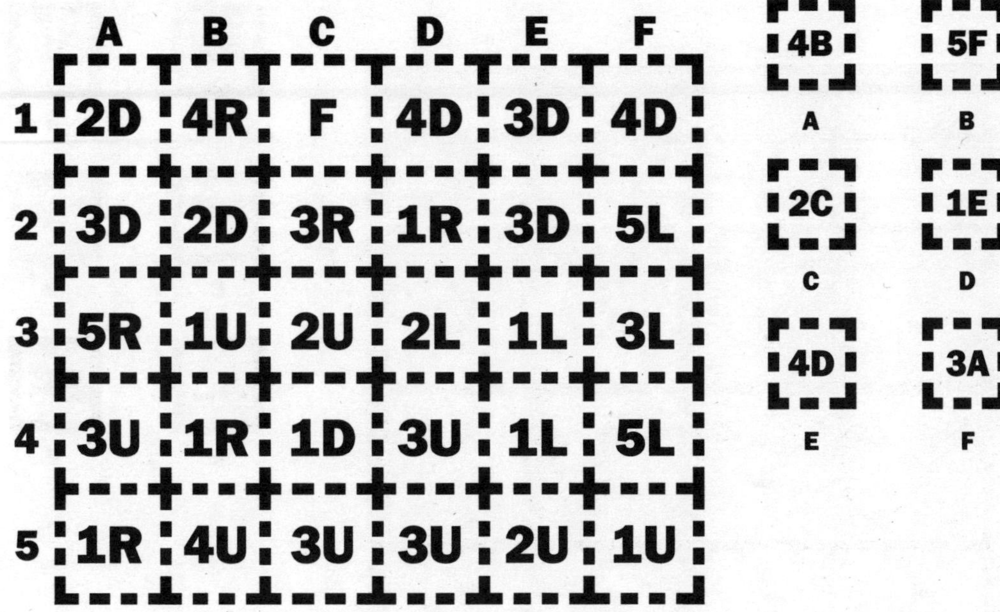

11 Here is an unusual safe. Each of the buttons must be pressed only once in the correct order to open it. The last button is marked F. The number of moves and the direction is marked on each button. Thus 1U would mean one move up, while 1L would mean one move to the left. Using the grid reference, which button is the first you must press?

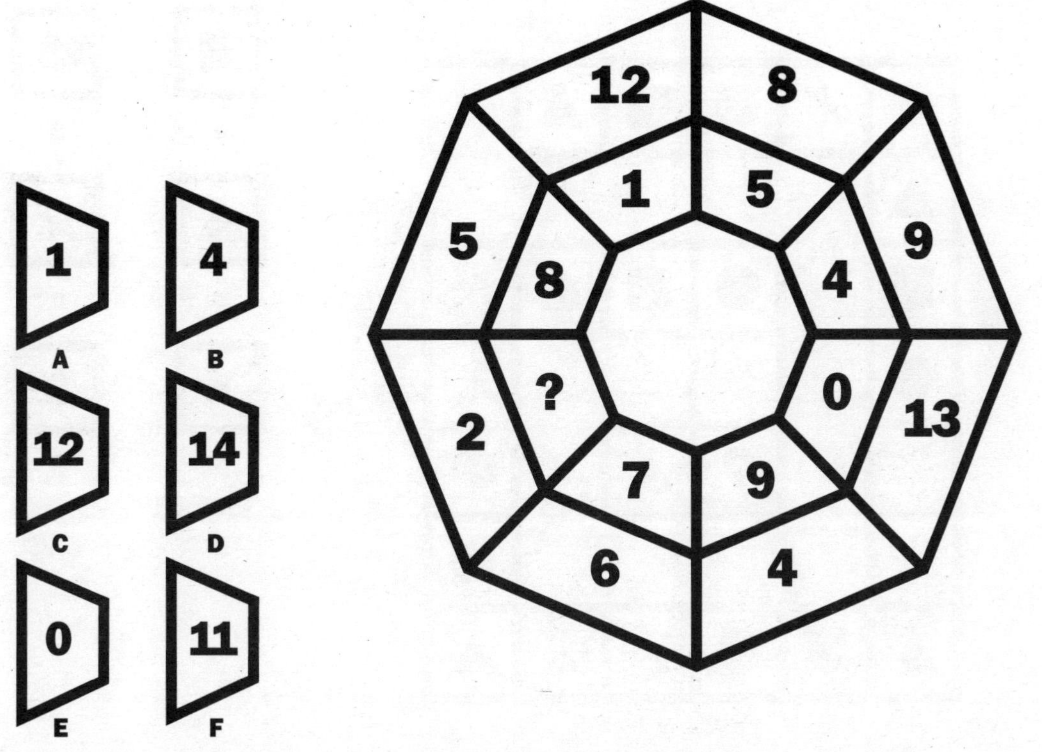

12 Which of the numbers should logically replace the question mark in the octagon?

TEST 3 time limit 25 minutes

TEST 3

13 Which of the numbers should replace the question mark?

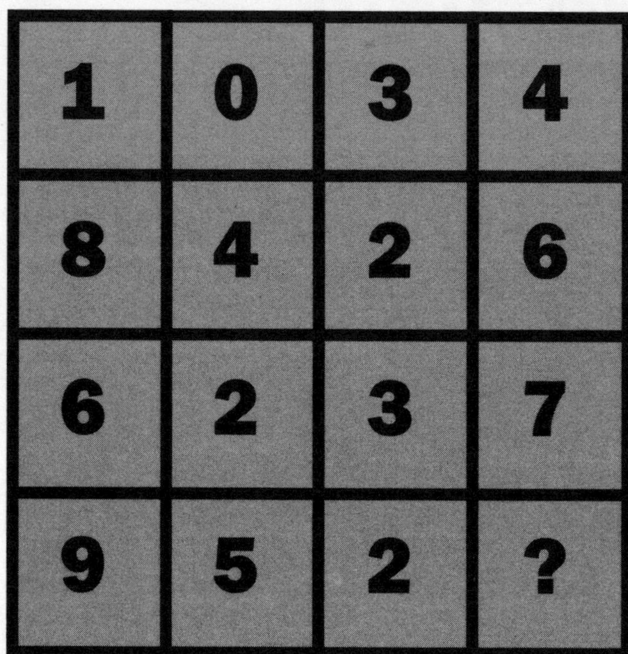

6	9
A	B
5	3
C	D
2	7
E	F

14 Which of the boxes should be used to replace the question mark?

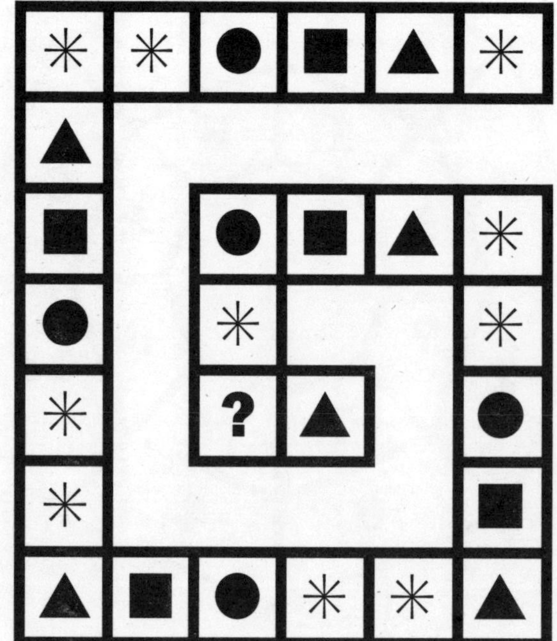

A B

C D

E F

TEST 3 time limit 25 minutes

TEST 3

15 Which of the numbers should replace the question mark?

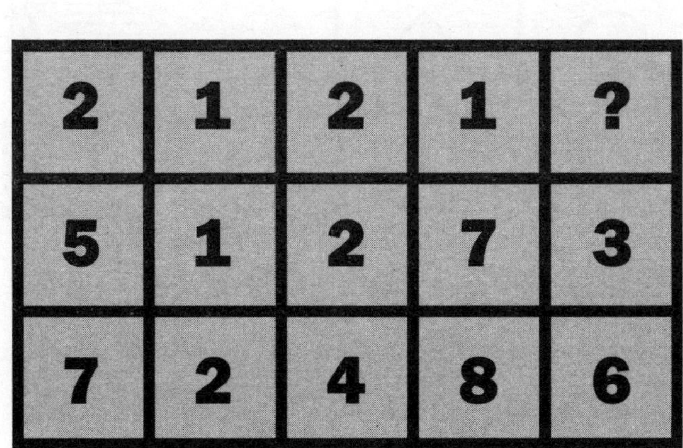

8	1
A	B
7	9
C	D
3	4
E	F

16 This square follows a logical pattern. Which of the tiles should be used to complete the square?

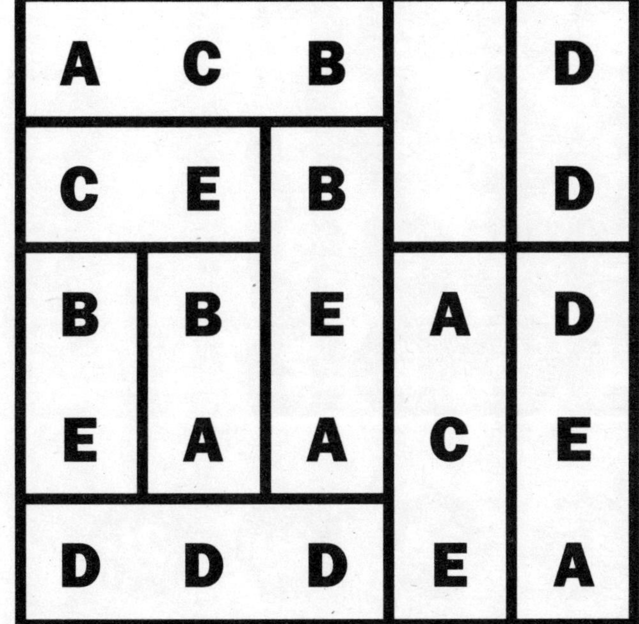

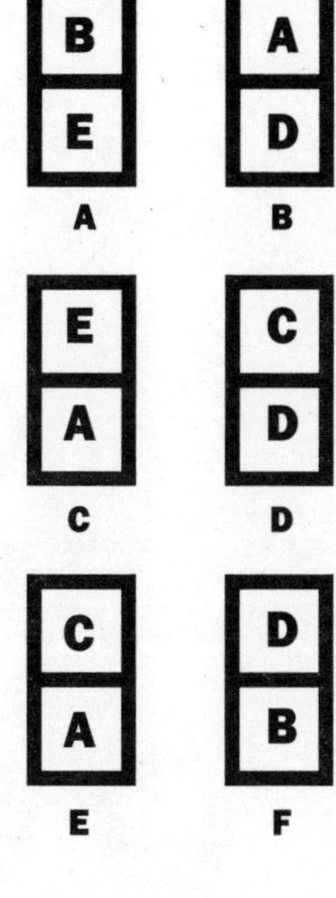

TEST 3 time limit 25 minutes

TEST 3

17 Which of the constructed boxes cannot be made from the pattern?

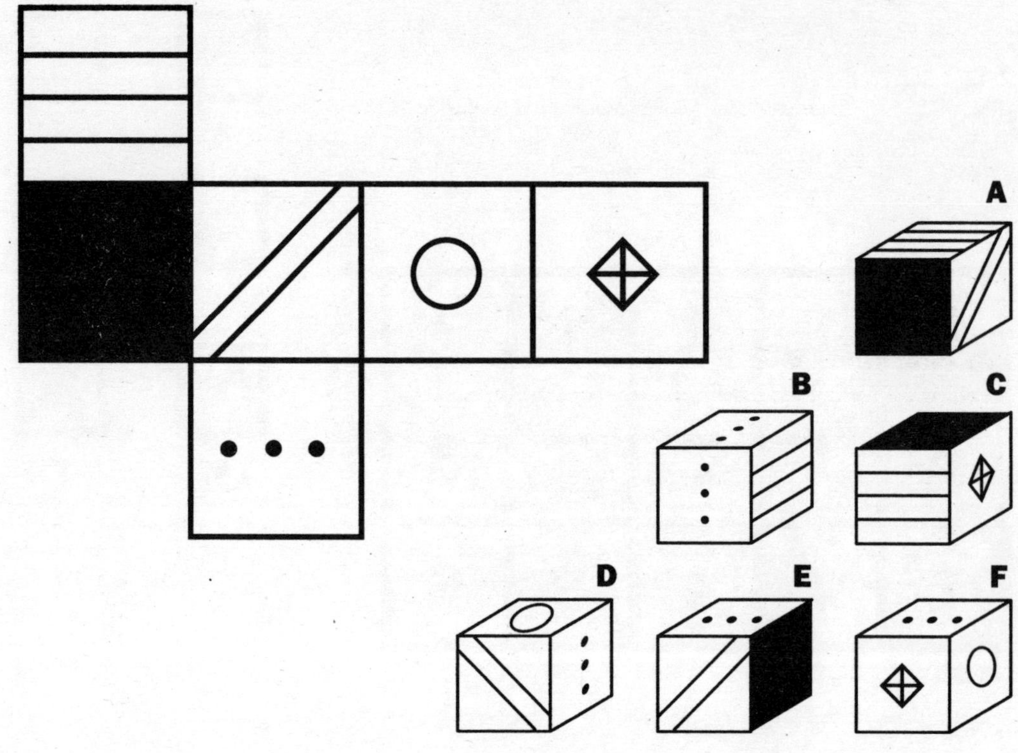

18 Move from ring to touching ring, starting from the bottom left corner and finishing in the top right corner. Collect nine numbers and total them. Which is the highest possible total?

TEST 3 time limit 25 minutes

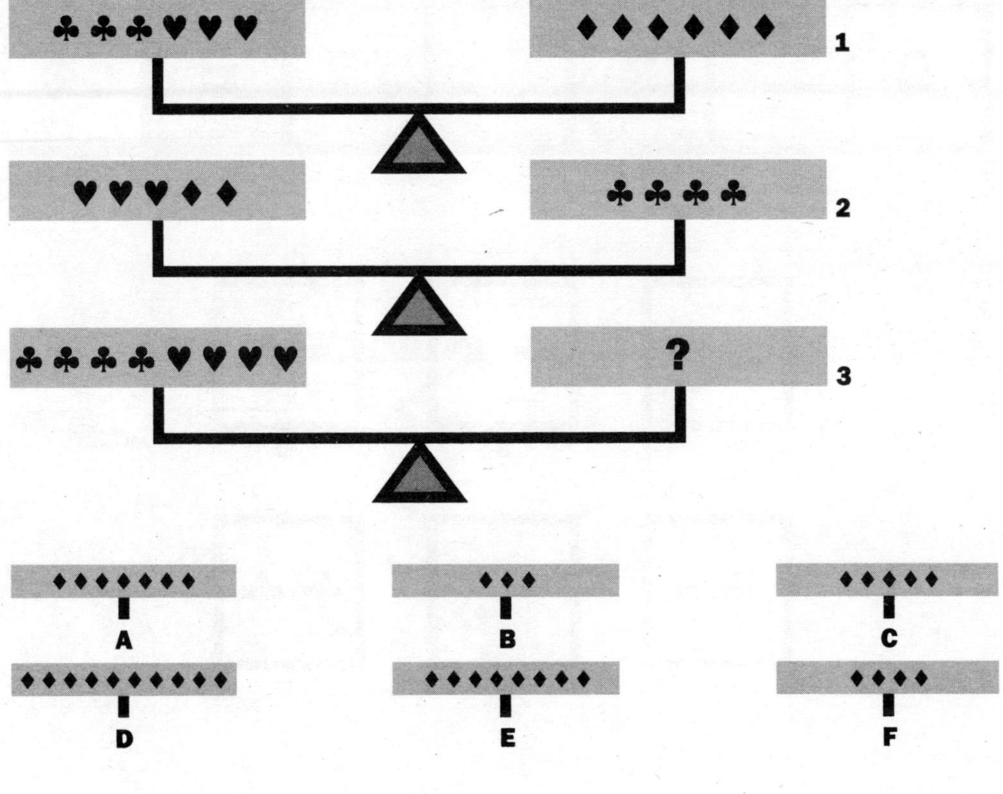

19 Scales one and two are in perfect balance. Which of the pans should replace the empty one?

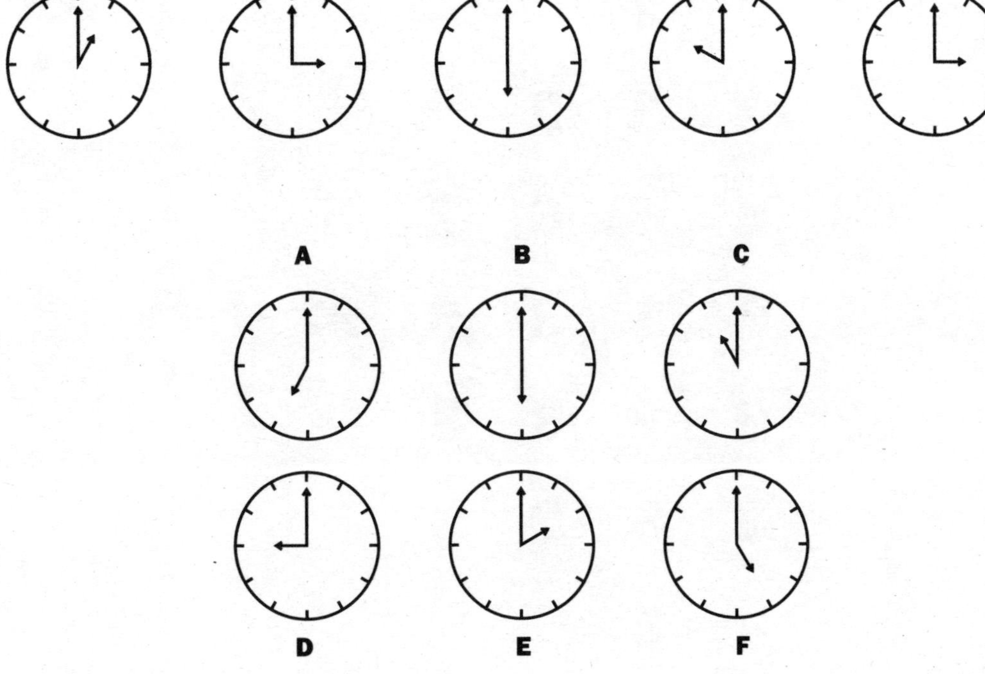

20 Which of the clocks continues this series?

TEST 3 time limit 25 minutes

TEST 4

1 Insert the correct mathematical signs between each number in order to resolve the equation. What are the signs?

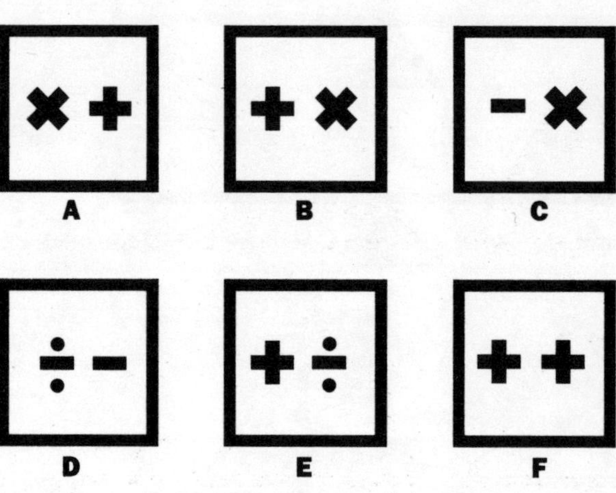

2 Start at 1 and move from circle to touching circle. Collect four numbers each time. How many different routes are there to collect 12? A reversed route counts twice.

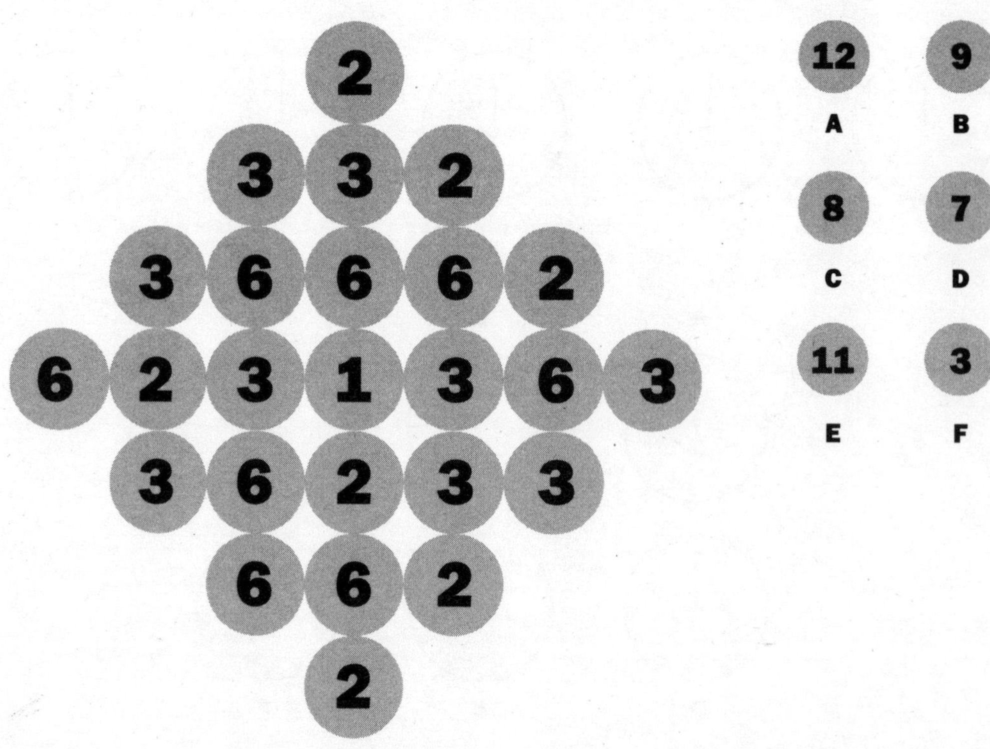

TEST 4 time limit 25 minutes

TEST 4

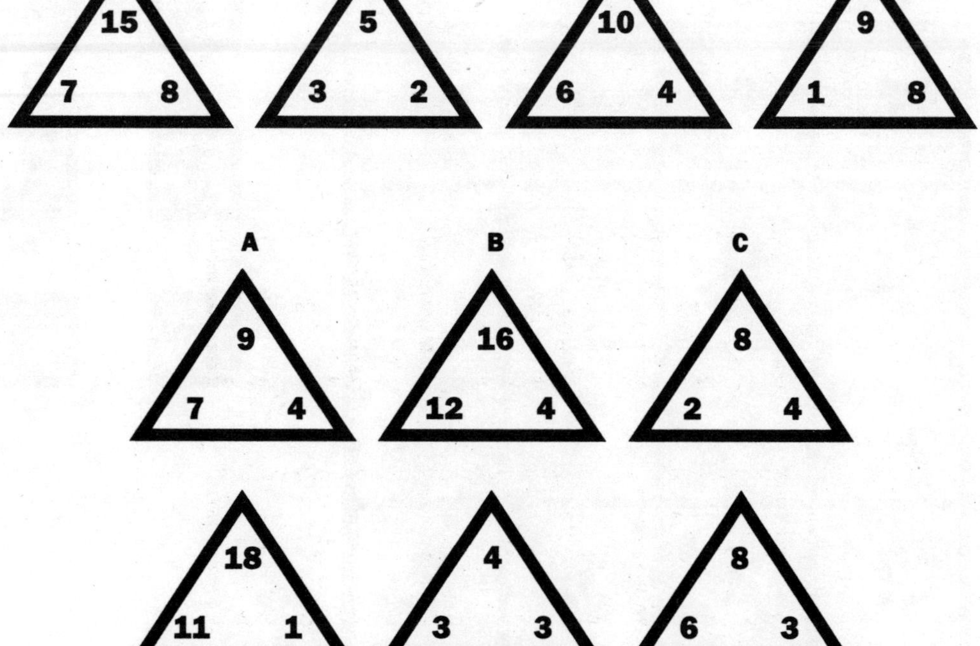

3 Which triangle belongs to this series?

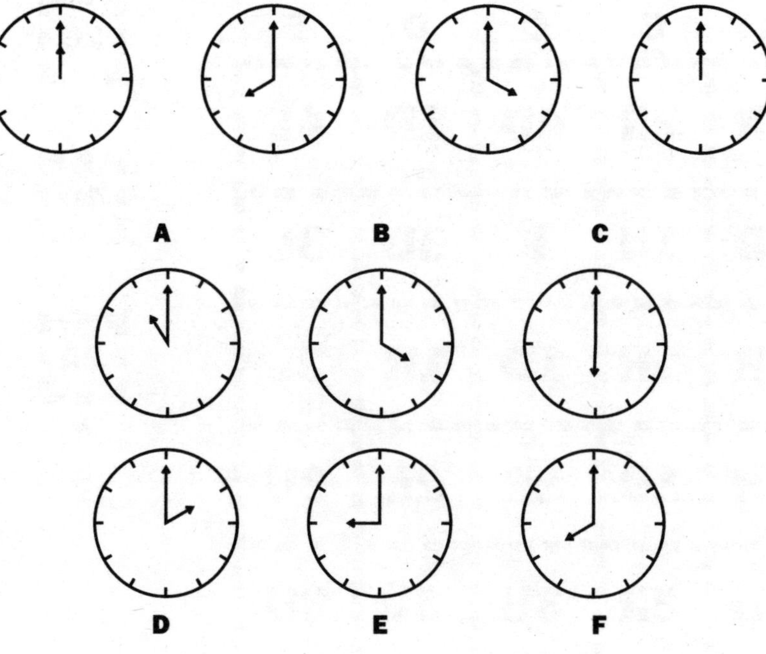

4 Which of the clocks continues this series?

TEST 4 time limit 25 minutes

TEST 4

5 Which of the numbers should replace the question mark?

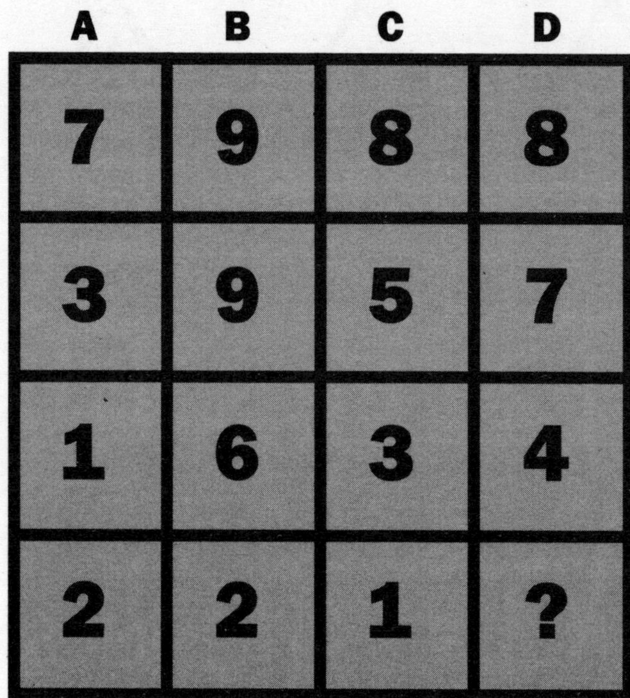

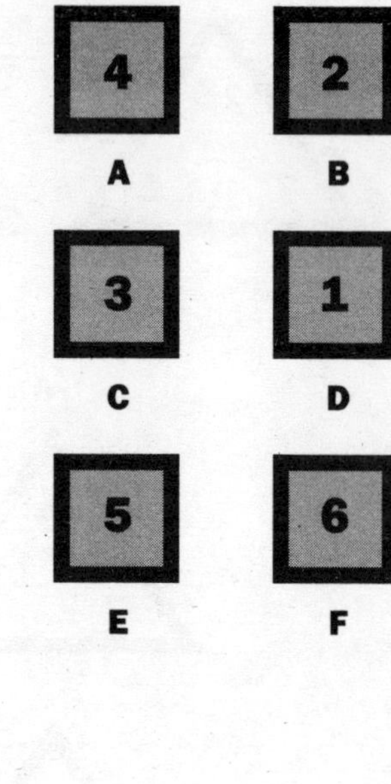

6 Here is an unusual safe. Each of the buttons must be pressed only once in the correct order to open it. The last button is marked F. The number of moves and the direction is marked on each button. Thus 1U would mean one move up, while 1L would mean one move to the left. Using the grid reference, which button is the first you must press?

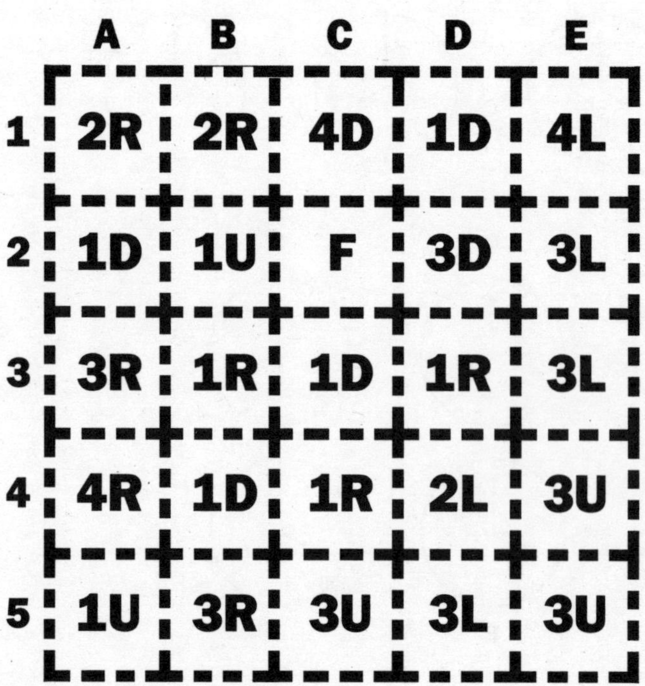

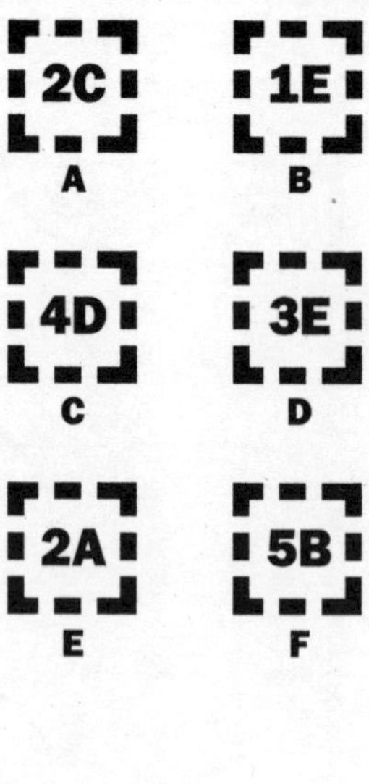

TEST 4 time limit 25 minutes

TEST 4

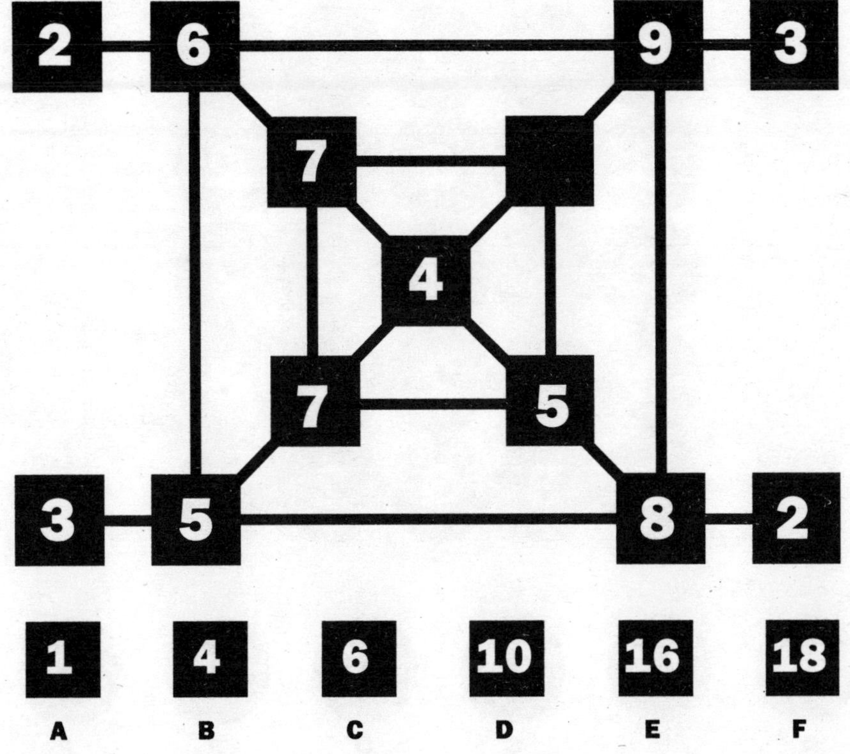

7 Start at any corner and follow the lines. Collect another four numbers and total the five. One of the numbers in the squares below can be used to complete the diagram. If the correct one has been chosen, one of the routes involving it will give a total of 33. Which one is it?

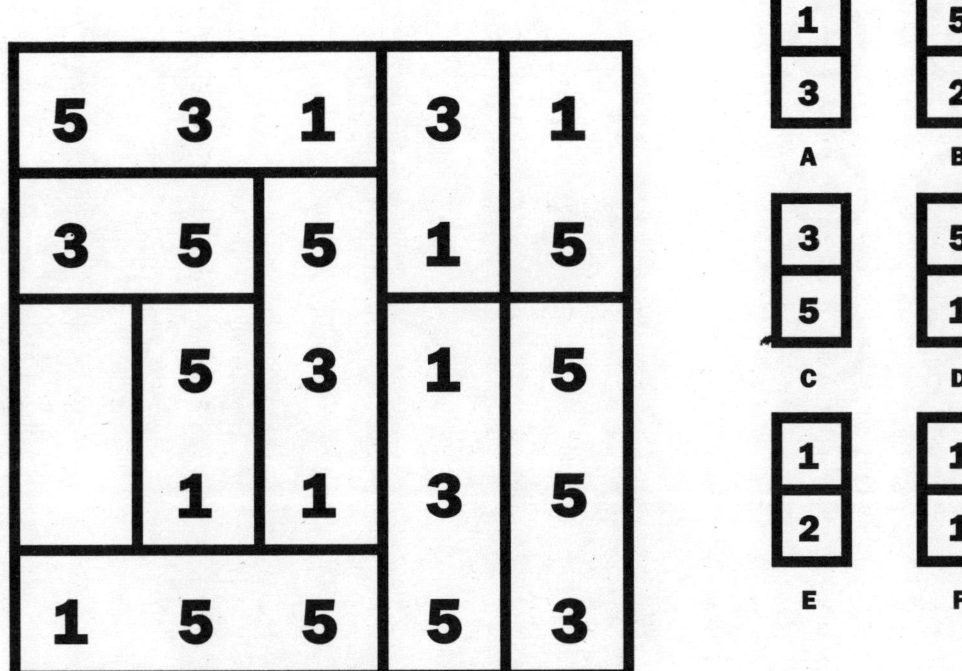

8 This square follows a logical pattern. Which of the tiles should be used to complete the square?

TEST 4 time limit 25 minutes

TEST 4

9 Move from ring to touching ring, starting from the bottom left corner and finishing in the top right corner. Collect nine numbers and total them. Which is the highest possible total?

10 When rearranged the shapes will give a number. Which of the numbers is it?

TEST 4 time limit 25 minutes

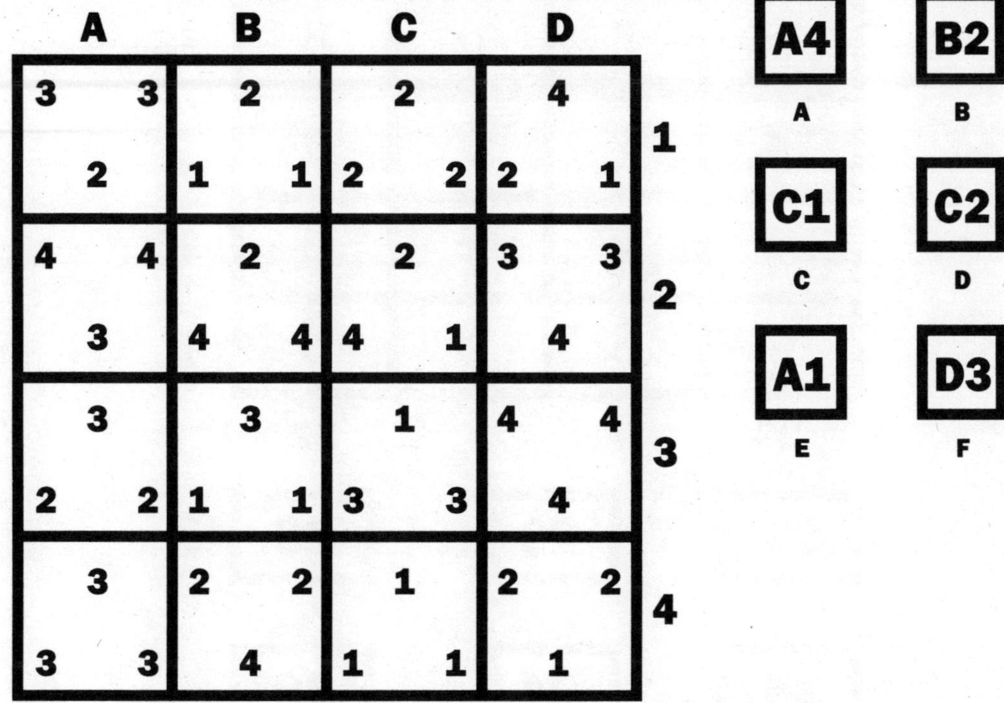

11 Which square's contents matches D1?

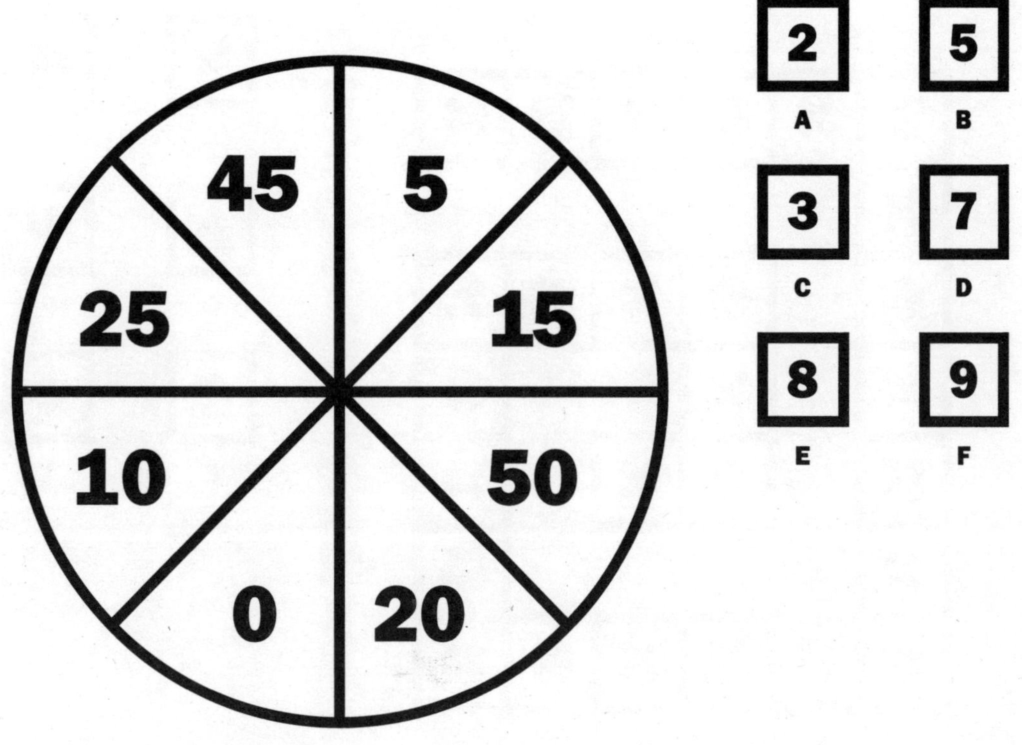

12 How many ways are there to score 60 on this dartboard using three darts only? Each dart always lands in a sector and no dart falls to the floor.

TEST 4 time limit 25 minutes

TEST 4

13 Each same symbol has a value. Work out the logic and discover what should replace the question mark.

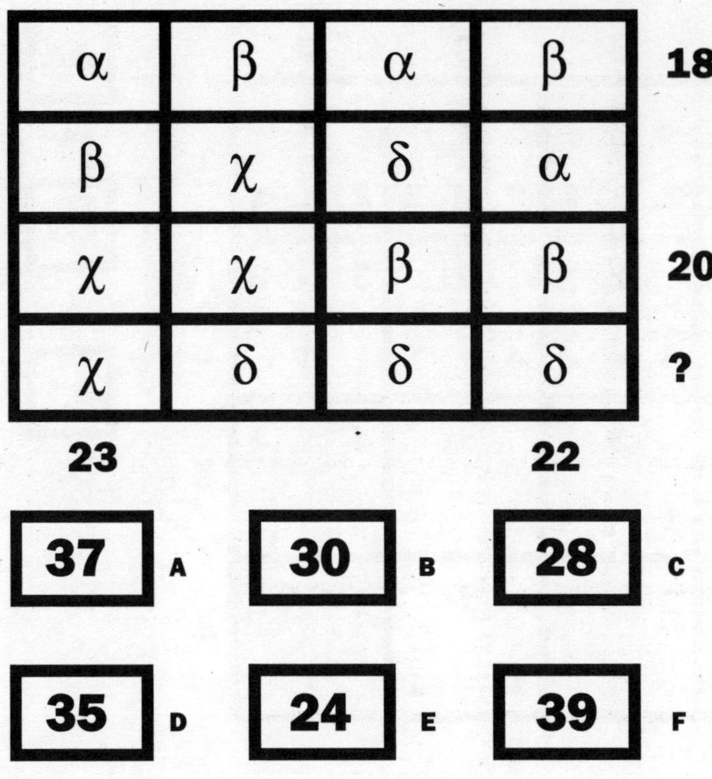

14 Which of the boxes should be used to replace the question mark?

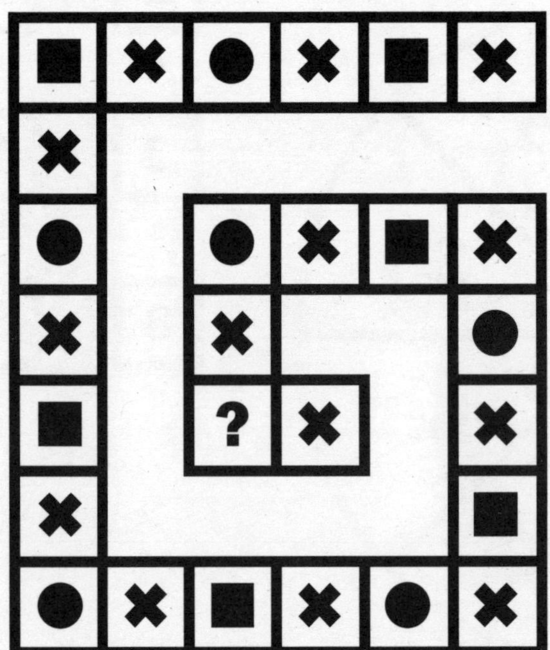

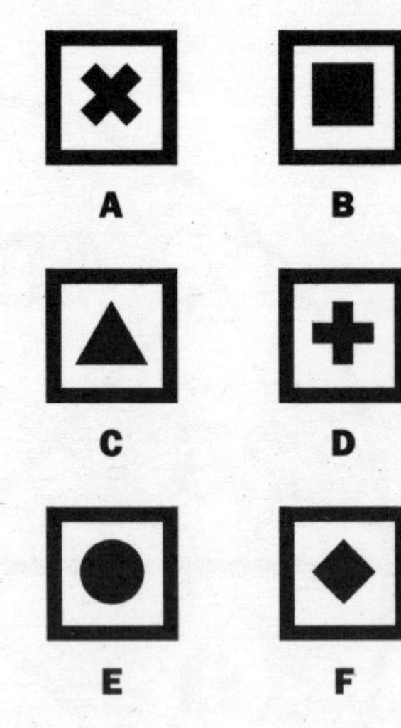

TEST 4 time limit 25 minutes

TEST 4

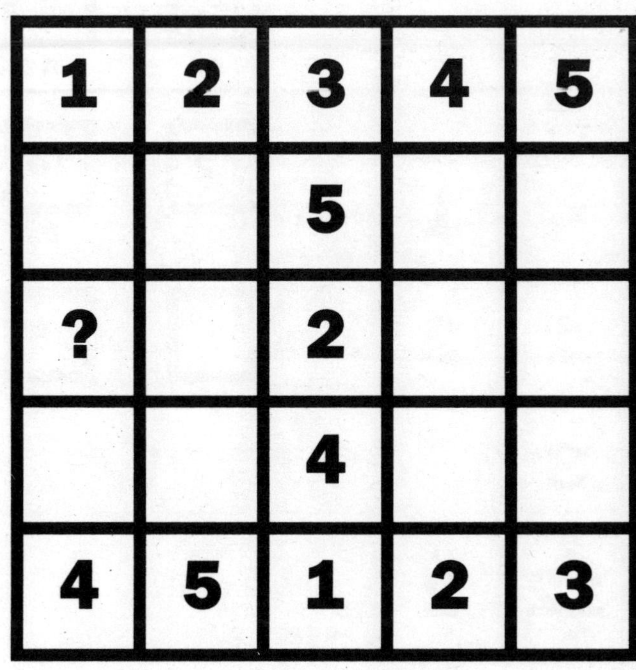

1	2	3	4	5
		5		
?		2		
		4		
4	5	1	2	3

2 A

4 B

3 C

5 D

1 E

15 Complete the square using the five numbers shown. When completed no row, column or diagonal line will use the same number more than once. What should replace the question mark?

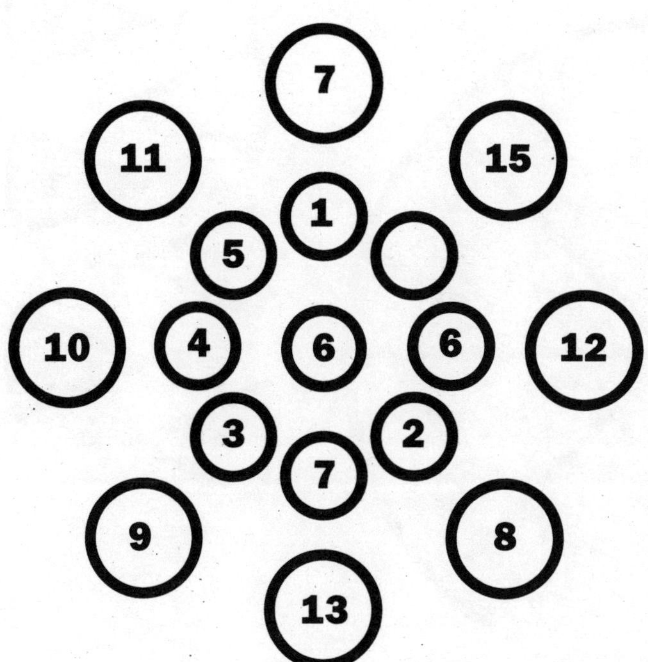

16 Which circle should replace the empty one?

TEST 4 time limit 25 minutes

TEST 4

17 Each straight line of five numbers should total 25. Which of the numbers will replace the question mark?

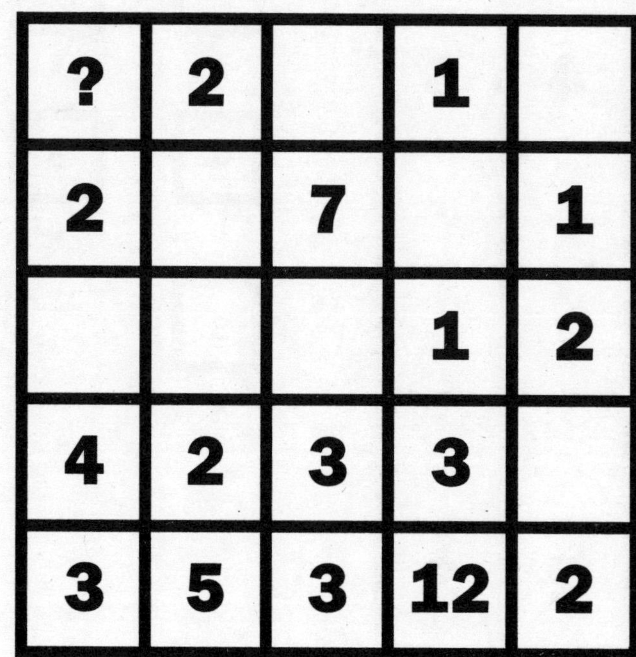

A 8
B 6
C 12
D 10
E 2
F 15

18 Which of the slices should be used to replace the question mark and complete the cake?

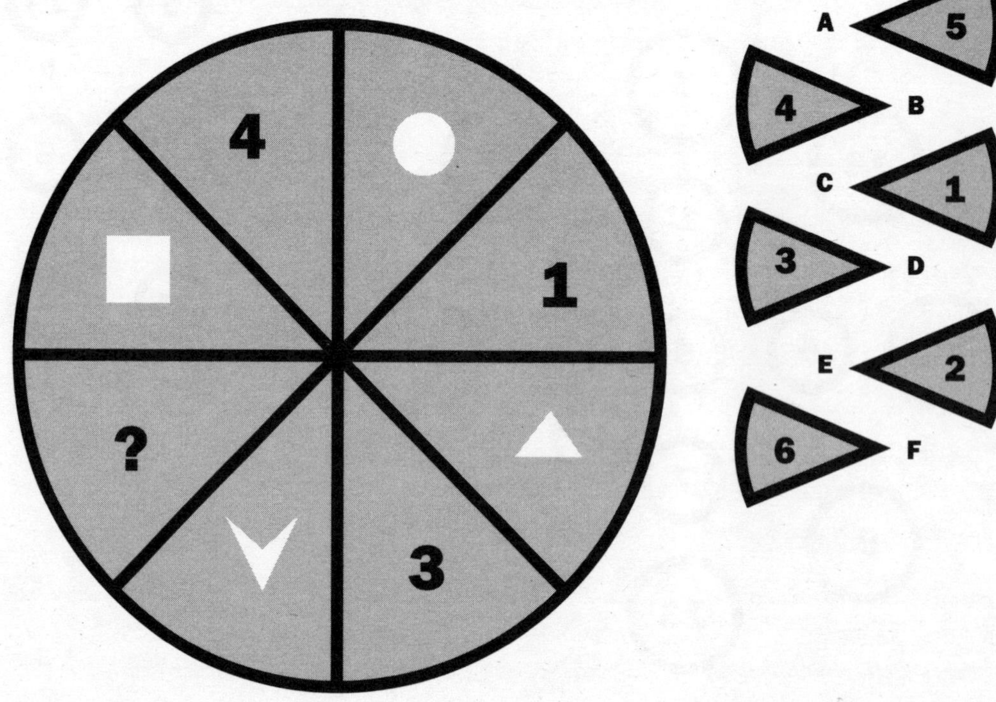

TEST 4 time limit 25 minutes

5	9	1	2	1
8	9	6	4	3
3	0	5	2	?

9	6
A	B
2	7
C	D
4	5
E	F

19 Which of the numbers should replace the question mark?

S	?	K
E	516	P
Z	262	B
I	914	N
A	120	T

393	671	385
A	B	C
5482	1911	2363
D	E	F

20 Discover the connection between the letters and the numbers. Which number should replace the question mark?

TEST 4 time limit 25 minutes

TEST 5

1 Here is an unusual safe. Each of the buttons must be pressed only once in the correct order to open it. The last button is marked F. The number of moves and the direction is marked on each button. Thus 1i would mean one move in, while 1o would mean one move out. 1c would mean one move clockwise and 1a would mean one move anti-clockwise. Which button is the first you must press?

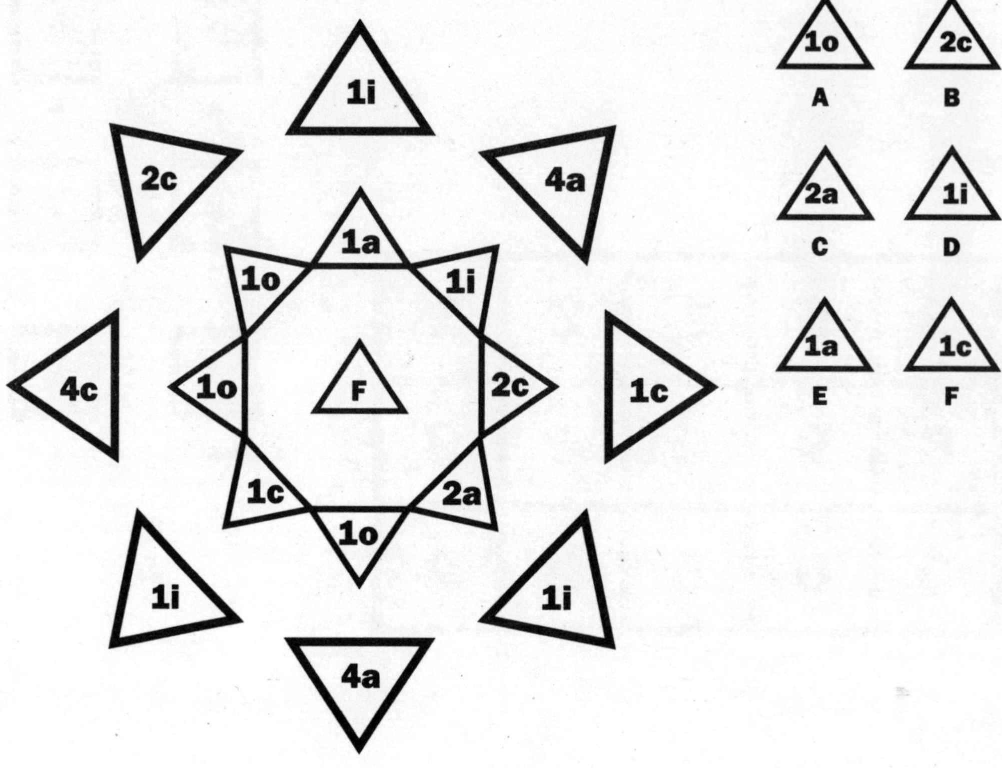

2 Complete the square using the five symbols shown. When completed no row, column or diagonal line will use the same symbol more than once. What should replace the question mark?

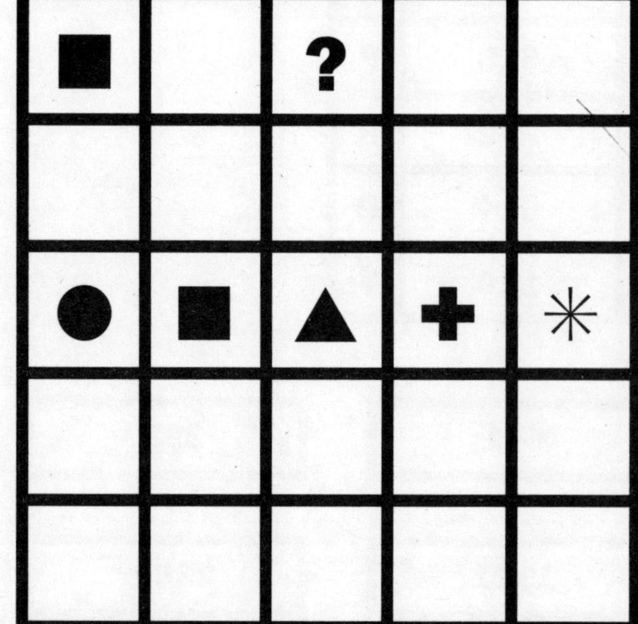

TEST 5 time limit 40 minutes

TEST 5

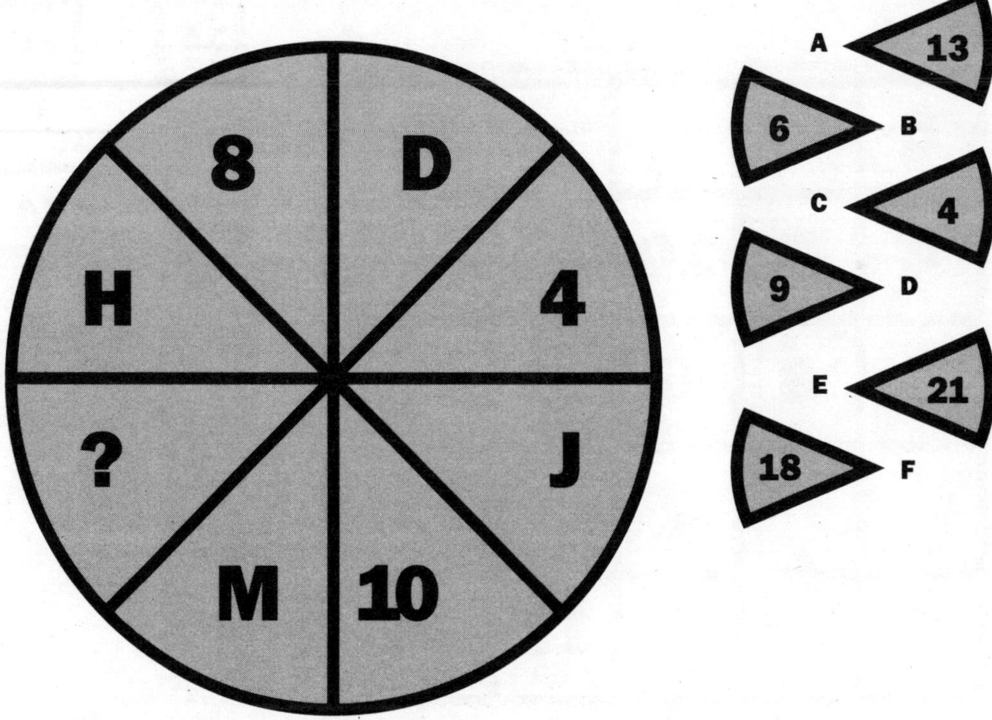

3 Which of the slices should be used to complete the cake?

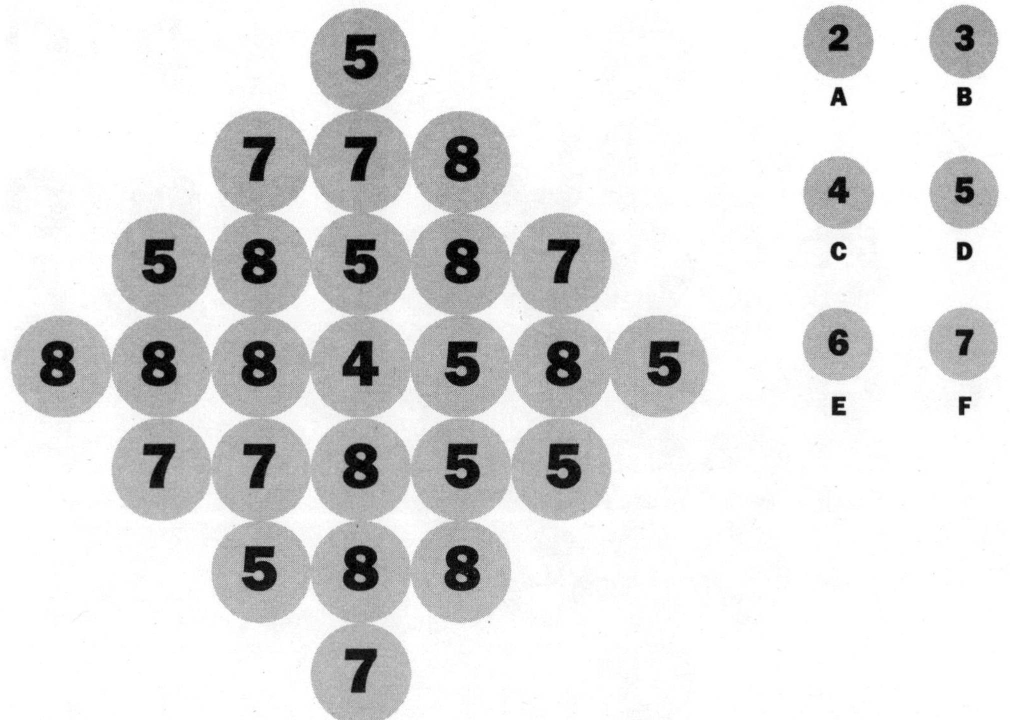

4 Start at 4 and move from circle to touching circle. Collect four numbers each time. How many different routes are there to collect 24? A reversed route counts twice.

TEST 5 time limit 40 minutes

TEST 5

5 Each straight line of five numbers should total 30. Which of the numbers will replace the question mark?

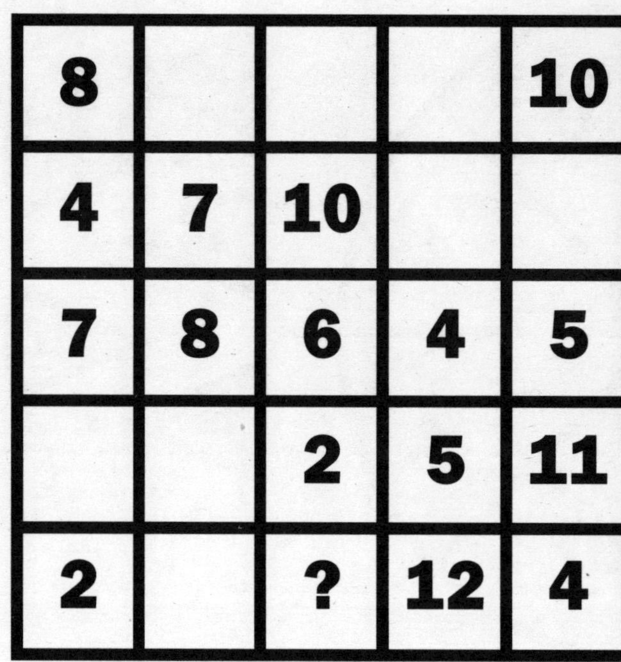

8				10
4	7	10		
7	8	6	4	5
		2	5	11
2		?	12	4

15 A | 13 B

19 C | 14 D

16 E | 3 F

6 Which number is missing from this series?

3 A | 4 B

1 C | 5 D

2 E | 6 F

TEST 5 time limit 40 minutes

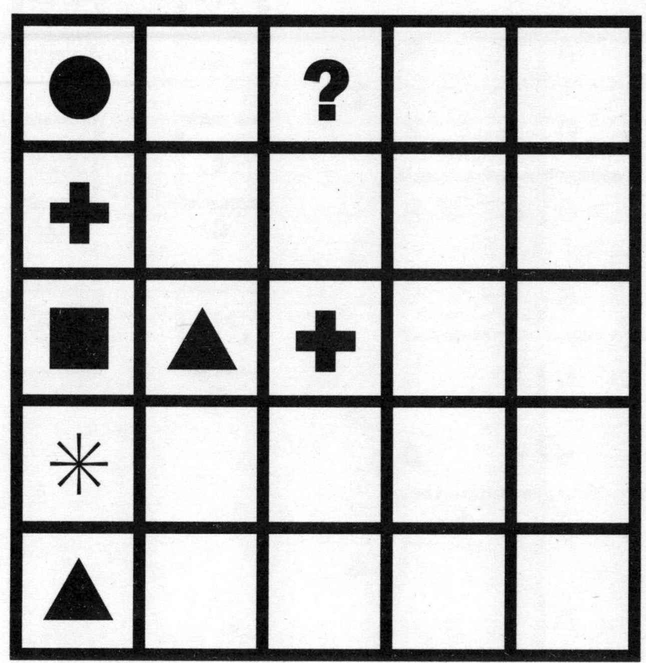

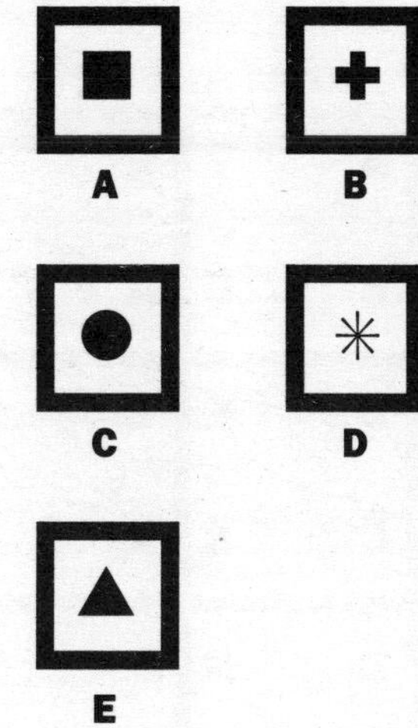

7 Complete the square using the five symbols shown. When completed no row, column or diagonal line will use the same symbol more than once. What should replace the question mark?

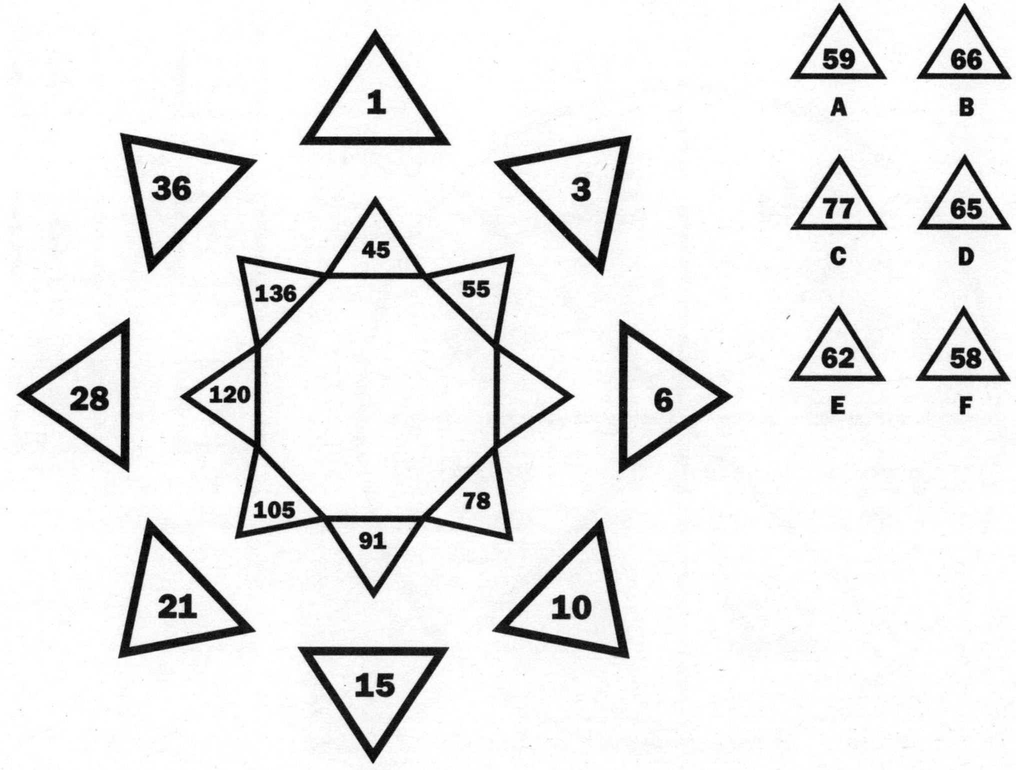

8 Which triangle should replace the empty one?

TEST 5 time limit 40 minutes

TEST 5

9 Which square's contents matches C1?

	A	B	C	D
1	A E B D	A A A A	A A B D	B B A B
2	D E B B	E E E E	B C E A	B B B C
3	D D A D	C A C B	C C E E	A B C D
4	B E D C	A E E D	B A A D	D D C D

4A	2D
A	B
4C	**1B**
C	D
3B	**1D**
E	F

10 How many ways are there to score 62 on this dartboard using four darts only? Each dart always lands in a sector and no dart falls to the floor.

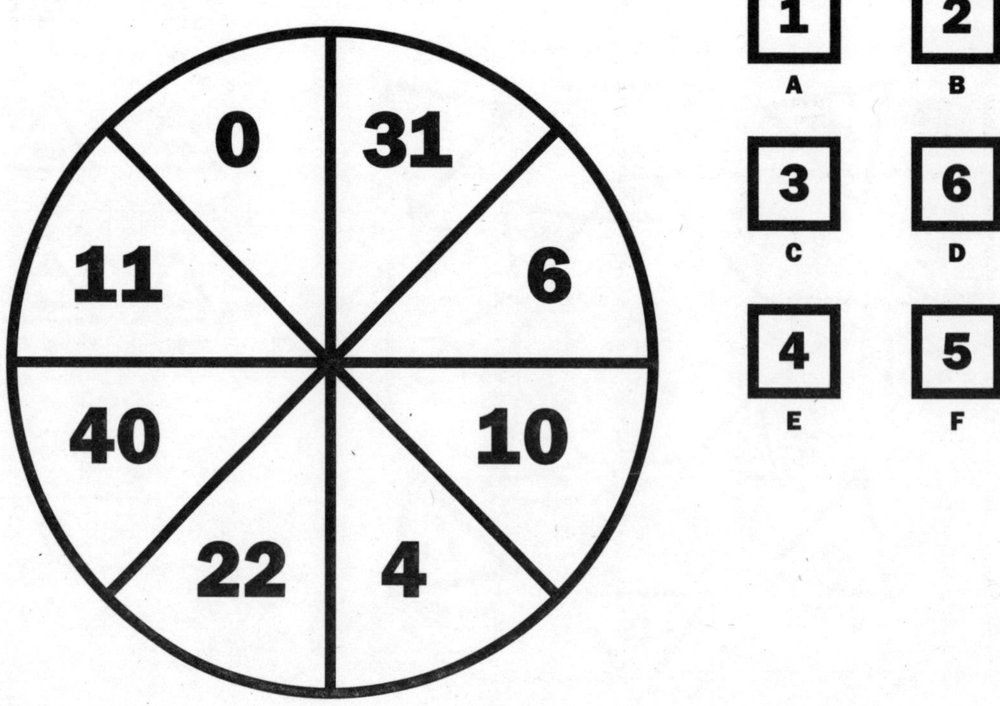

TEST 5 time limit 40 minutes

TEST 5

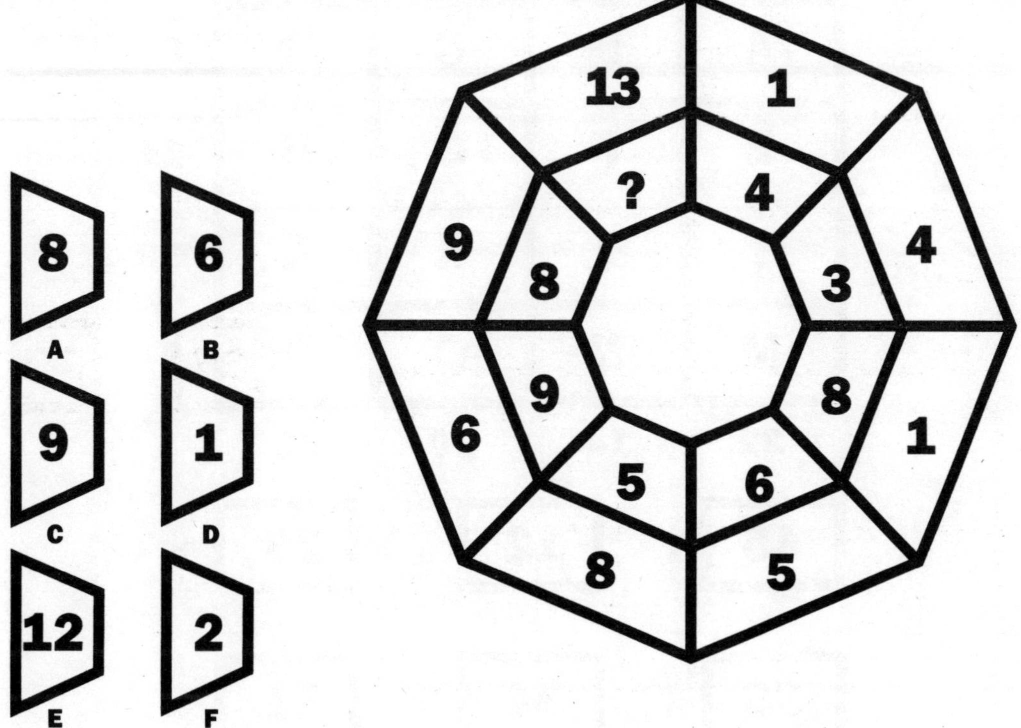

11 Which of the numbers should logically replace the question mark in the octagon?

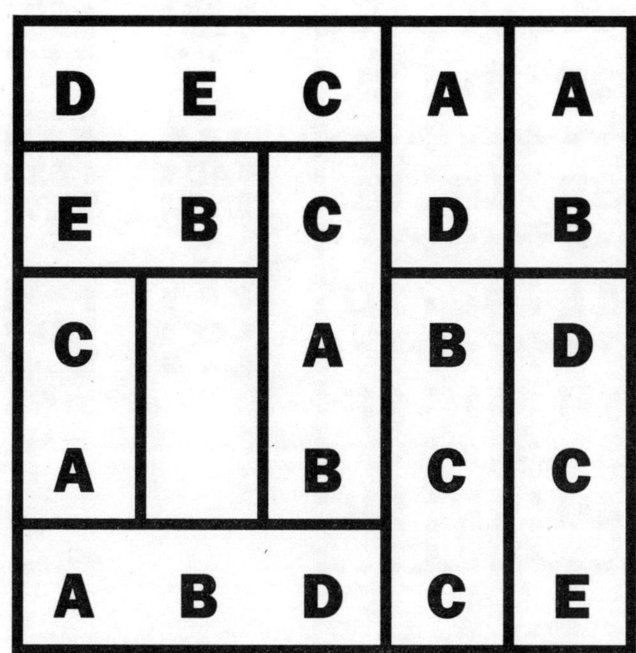

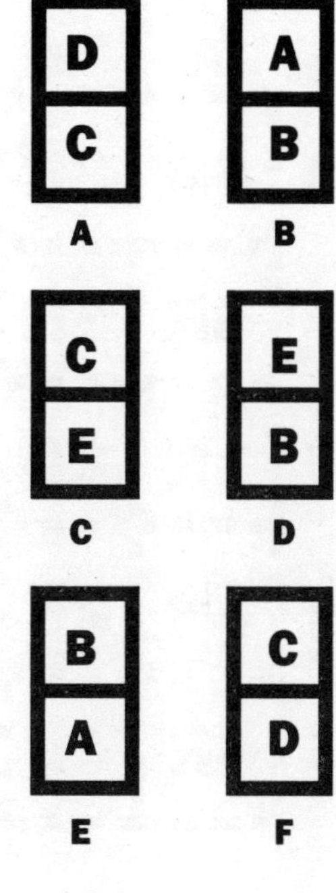

12 This square follows a logical pattern. Which of the tiles should be used to complete the square?

TEST 5 time limit 40 minutes

TEST 5

13 Each letter has a value. Work out the logic and discover what should replace the question mark.

A	B	C	D	5
E	F	G	H	11
I	J	K	L	32
M	N	O	P	?
22	14	20	30	

45 A	12 B	26 C
38 D	34 E	21 F

14 Here is an unusual safe. Each of the buttons must be pressed only once in the correct order to open it. The last button is marked F. The number of moves and the direction is marked on each button. Thus 1U would mean one move up, while 1L would mean one move to the left. Using the grid reference, which button is the first you must press?

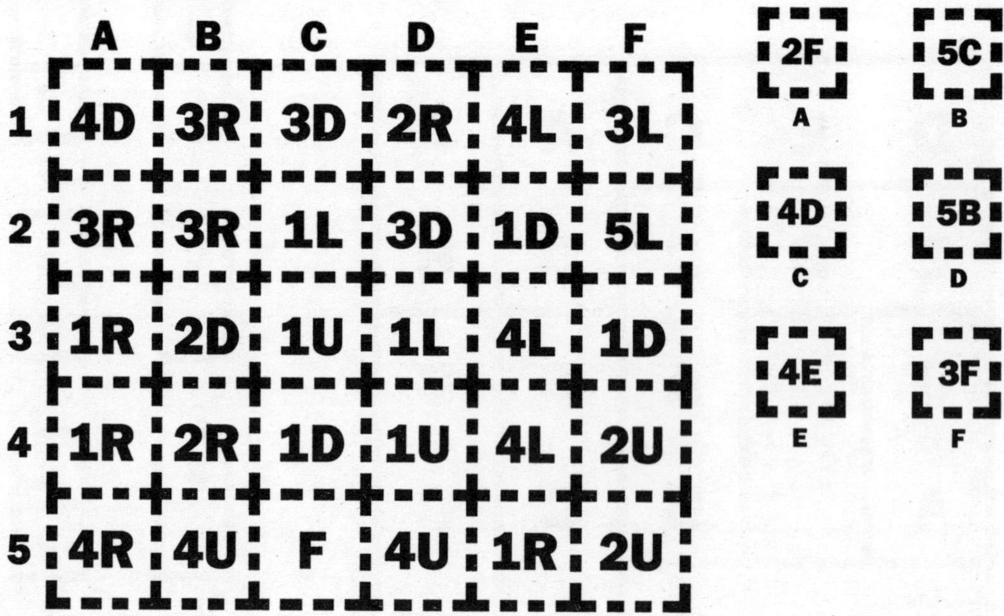

	A	B	C	D	E	F
1	4D	3R	3D	2R	4L	3L
2	3R	3R	1L	3D	1D	5L
3	1R	2D	1U	1L	4L	1D
4	1R	2R	1D	1U	4L	2U
5	4R	4U	F	4U	1R	2U

TEST 5 time limit 40 minutes

TEST 5

15 Move from ring to touching ring, starting from the bottom left corner and finishing in the top right corner. Collect nine numbers and total them. Which is the highest possible total?

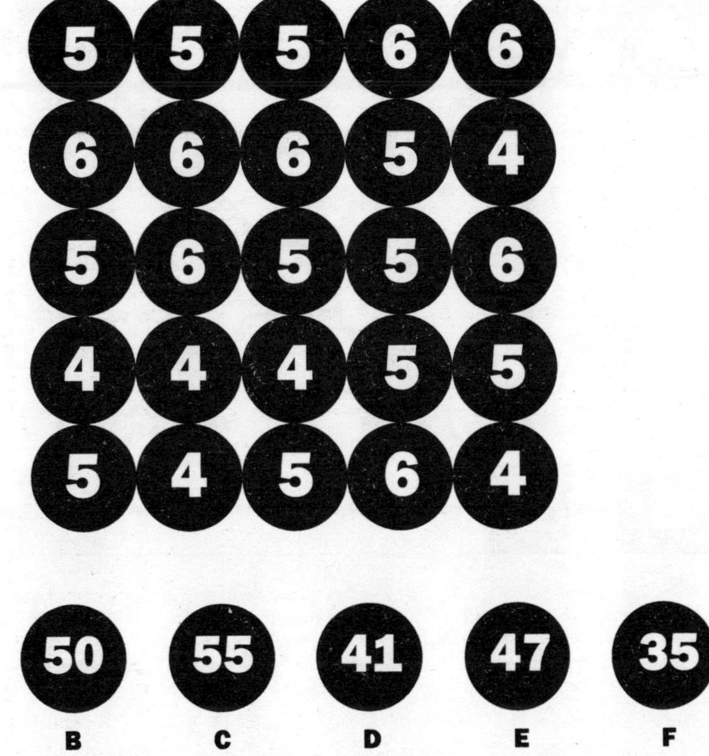

16 Which of the numbers should replace the question mark?

A	B	C	D
8	3	4	1
6	1	2	3
9	2	0	7
5	1	1	?

7 A	4 B
1 C	6 D
3 E	9 F

TEST 5 time limit 40 minutes

TEST 5

17 Start at any corner and follow the lines. Collect another four numbers and total the five. One of the numbers in the squares below can be used to complete the diagram. If the correct one has been chosen, one of the routes involving it will give a total of 20. Which one is it?

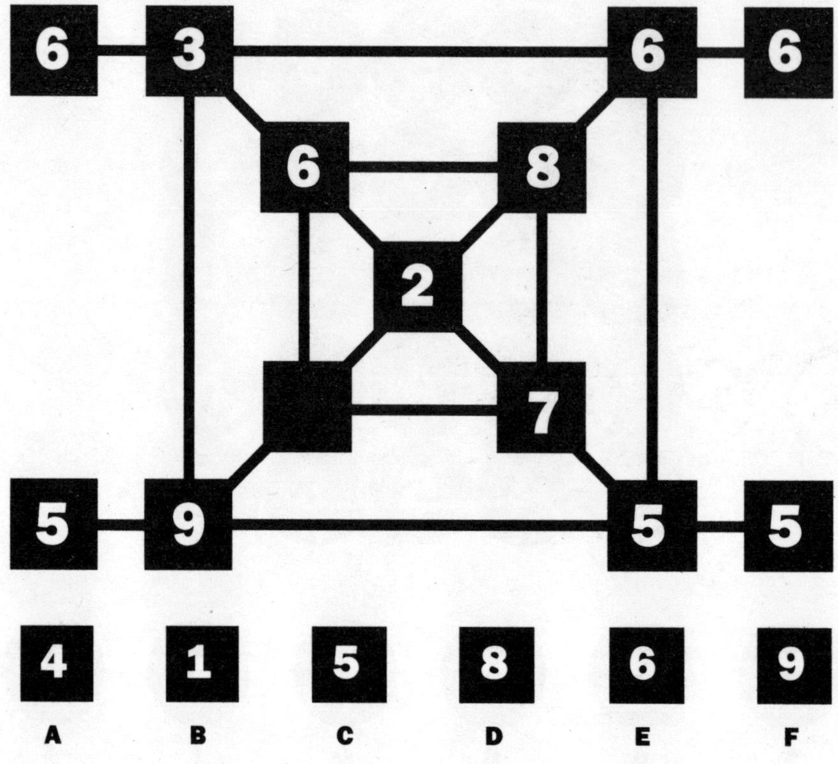

18 Scales one and two are in perfect balance. Which of these pans should replace the empty one?

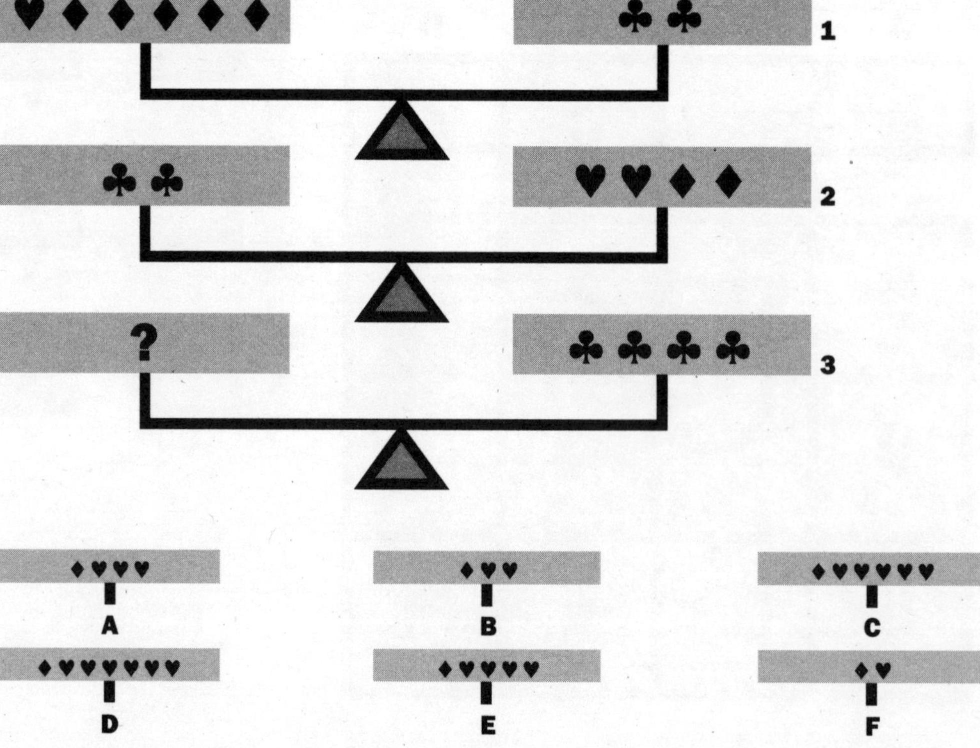

TEST 5 time limit 40 minutes

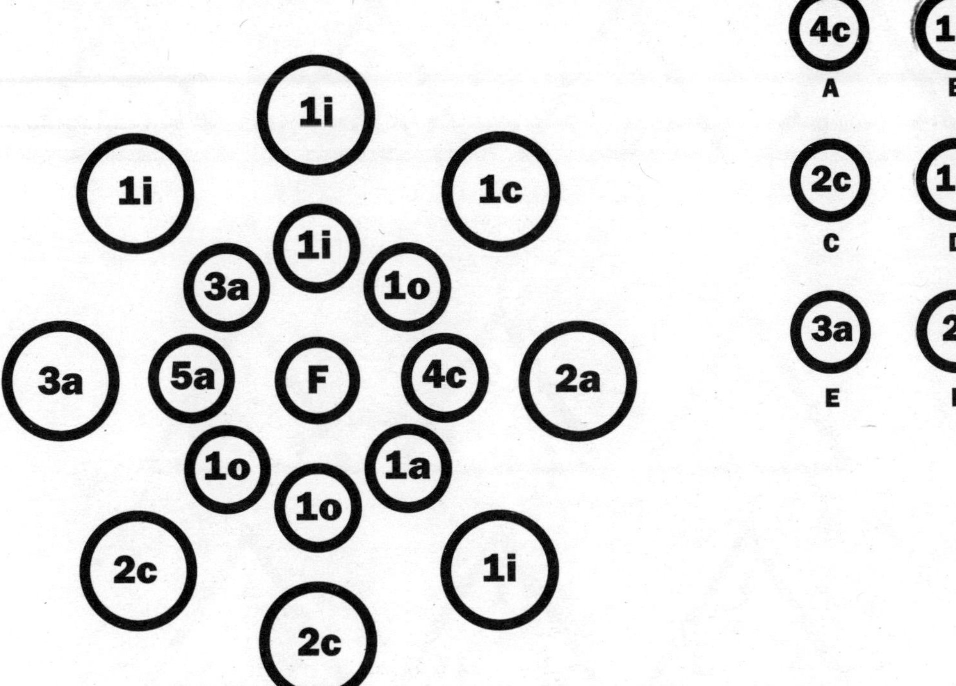

19 Here is an unusual safe. Each of the buttons must be pressed only once in the correct order to open it. The last button is marked F. The number of moves and the direction is marked on each button. Thus 1i would mean one move in, while 1o would mean one move out. 1c would mean one move clock-wise and 1a would mean one move anti-clockwise. Which button is the first you must press?

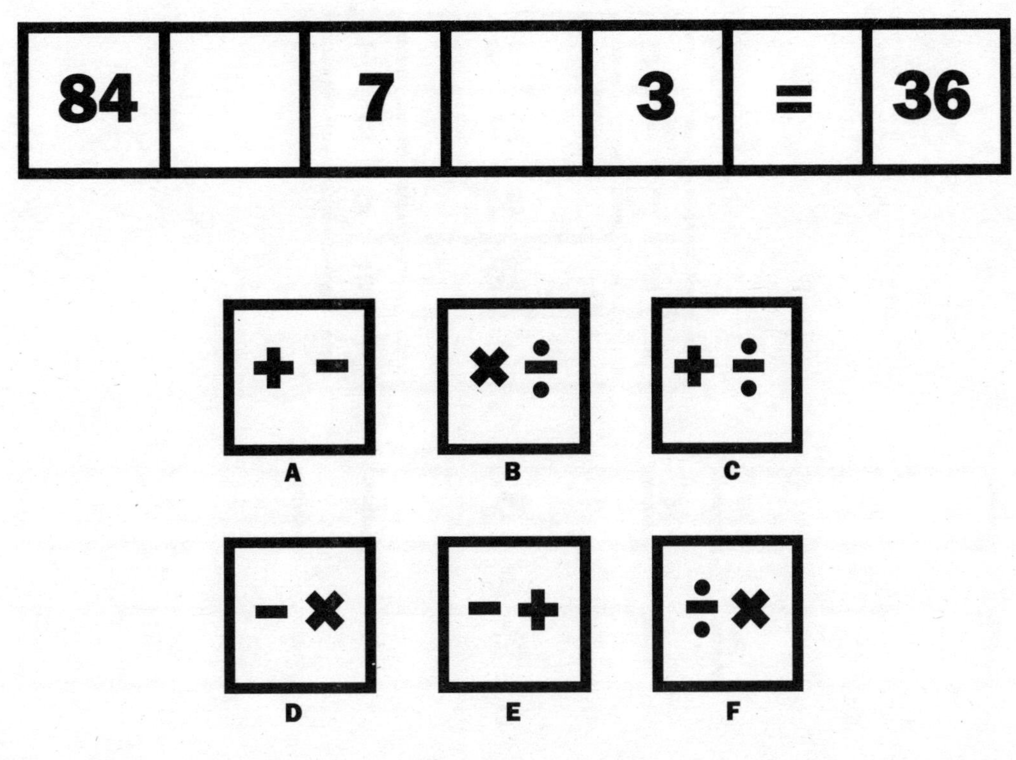

20 Insert the correct mathematical signs between each number in order to resolve the equation. What are the signs?

TEST 5 time limit 40 minutes

TEST 5

21 Which triangle belongs to this series?

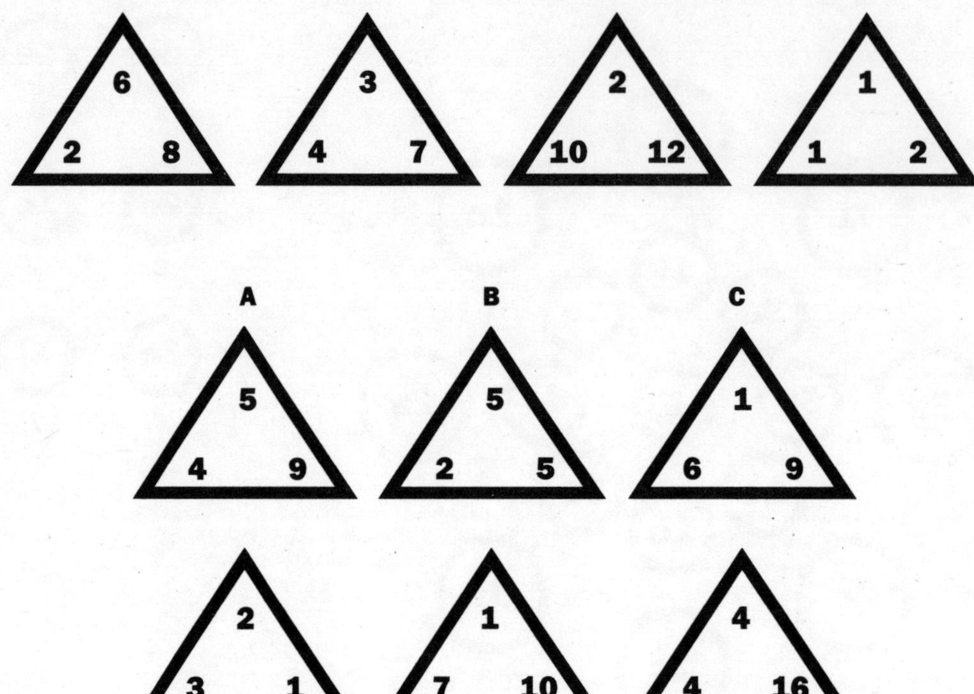

22 Discover the connection between the letters and the numbers. Which number should replace the question mark?

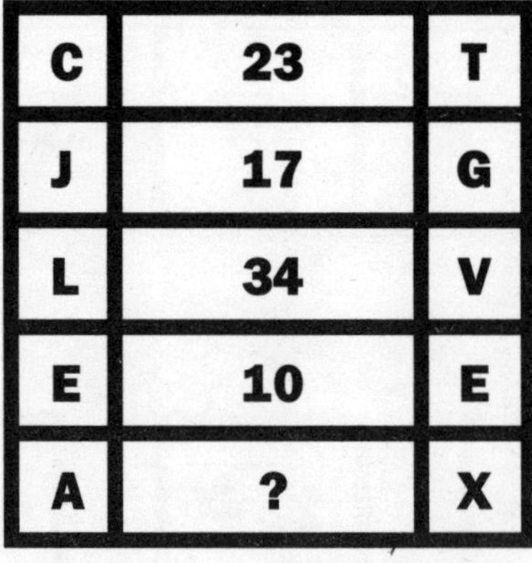

C	23	T
J	17	G
L	34	V
E	10	E
A	?	X

A	B	C
13	21	25

D	E	F
33	26	28

TEST 5 time limit 40 minutes

23 Which of the clocks continues this series?

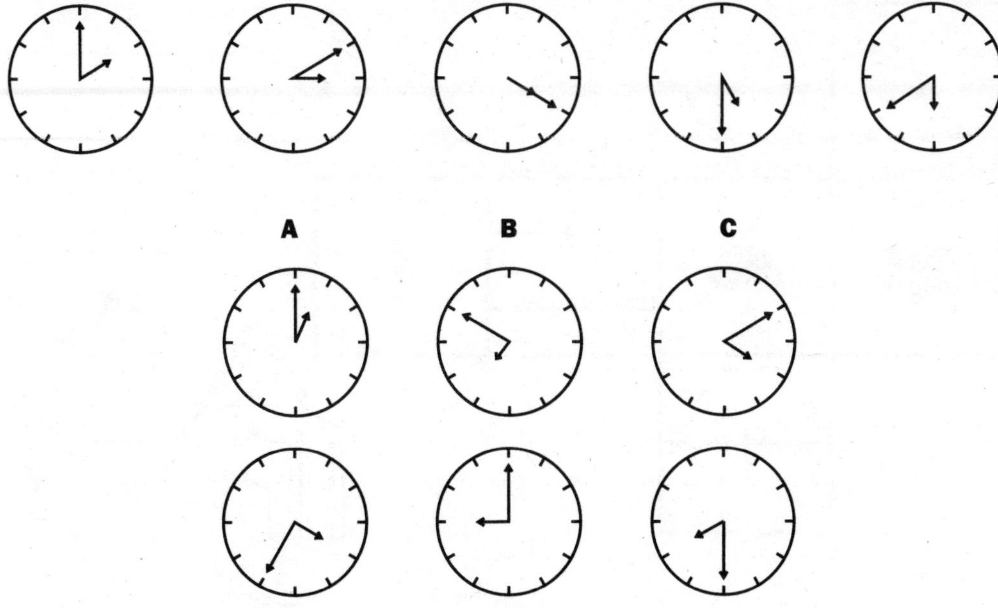

24 Which of the numbers should replace the question mark?

9	7	8	5
3	1	4	3
8	8	7	6
2	2	3	?

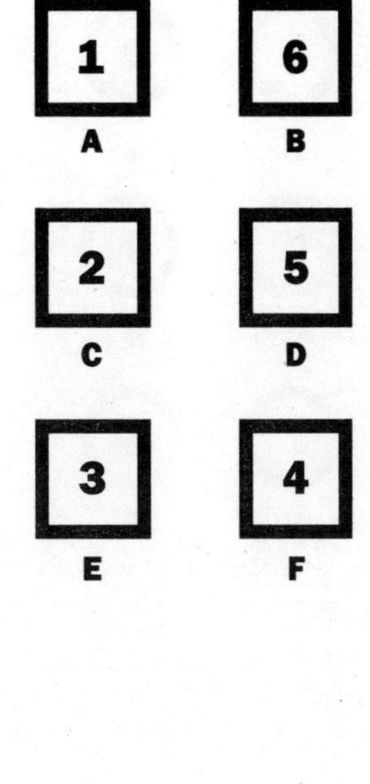

TEST 5 time limit 40 minutes

TEST 5

25 Which of the constructed boxes can be made from the pattern?

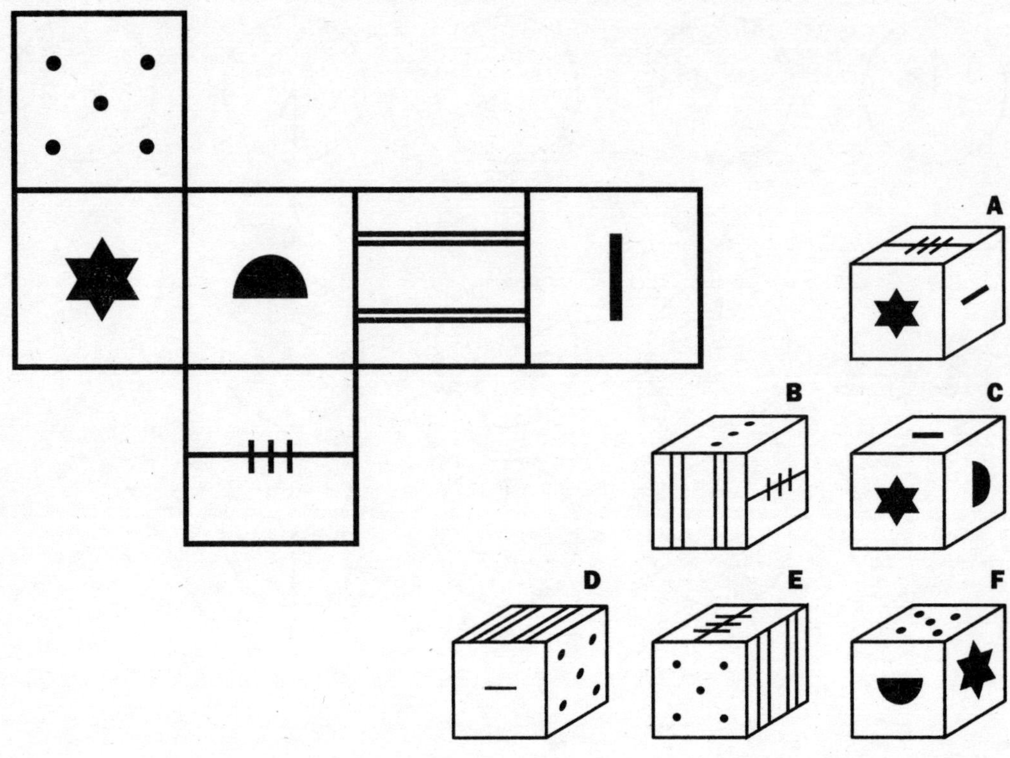

26 When rearranged the shapes will give a letter. Which of the letters is it?

TEST 5 time limit 40 minutes

TEST 5

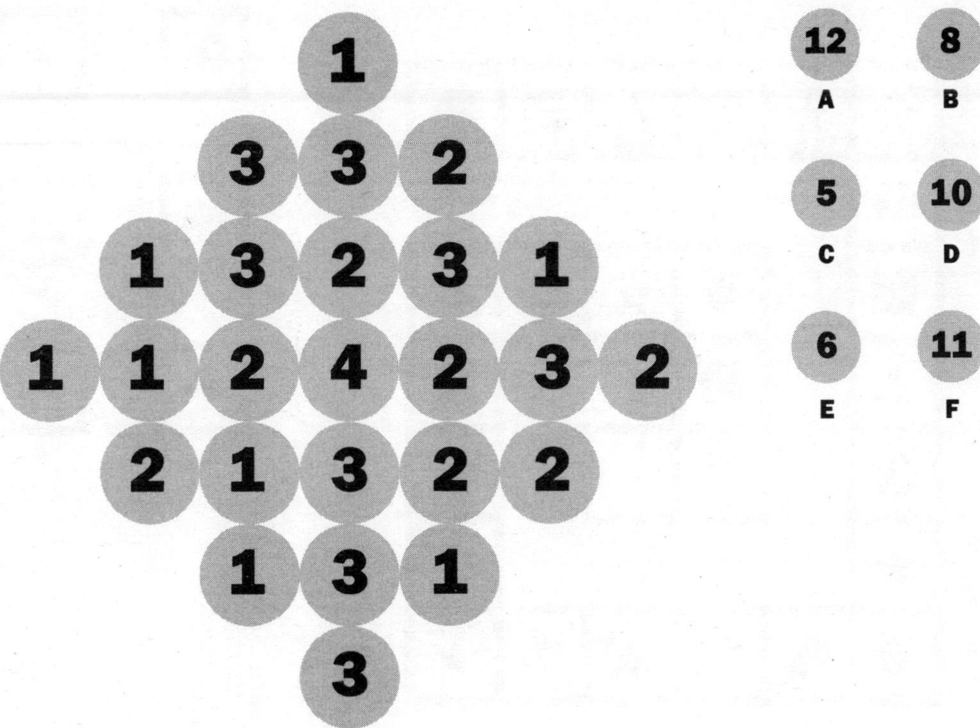

27 Start at 4 and move from circle to touching circle. Collect four numbers each time. How many different routes are there to collect 10? A reversed route counts twice.

12	10	14		12
7	14	14	14	1
12	18			8
11			?	21
8	2		26	8

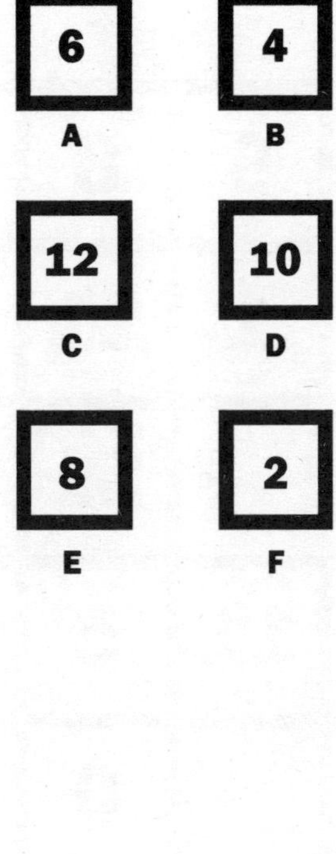

28 Each straight line of five numbers should total 50. Which of the numbers will replace the question mark?

TEST 5 time limit 40 minutes

TEST 5

29 Which of the boxes should be used to replace the question mark?

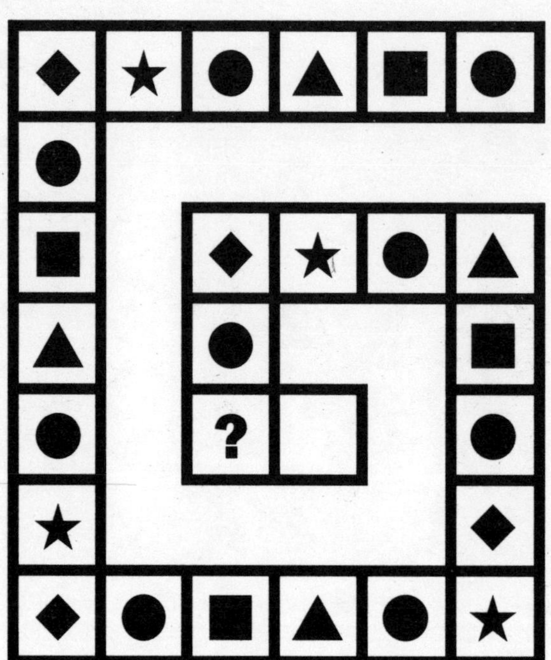

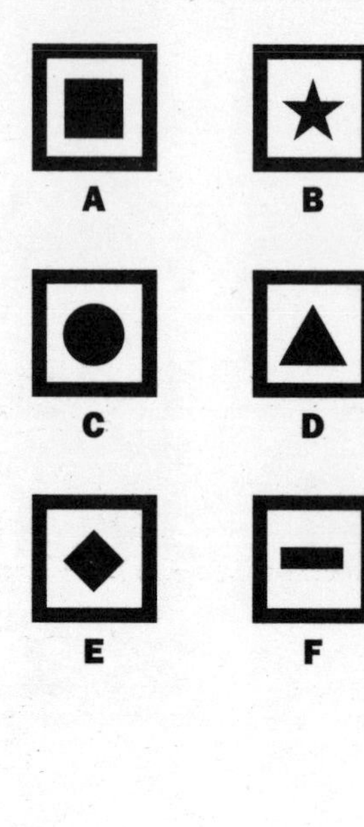

30 Each straight line of five numbers should total 35. Only two numbers must be used to complete the square. Which of the numbers will replace the question mark?

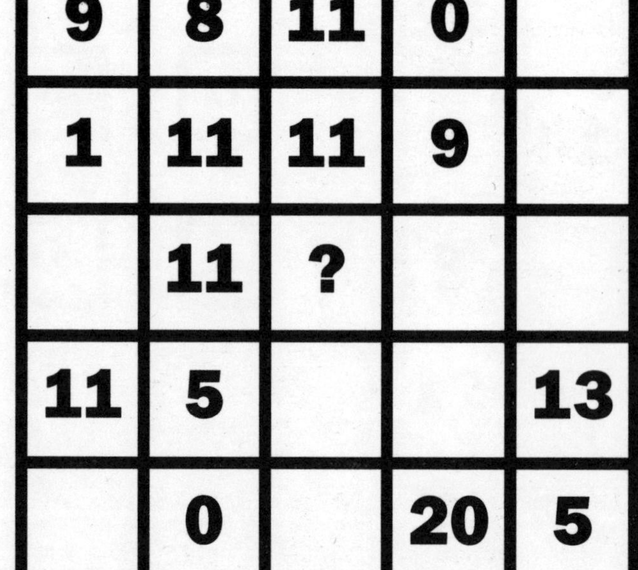

9	8	11	0	
1	11	11	9	
	11	?		
11	5			13
	0		20	5

12	9
A	B
1	10
C	D
7	4
E	F

TEST 5 time limit 40 minutes

TEST 6

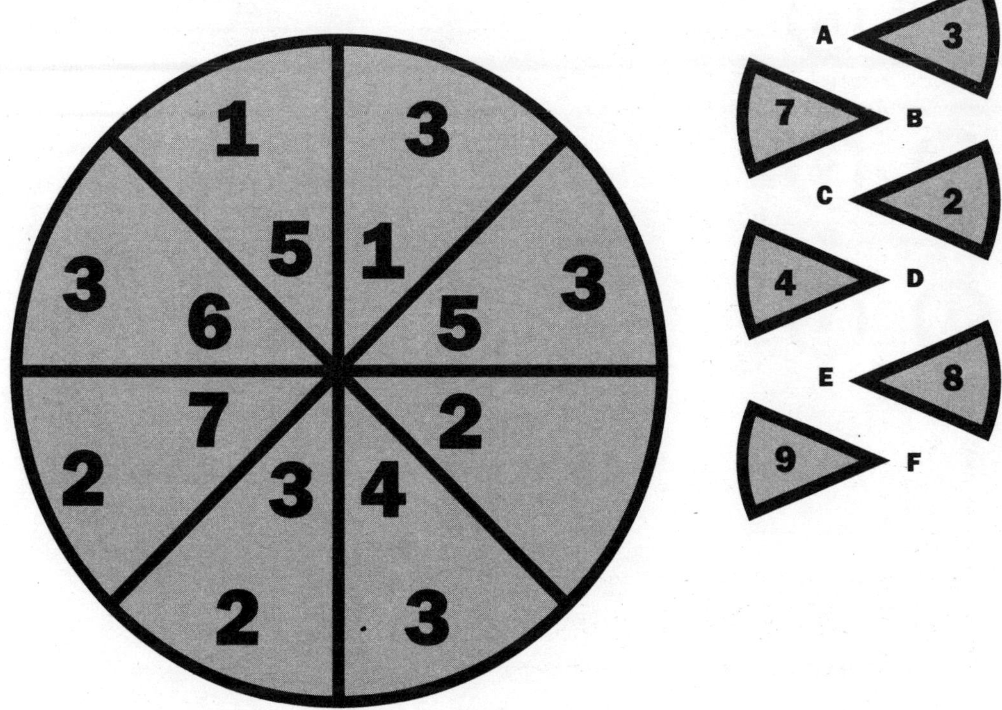

1 Which of the slices should be used to complete the cake?

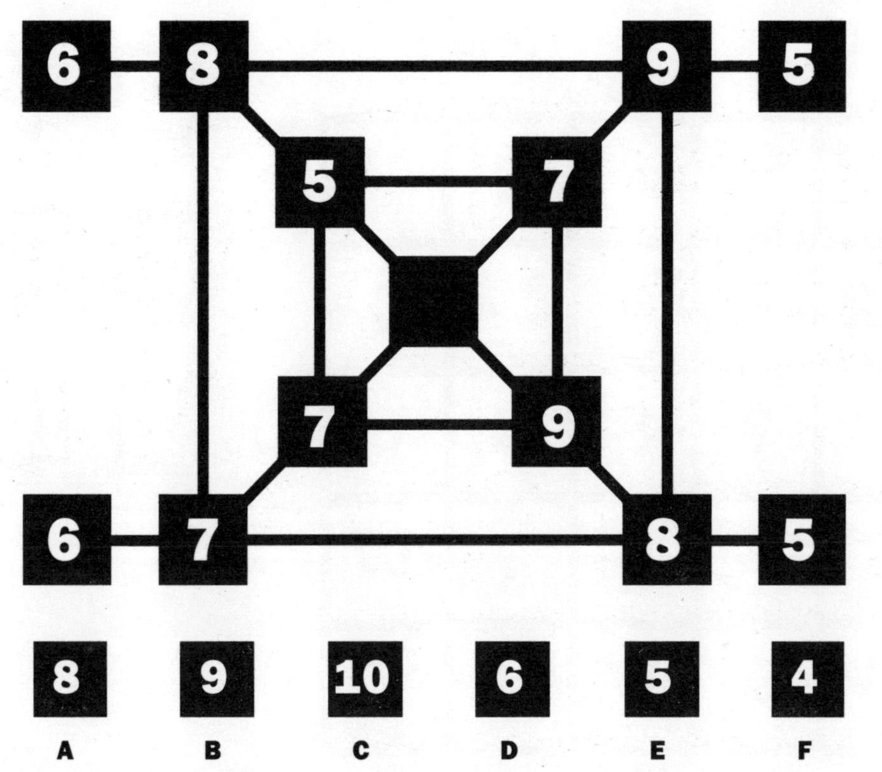

2 Start at any corner and follow the lines. Collect another four numbers and total the five. One of the numbers in the squares below can be used to complete the diagram. If the correct one has been chosen, one of the routes involving it will give a total of 41. Which one is it?

TEST 6 time limit 45 minutes

TEST 6

3 When rearranged the shapes will give a letter. Which of the letters is it?

4 Each straight line of five numbers should total 40. Only two numbers are used to complete the square. Which of the numbers will replace the question mark?

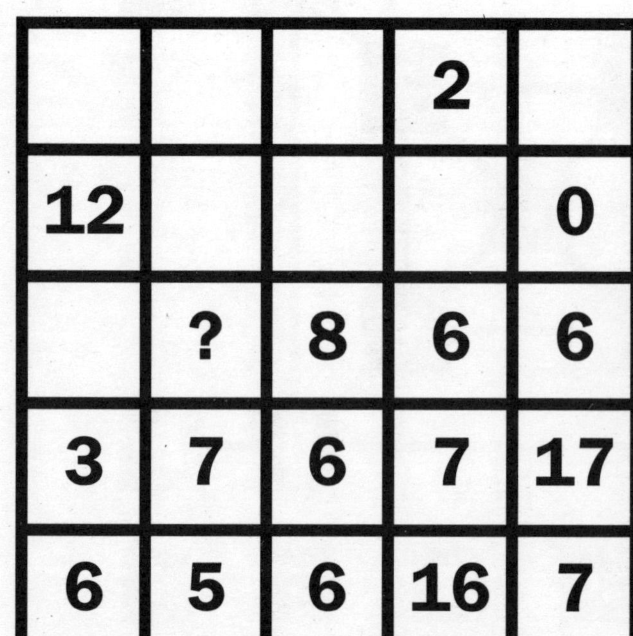

			2	
12				0
	?	8	6	6
3	7	6	7	17
6	5	6	16	7

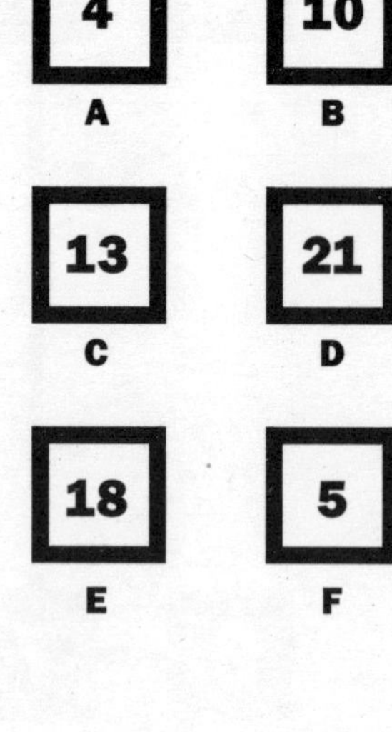

TEST 6 time limit 45 minutes

TEST 6

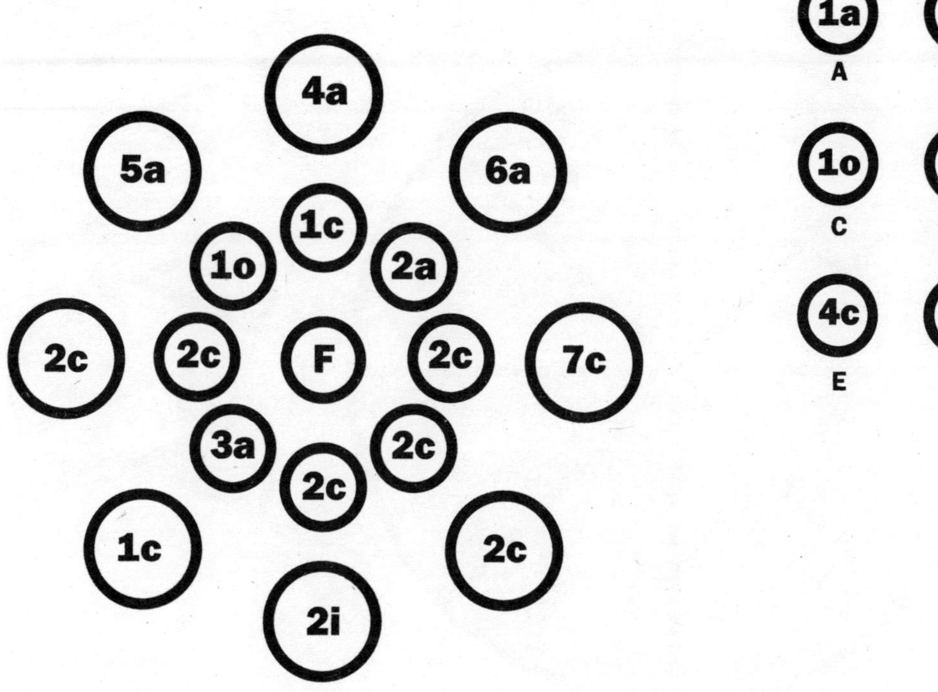

5 Here is an unusual safe. Each of the buttons must be pressed only once in the correct order to open it. The last button is marked F. The number of moves and the direction is marked on each button. Thus 1i would mean one move in, while 1o would mean one move out. 1c would mean one move clockwise and 1a would mean one move anti-clockwise. Which button is the first you must press?

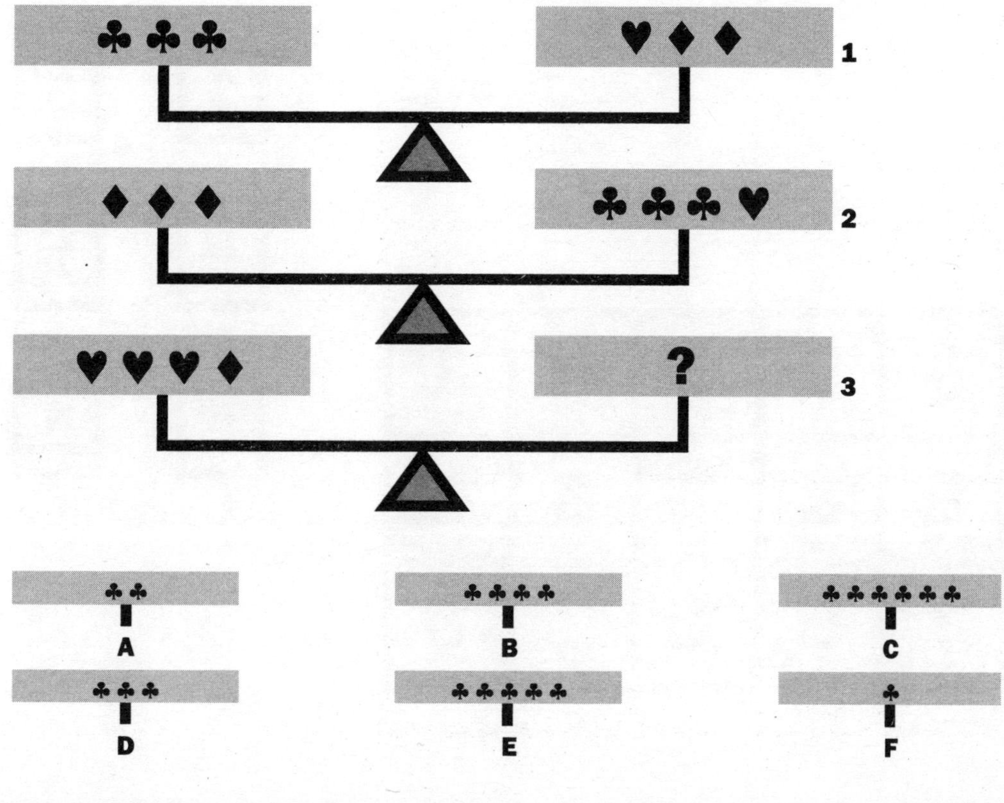

6 Scales one and two are in perfect balance. Which of these pans should replace the empty one?

TEST 6 time limit 45 minutes

TEST 6

7 Which of the slices should be used to complete the cake?

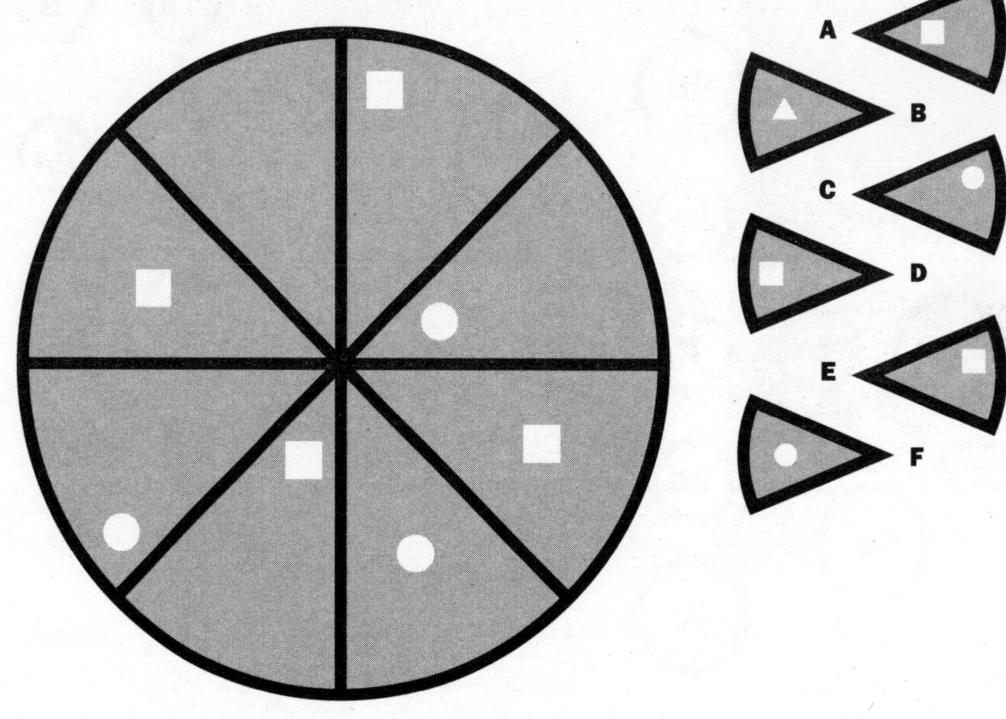

8 Which of the numbers should replace the question mark?

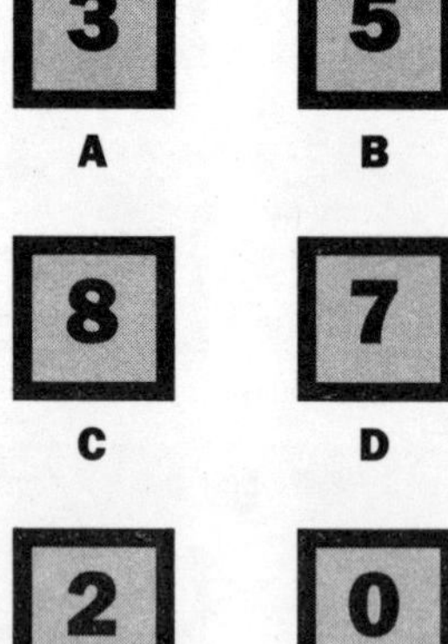

6	3	9	4	1
5	8	7	6	3
?	5	1	7	8

TEST 6 time limit 45 minutes

TEST 6

E F

9 Which arrow is missing from this series?

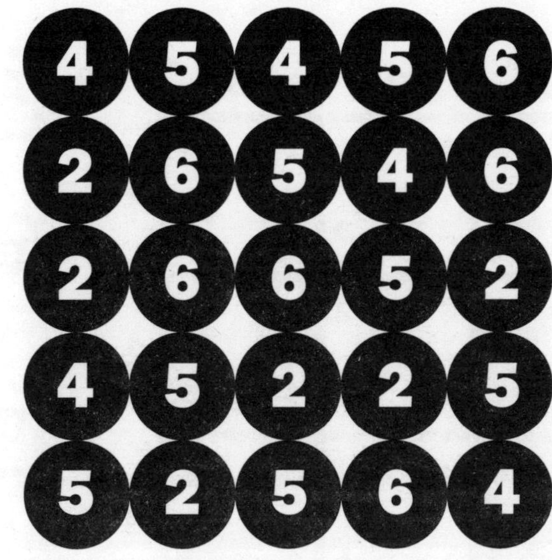

53
C

10 Move from ring to touching ring, starting from the bottom left corner and finishing in the top right corner. Collect nine numbers and total them. Which is the highest possible total?

TEST 6 time limit 45 minutes

TEST 6

11 This square follows a logical pattern. Which of the tiles should be used to complete the square?

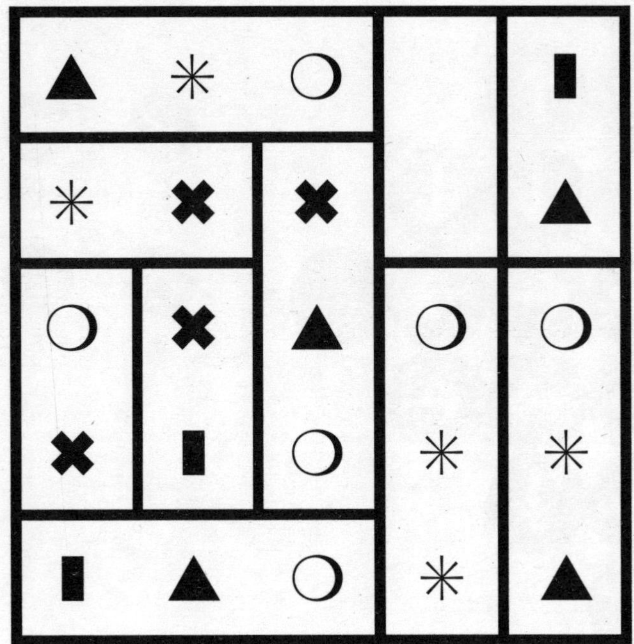

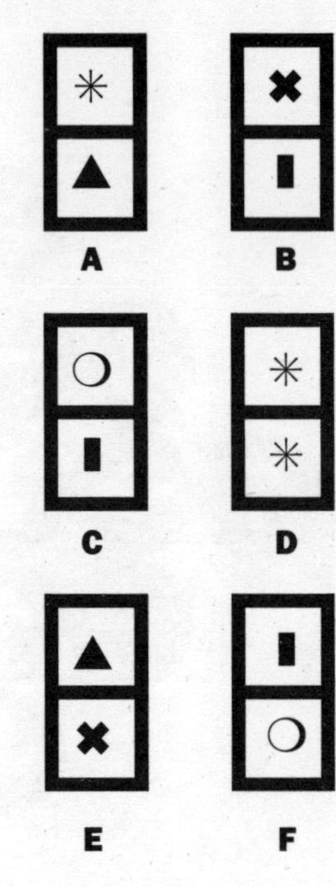

12 Which square's contents matches D4?

	A	B	C	D
1	1 1 5 5	5 1 2 3	3 1 2 3	1 3 5 4
2	2 3 4 3	4 4 1 4	4 2 2 5	3 3 4 5
3	3 3 4 3	1 4 2 5	4 4 1 1	2 5 4 3
4	3 4 2 2	5 3 4 4	4 2 3 1	3 5 1 2

A	B
A2	C1

C	D
D3	C3

E	F
B4	B1

TEST 6 time limit 45 minutes

TEST 6

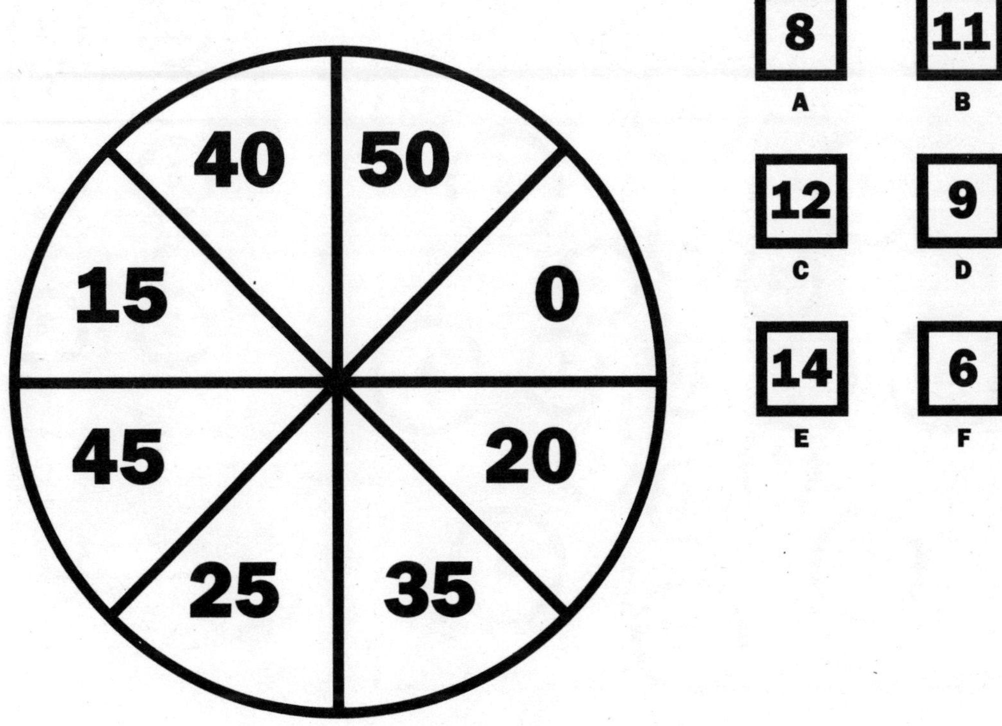

13 How many ways are there to score 85 on this dartboard using four darts only? Each dart always lands in a sector and no dart falls to the floor.

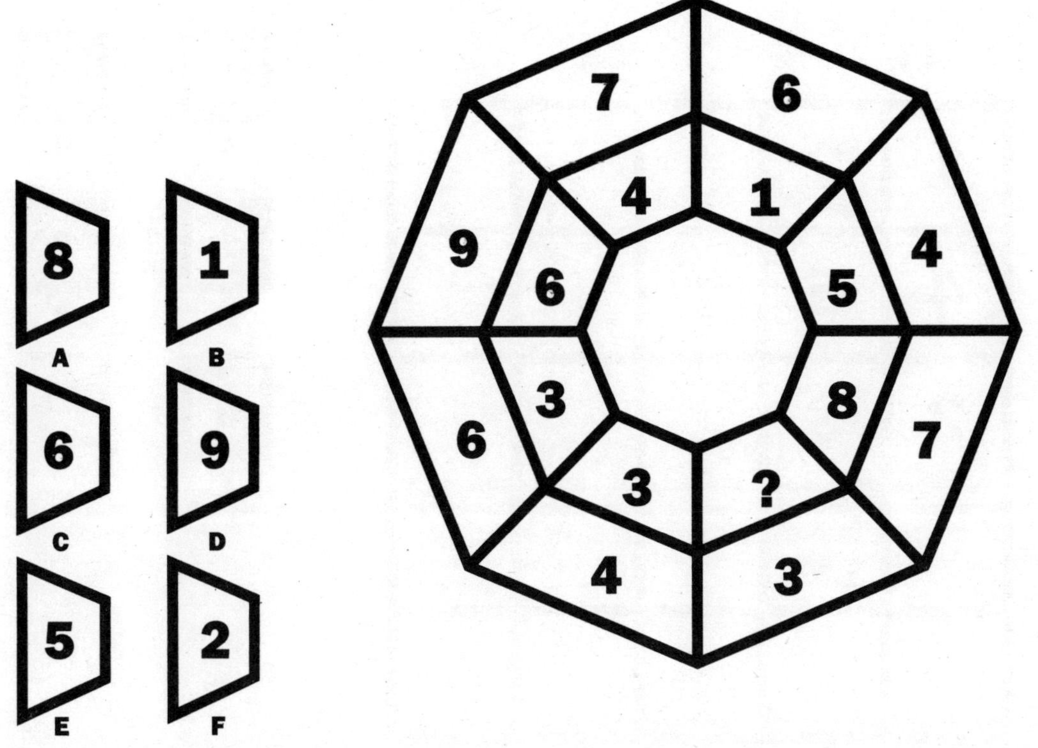

14 Which of the numbers should logically replace the question mark in the octagon?

TEST 6 time limit 45 minutes

TEST 6

15 Which circle should replace the empty one?

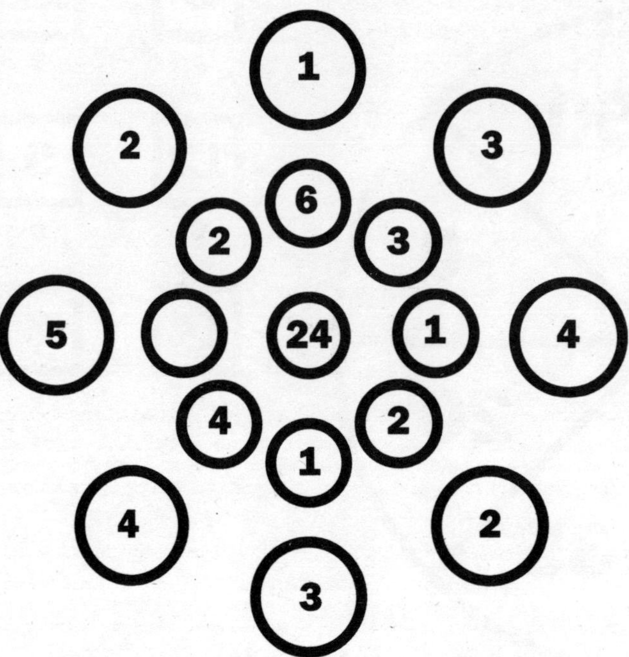

8 A
3 B
6 C
1 D
5 E
2 F

16 Complete the square using the five numbers shown. When completed no row, column or diagonal line will use the same number more than once. What should replace the question mark?

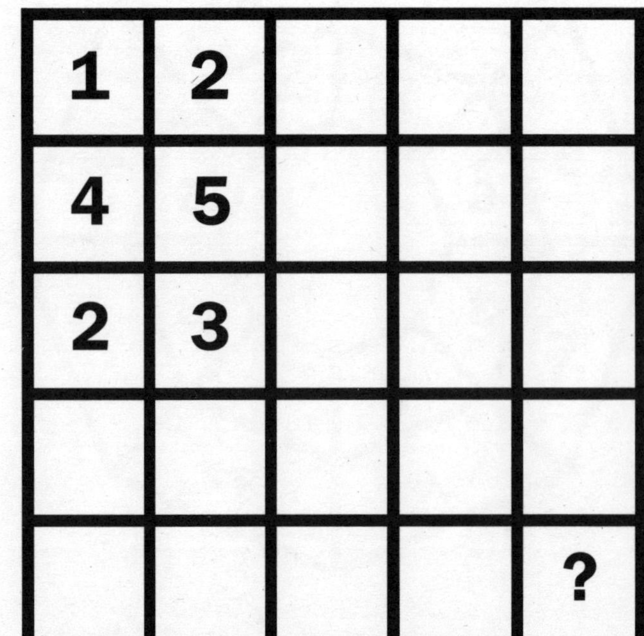

4 A
5 B
1 C
2 D
3 E

TEST 6 time limit 45 minutes

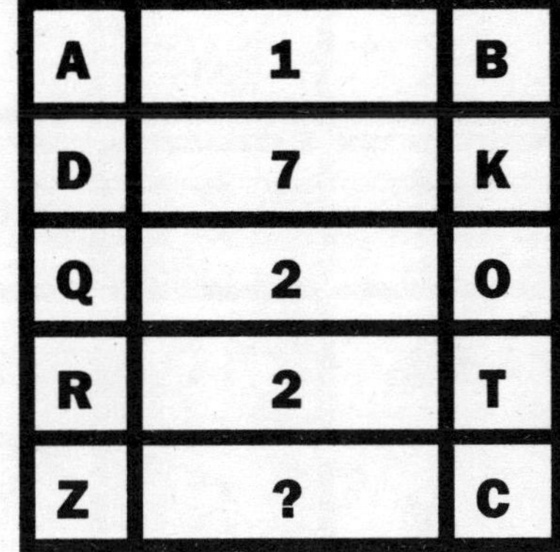

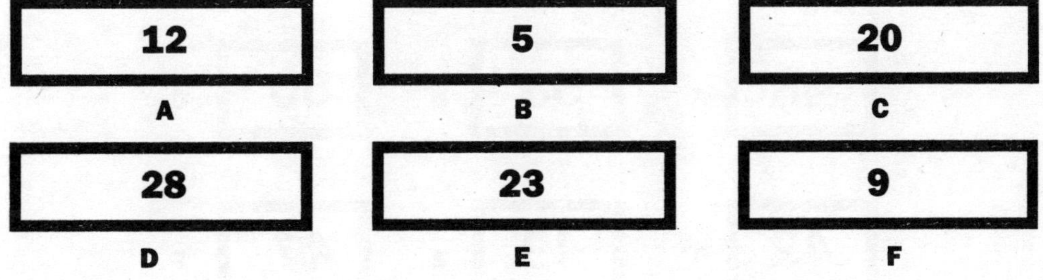

17 Discover the connection between the letters and the numbers. Which number should replace the question mark?

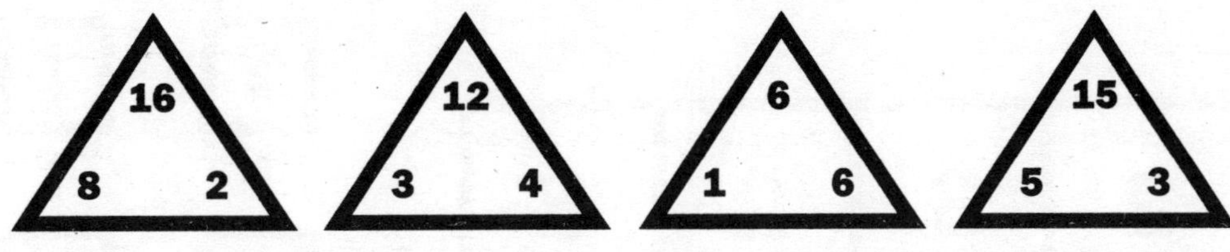

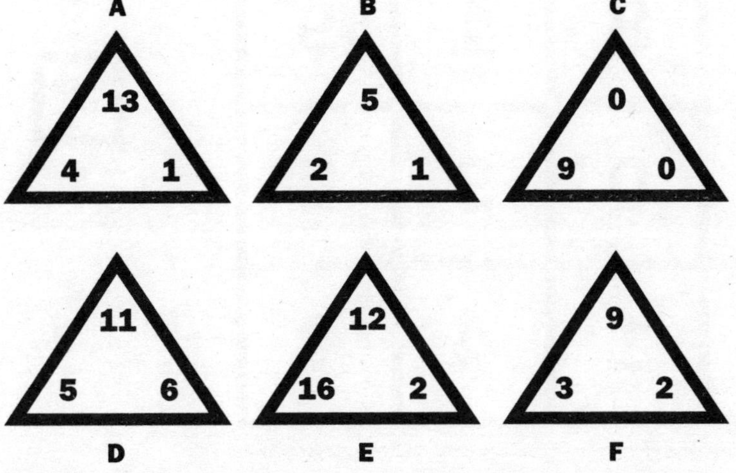

18 Which triangle belongs to this series?

TEST 6

19 Each same symbol has a value. Work out the logic and discover what should replace the question mark.

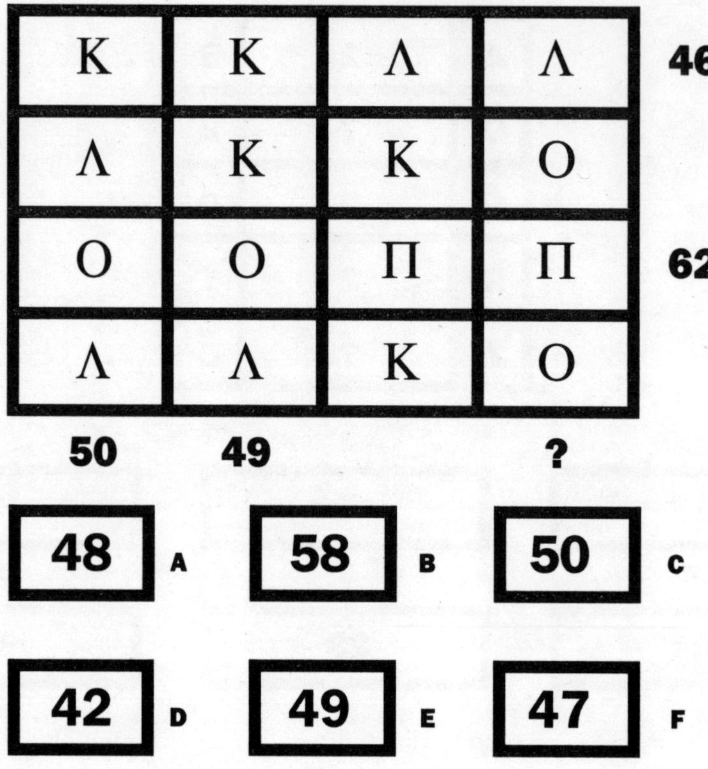

20 Which of the numbers should replace the question mark?

2	3	2	8
1	8	1	9
3	0	3	3
1	1	4	?

2 A

1 B

4 C

5 D

8 E

7 F

TEST 6 time limit 45 minutes

TEST 6

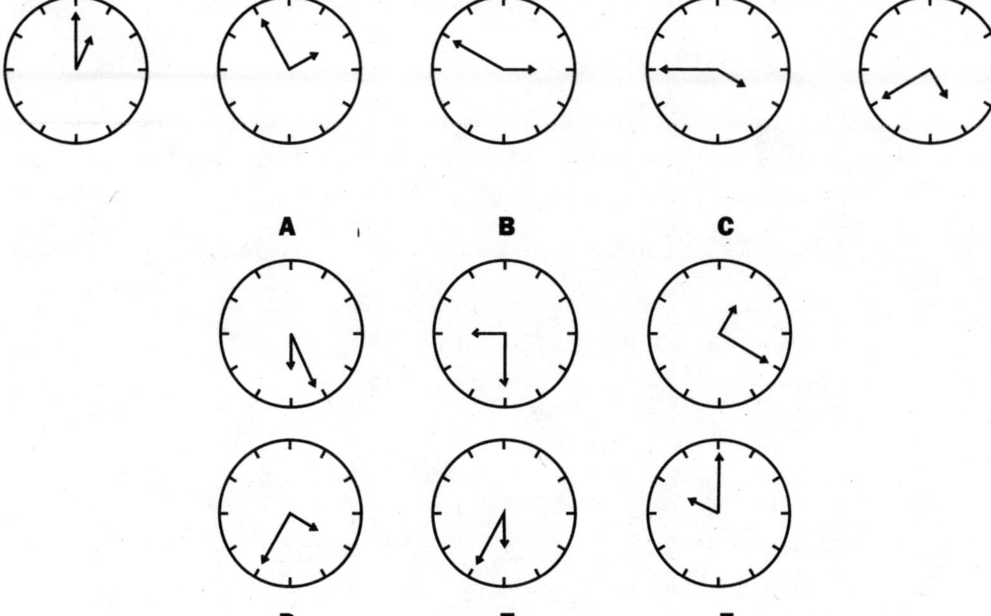

21 Which of the clocks continues this series?

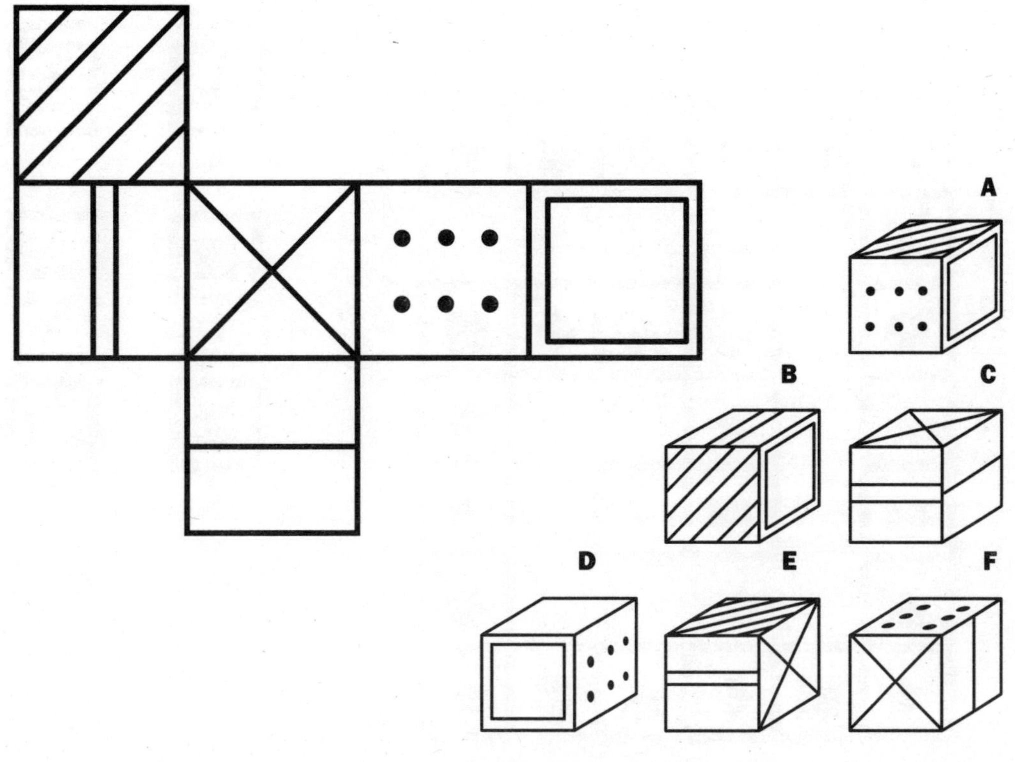

22 Which of the constructed boxes cannot be made from the pattern?

TEST 6 time limit 45 minutes

TEST 6

23 Which of the slices should be used to complete the cake?

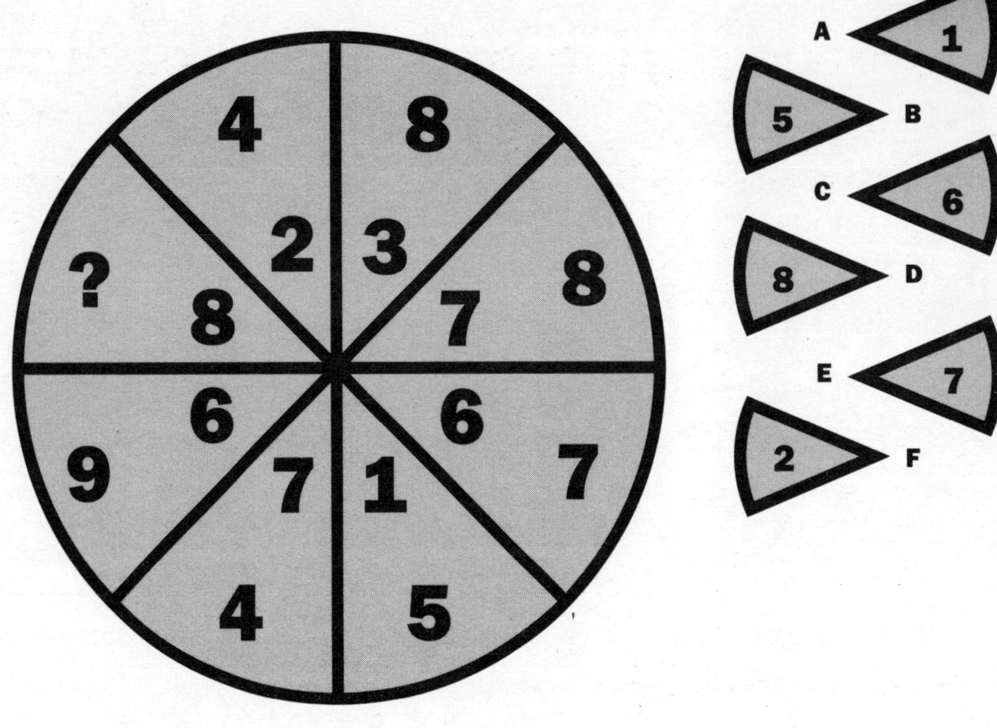

24 Which of the boxes should be used to replace the question mark?

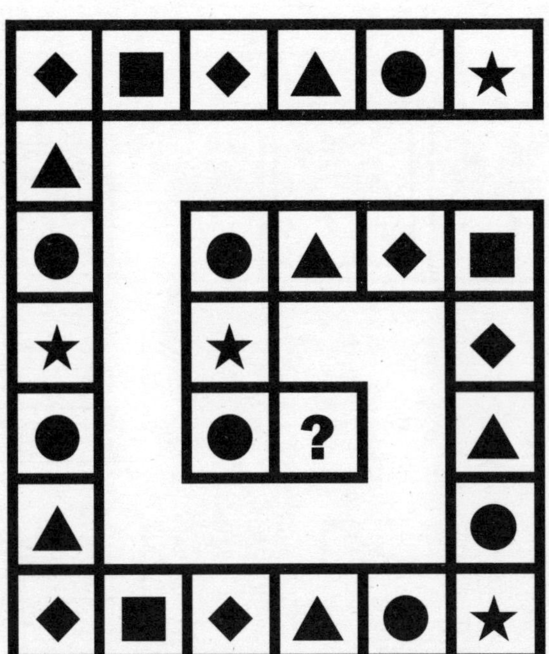

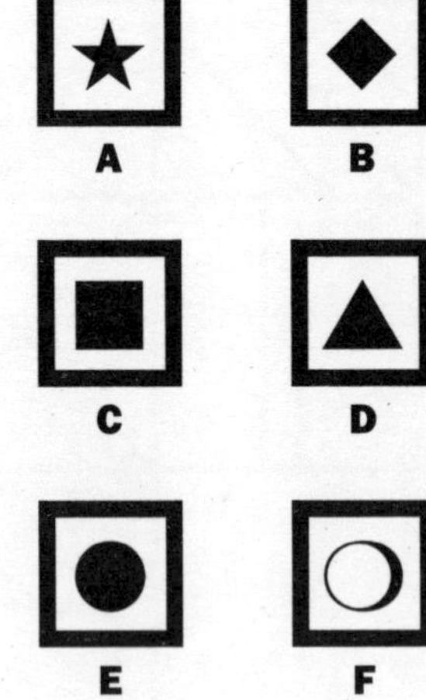

TEST 6 time limit 45 minutes

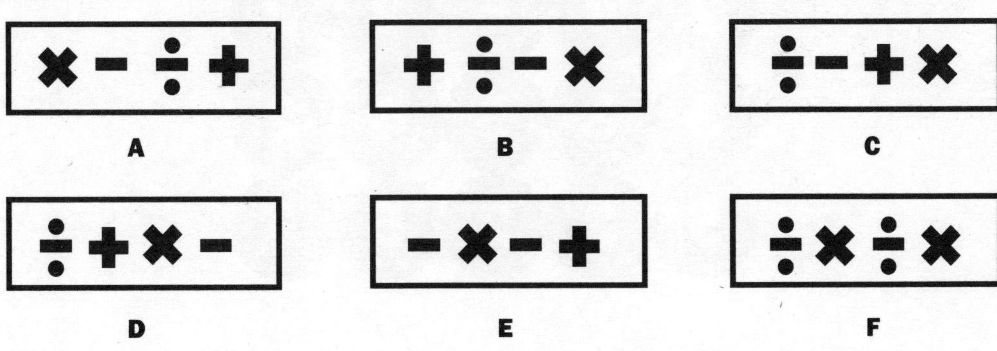

25 Insert the correct mathematical signs between each number in order to resolve the equation. What are the signs?

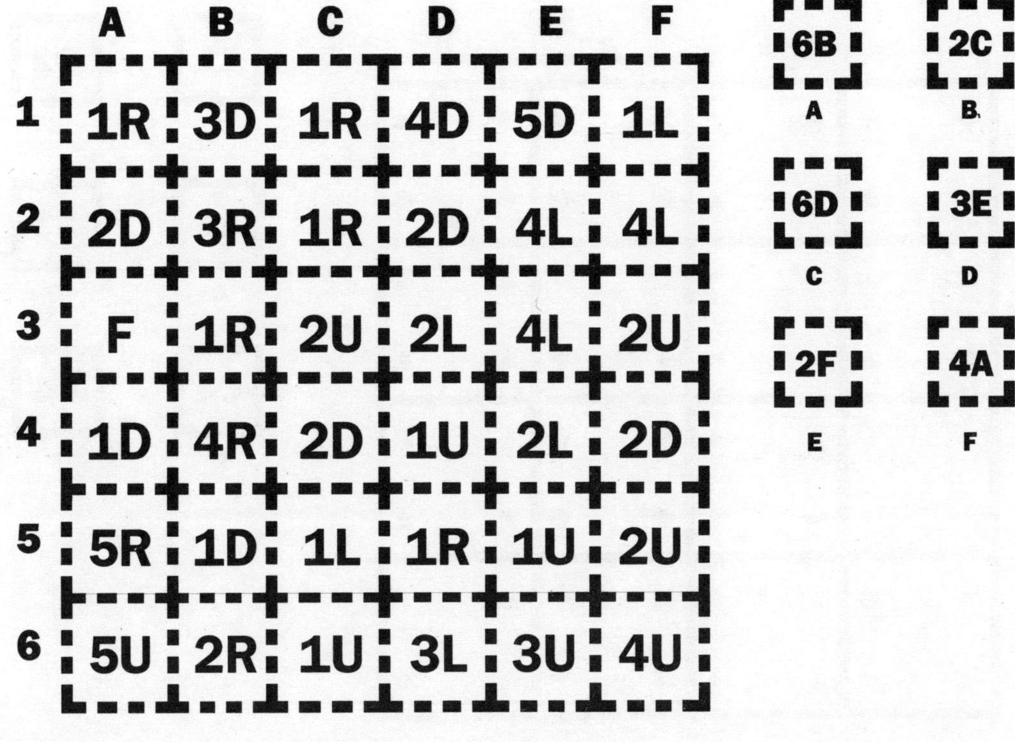

	A	B	C	D	E	F
1	1R	3D	1R	4D	5D	1L
2	2D	3R	1R	2D	4L	4L
3	F	1R	2U	2L	4L	2U
4	1D	4R	2D	1U	2L	2D
5	5R	1D	1L	1R	1U	2U
6	5U	2R	1U	3L	3U	4U

26 Here is an unusual safe. Each of the buttons must be pressed only once in the correct order to open it. The last button is marked F. The number of moves and the direction is marked on each button. Thus 1U would mean one move up, while 1Lwould mean one move to the left. Using the grid reference, which button is the first you must press?

TEST 6 time limit 45 minutes

TEST 6

27 Move from ring to touching ring, starting from the bottom left corner and finishing in the top right corner. Collect nine numbers and total them. Which is the highest possible total?

28 Which square's contents matches B1?

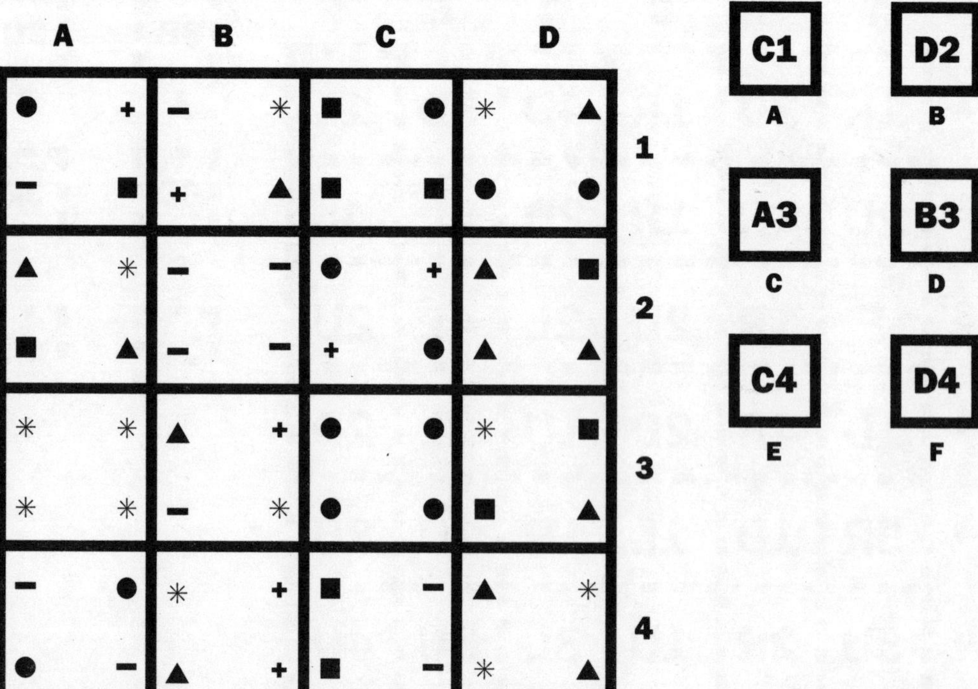

TEST 6 time limit 45 minutes

TEST 6

29 Which arrow is missing from this series?

30 How many ways are there to score 58 on this dartboard using four darts only? Each dart always lands in a sector and no dart falls to the floor.

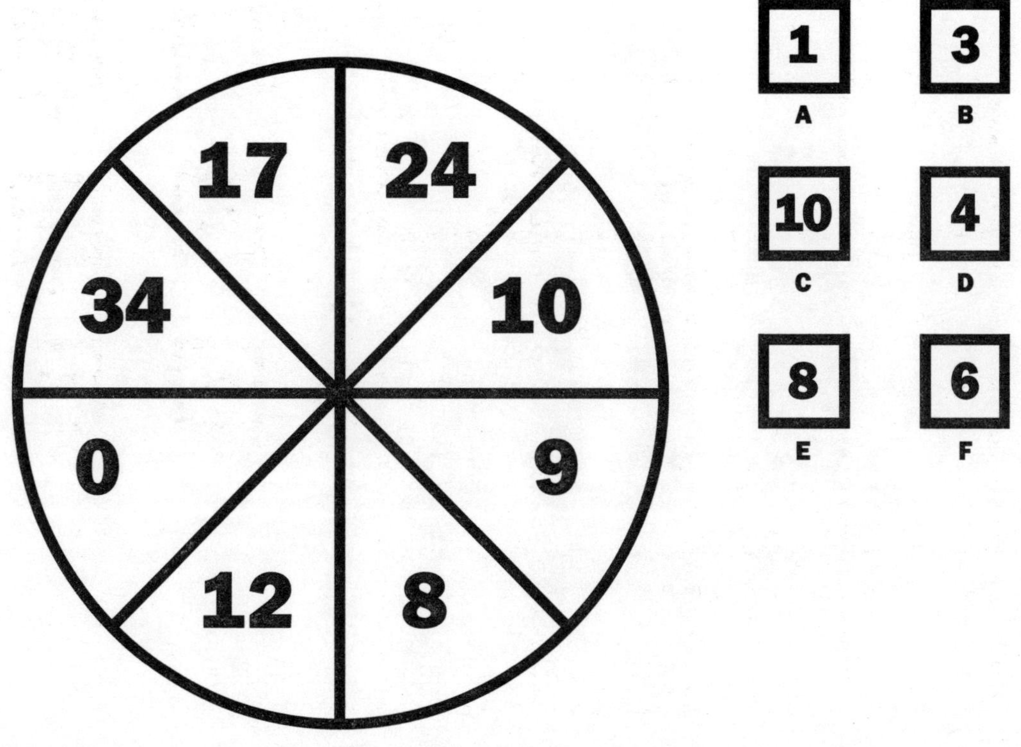

TEST 6 time limit 45 minutes

TEST 7

1 Which triangle belongs to this series?

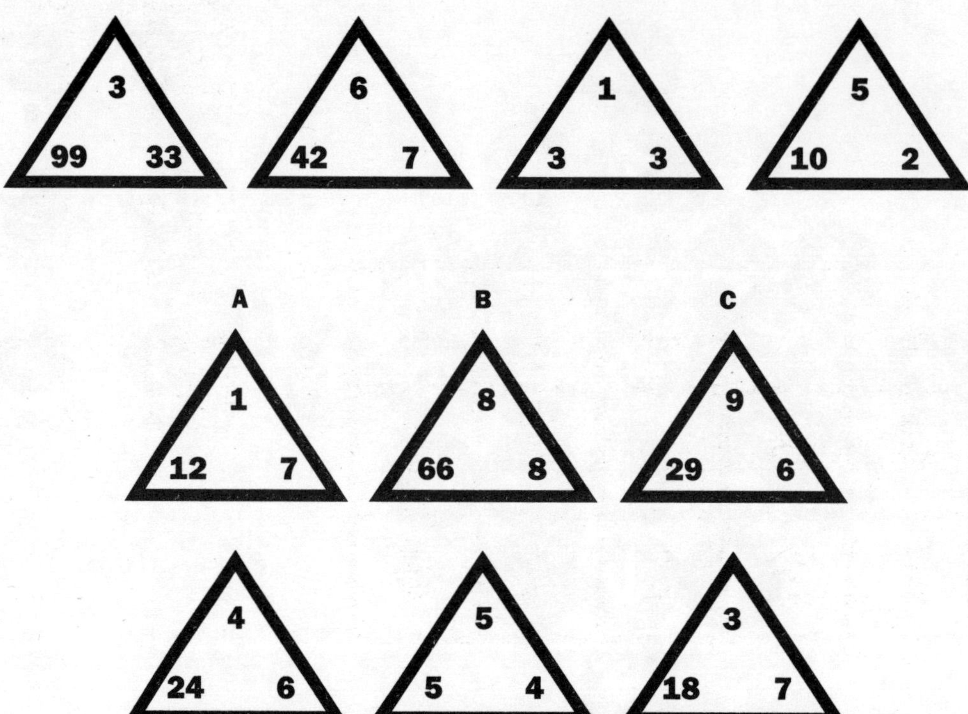

2 Start at 15 and move from circle to touching circle. Collect four numbers each time. How many different routes are there to collect 50? A reversed route counts twice.

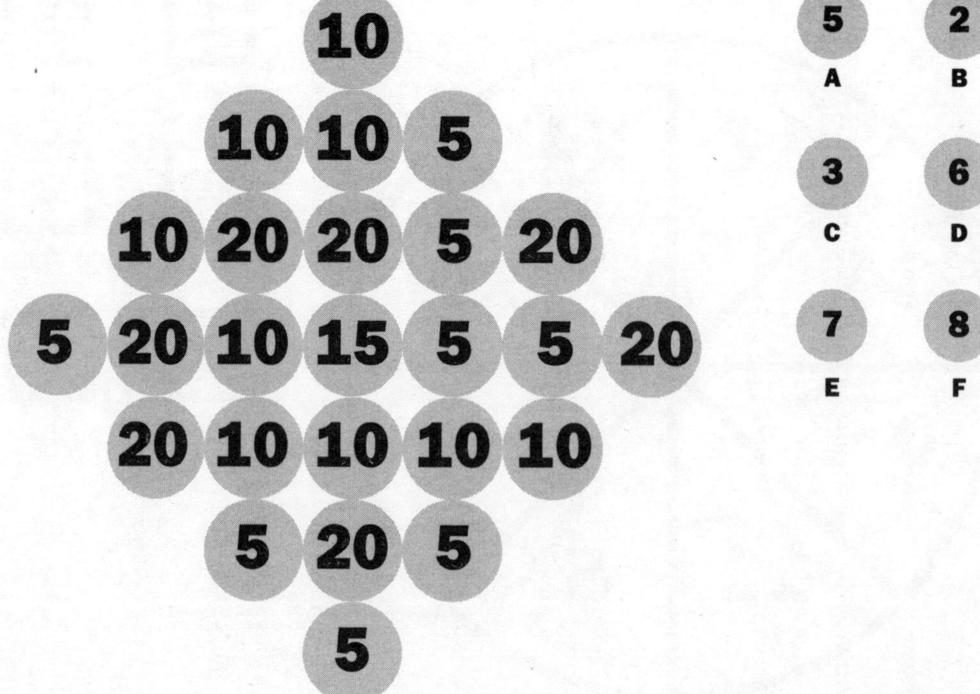

TEST 7 time limit 1 hour

3 Which of the numbers should replace the question mark?

2	2	5	7	0
4	9	5	7	?
7	2	1	4	6

1 (A)	3 (B)
8 (C)	9 (D)
6 (E)	4 (F)

4 Which of the numbers should logically replace the question mark in the octagon?

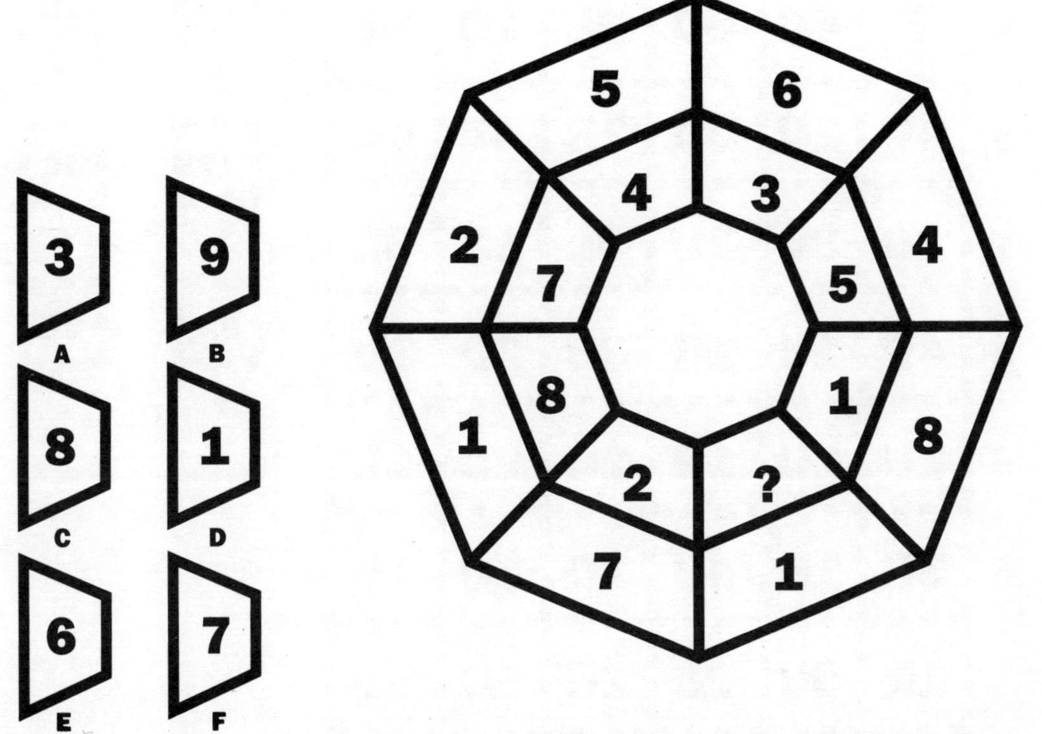

TEST 7 time limit 1 hour

TEST 7

5 Complete the square using the five symbols shown. When completed no row, column or diagonal line will use the same symbol more than once. What should replace the question mark?

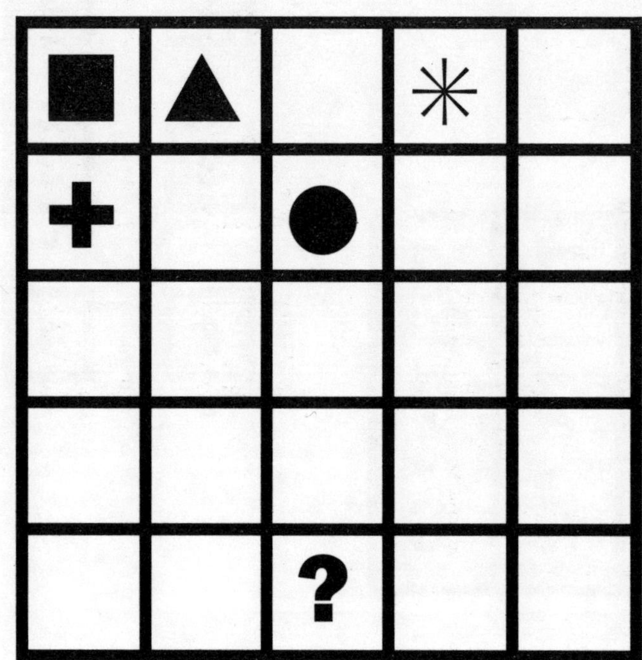

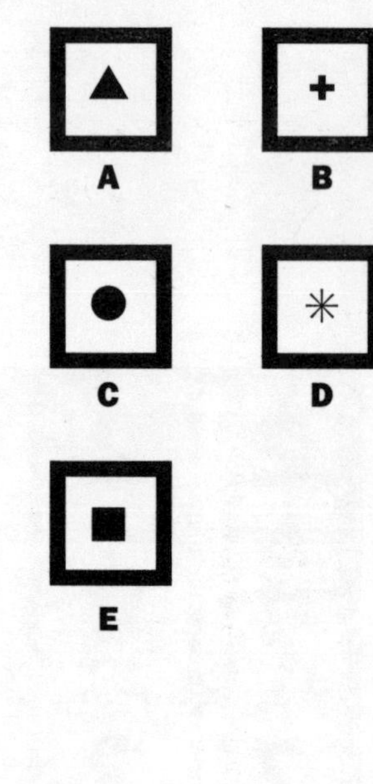

6 Here is an unusual safe. Each of the buttons must be pressed only once in the correct order to open it. The last button is marked F. The number of moves and the direction is marked on each button. Thus 1U would mean one move up, whilst 1L would mean one move to the left. Using the grid reference, which button is the first you must press?

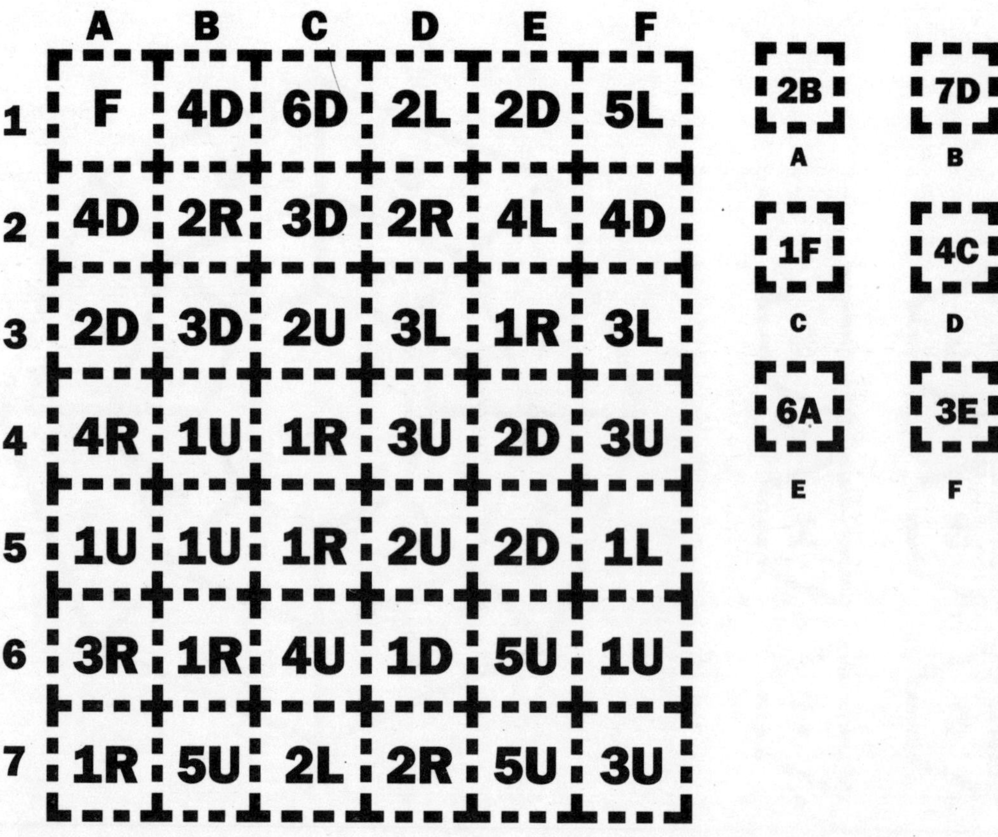

TEST 7 time limit 1 hour

TEST 7

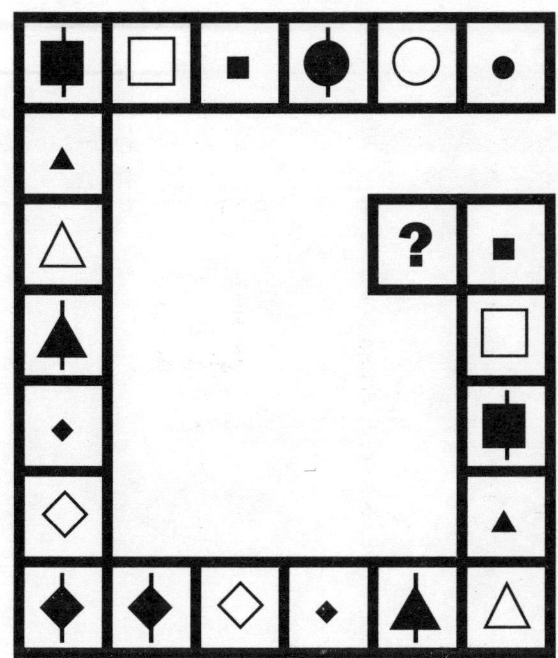

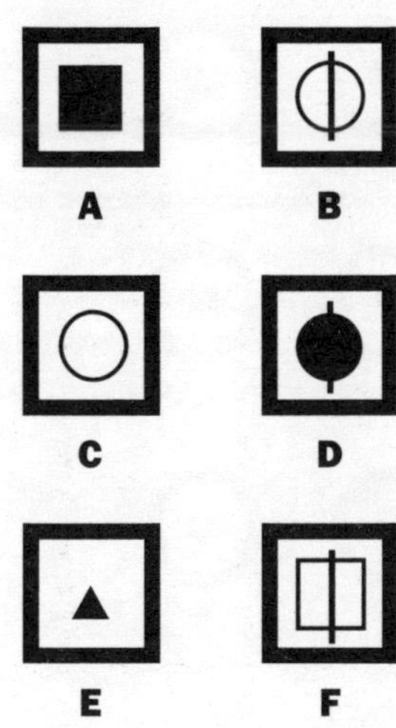

7 Which of the boxes should be used to replace the question mark?

8	4	2	2	4
9	1	1	2	2
?	2	1	0	2

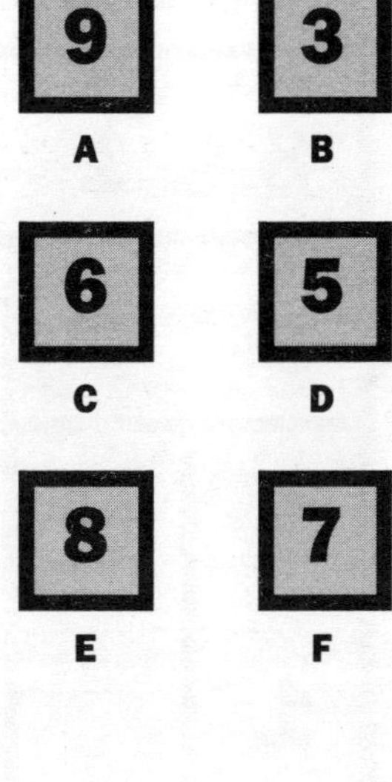

8 Which of the numbers should replace the question mark?

TEST 7 time limit 1 hour

TEST 7

9 When rearranged the shapes will give a letter. Which of the letters is it?

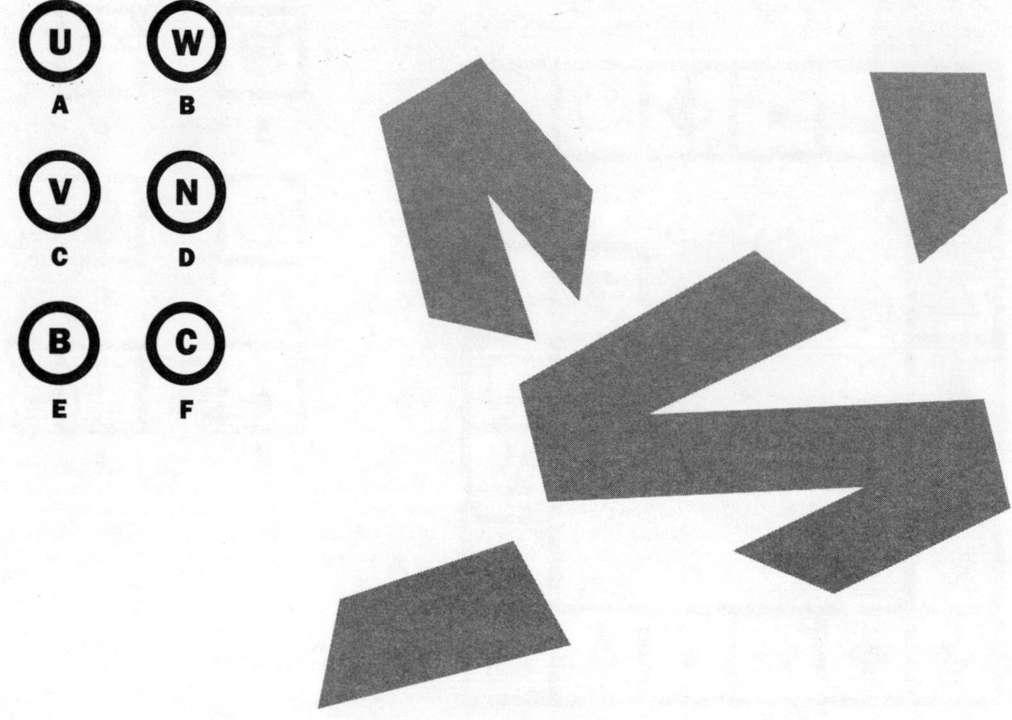

10 When the tiles in this square are rearranged a logical pattern will emerge. Which of the tiles should be used to complete the square?

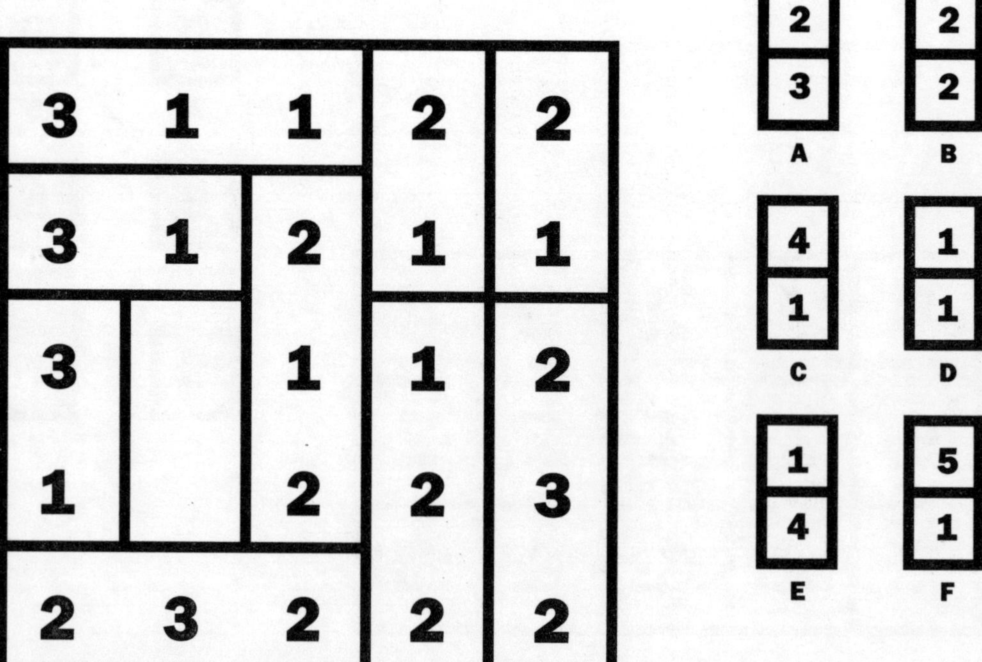

TEST 7 time limit 1 hour

TEST 7

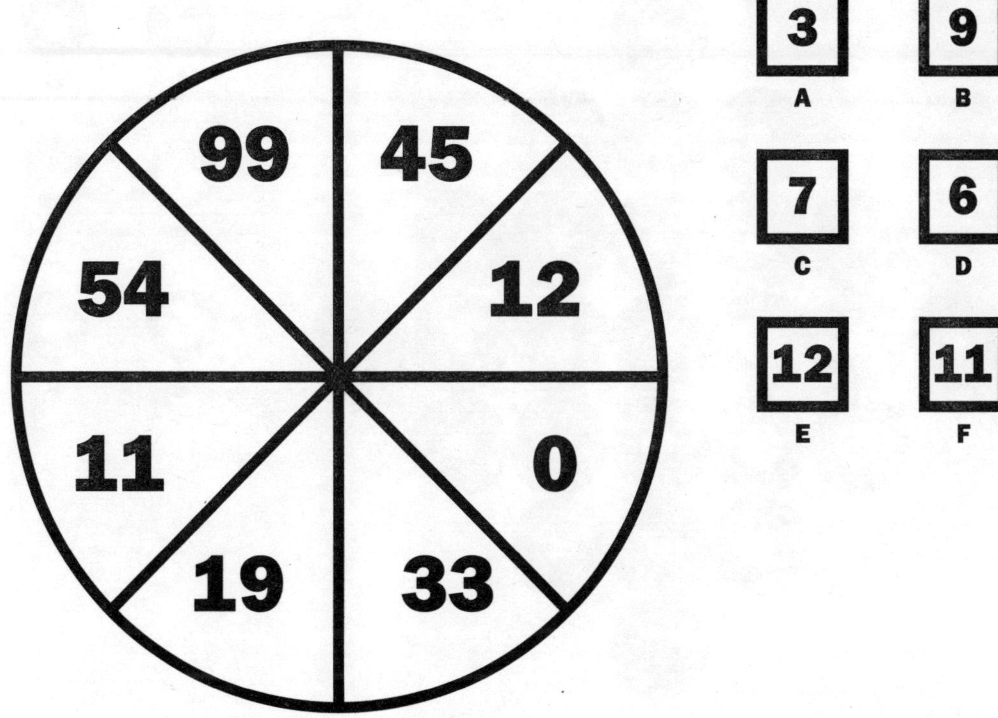

11 How many ways are there to score 99 on this dartboard using five darts only? Each dart always lands in a sector and no dart falls to the floor.

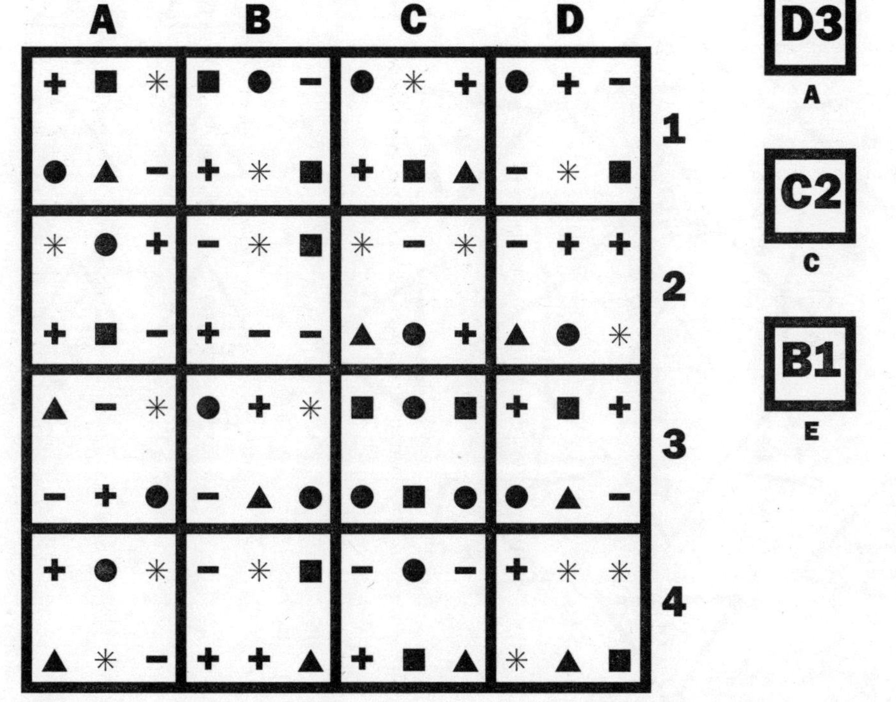

12 Which square's contents matches A4?

TEST 7 time limit 1 hour

TEST 7

13 Which shape is missing from this series?

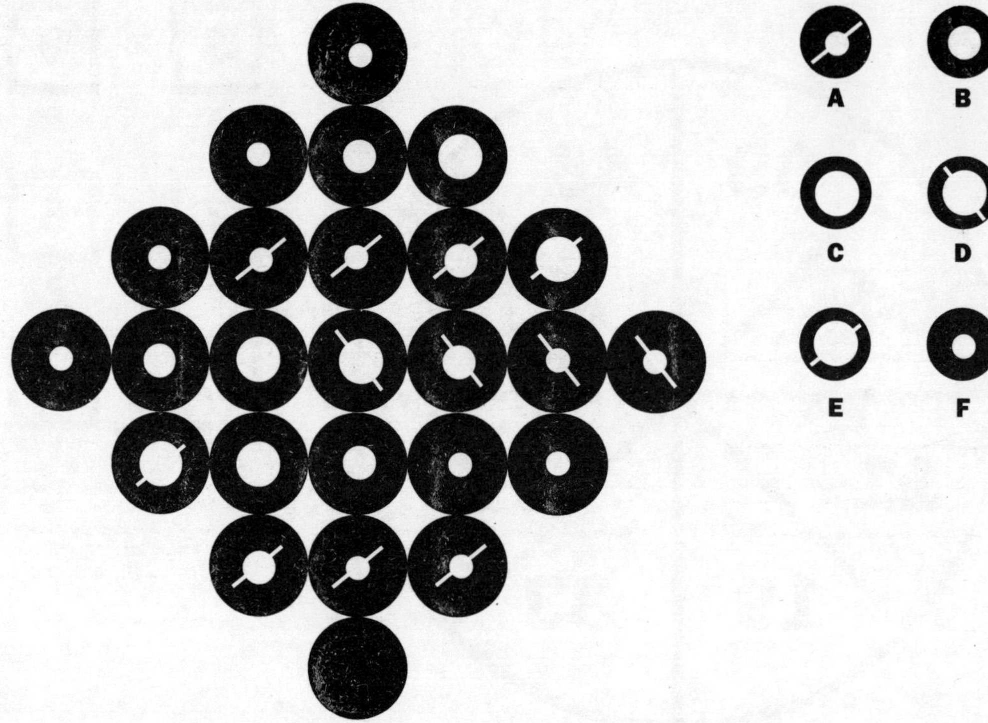

14 Which triangle should replace the empty one?

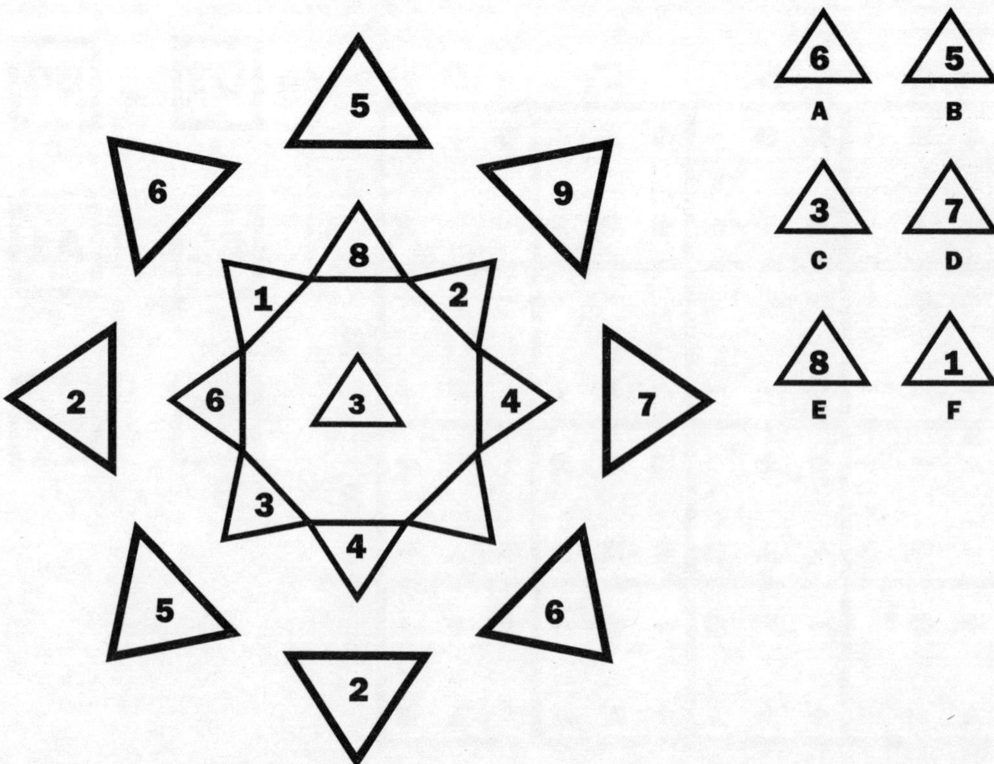

TEST 7 time limit 1 hour

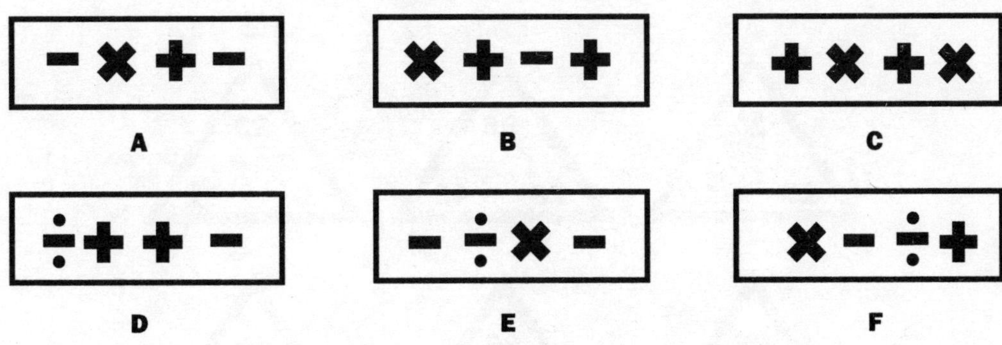

15 Insert the correct mathematical signs between each number in order to resolve the equation. What are the signs?

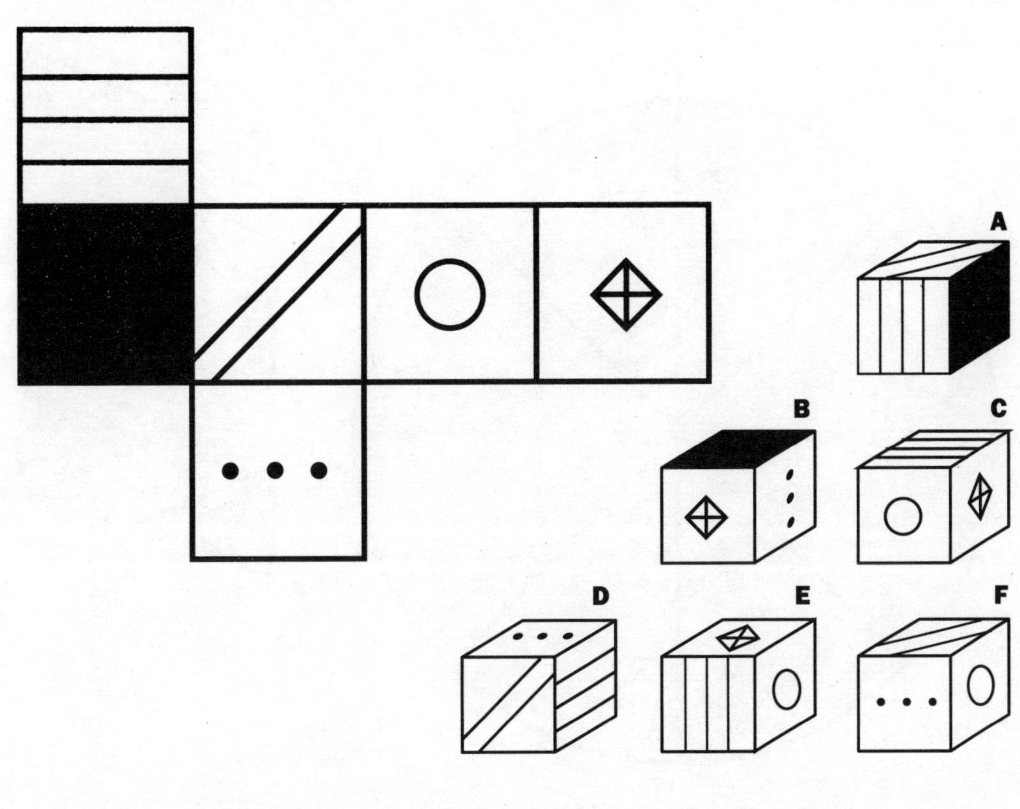

16 Which of the constructed boxes cannot be made from the pattern?

TEST 7 time limit 1 hour

TEST 7

17 Which triangle continues this series?

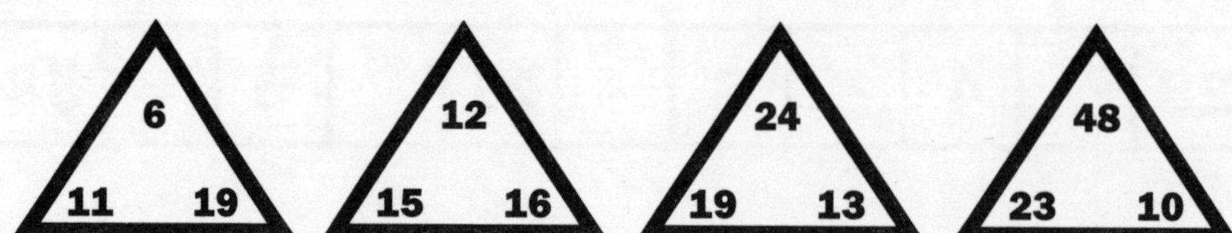

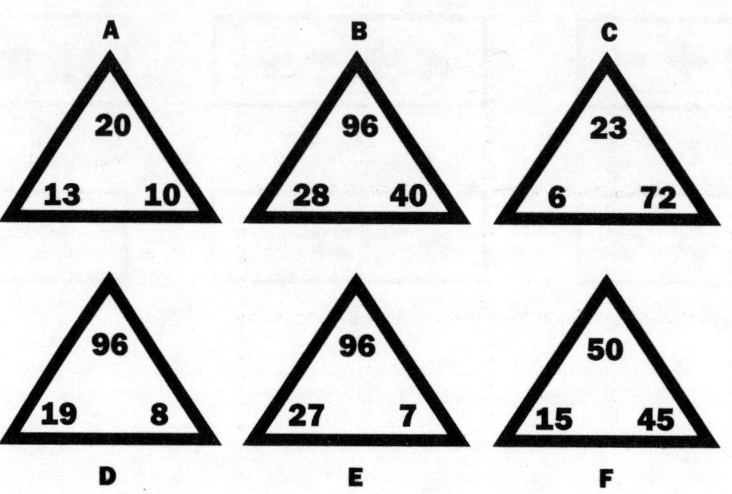

18 Which of the slices should be used to complete the cake?

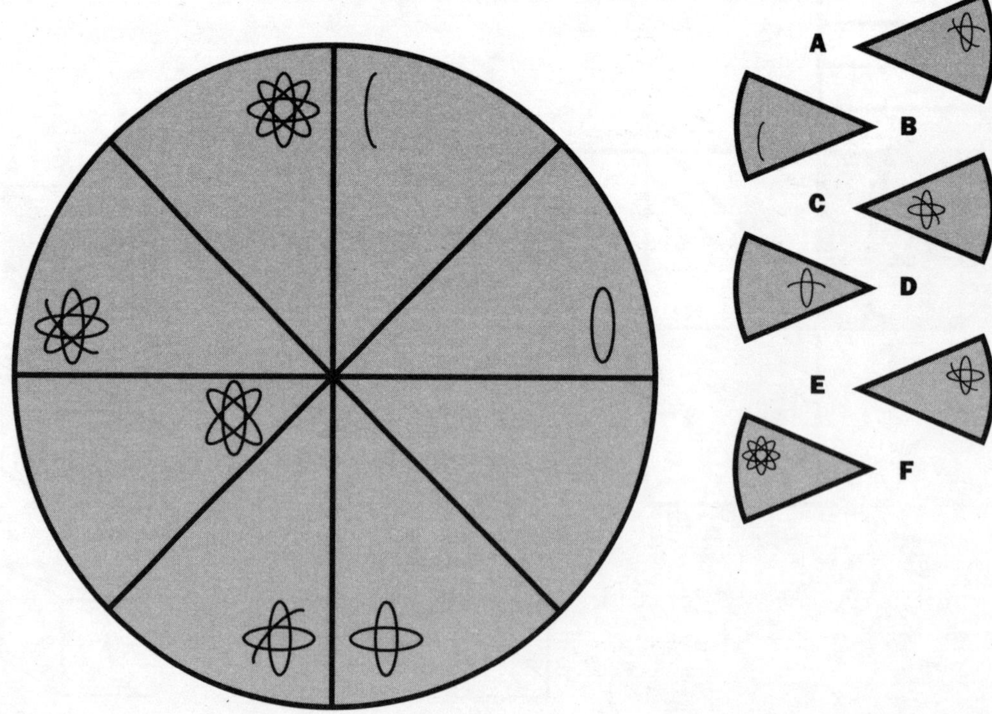

TEST 7 time limit 1 hour

TEST 7

11	12	13	0	
8	13	13	11	0
11	13			3
6				
	0	?	24	

5	2
A	B
3	4
C	D
1	6
E	F

19 Each straight line of five numbers should total 45. Which of the numbers will replace the question mark?

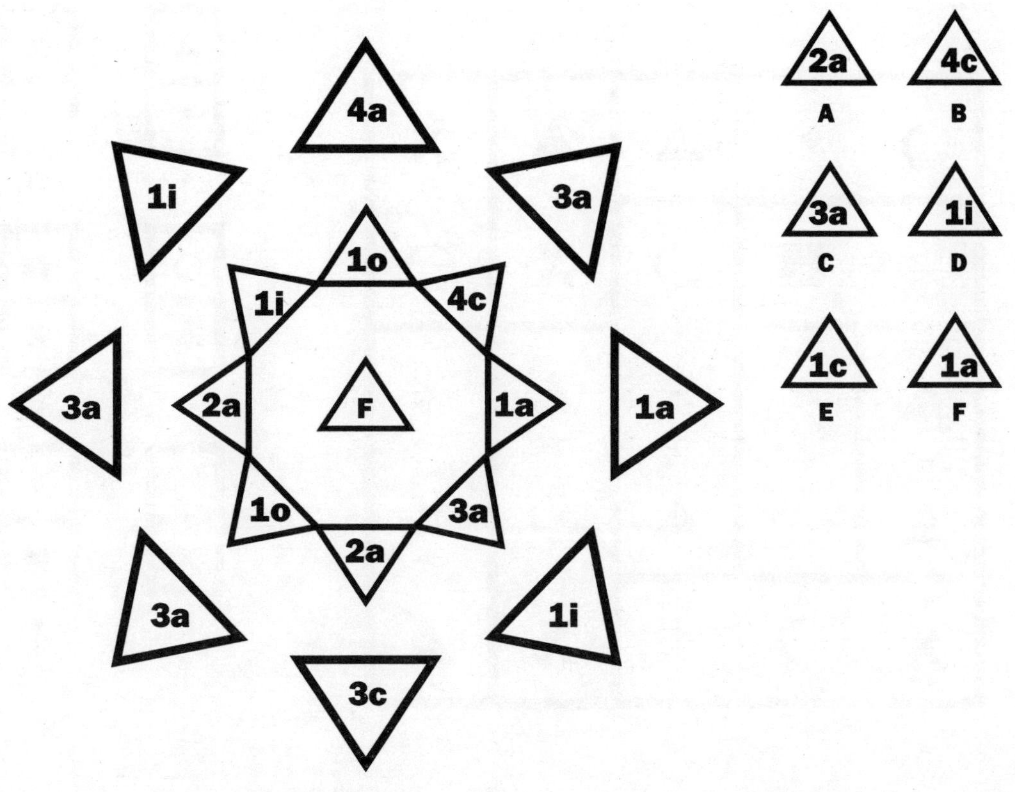

20 Here is an unusual safe. Each of the buttons must be pressed only once in the correct order to open it. The last button is marked F. The number of moves and the direction is marked on each button. Thus 1i would mean one move in, whilst 1o would mean one move out. 1c would mean one move clockwise and 1a would mean one move anti-clockwise. Which button is the first you must press?

TEST 7 time limit 1 hour

TEST 7

21 Each same symbol has a value. Work out the logic and discover what should replace the question mark.

φ	φ	φ	γ	**?**
γ	γ	γ	η	**29**
τ	τ	τ	η	**68**
η	η	φ	γ	
41			**30**	

35 A	**20** B	**25** C
27 D	**31** E	**32** F

22 This square follows a logical pattern. Which of the tiles should be used to complete the square?

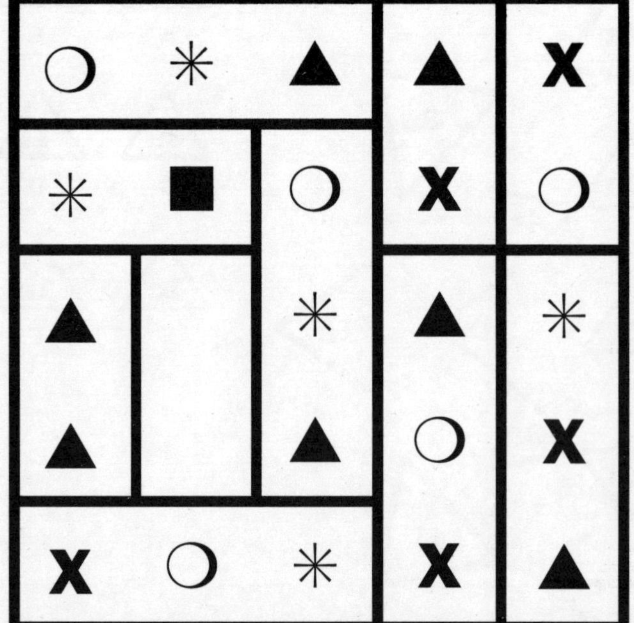

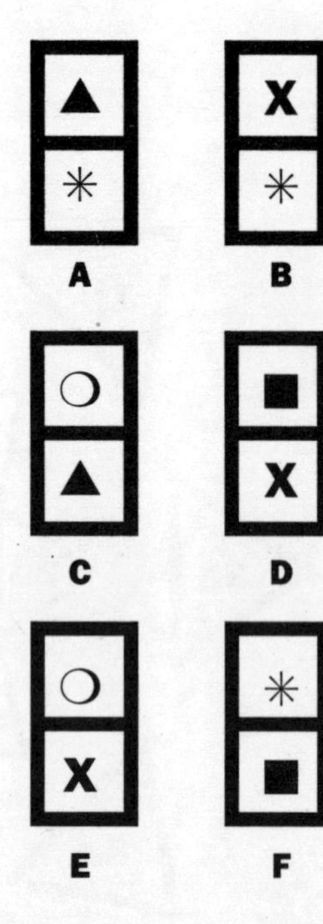

TEST 7 time limit 1 hour

23 When rearranged the shapes will give a number. Which of the numbers is it?

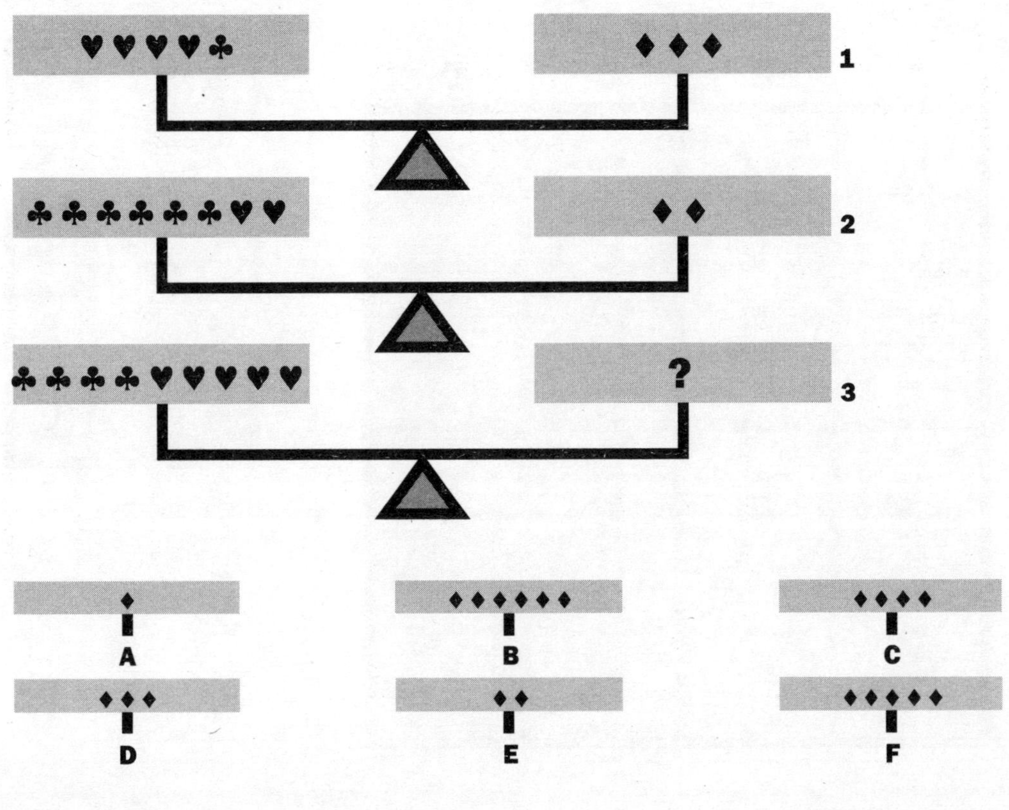

24 Scales one and two are in perfect balance. Which of these pans should replace the empty one?

TEST 7 time limit 1 hour

TEST 7

25 Start at any corner and follow the lines. Collect another four numbers and total the five. One of the numbers in the squares below can be used to complete the diagram. If the correct one has been chosen, one of the routes involving it will give a total of 45. Which one is it?

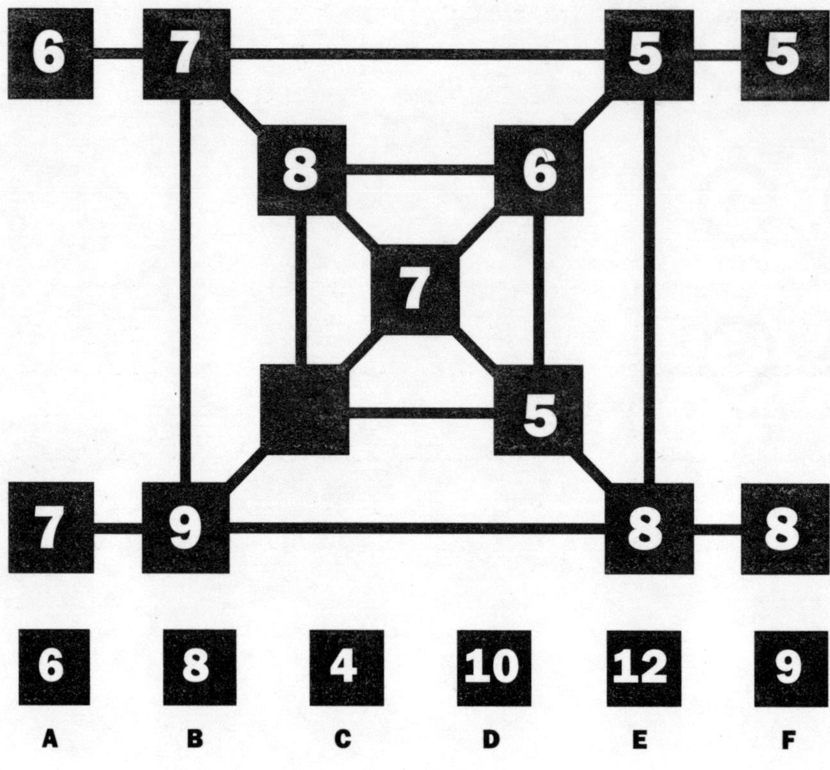

26 Which of the numbers should replace the question mark?

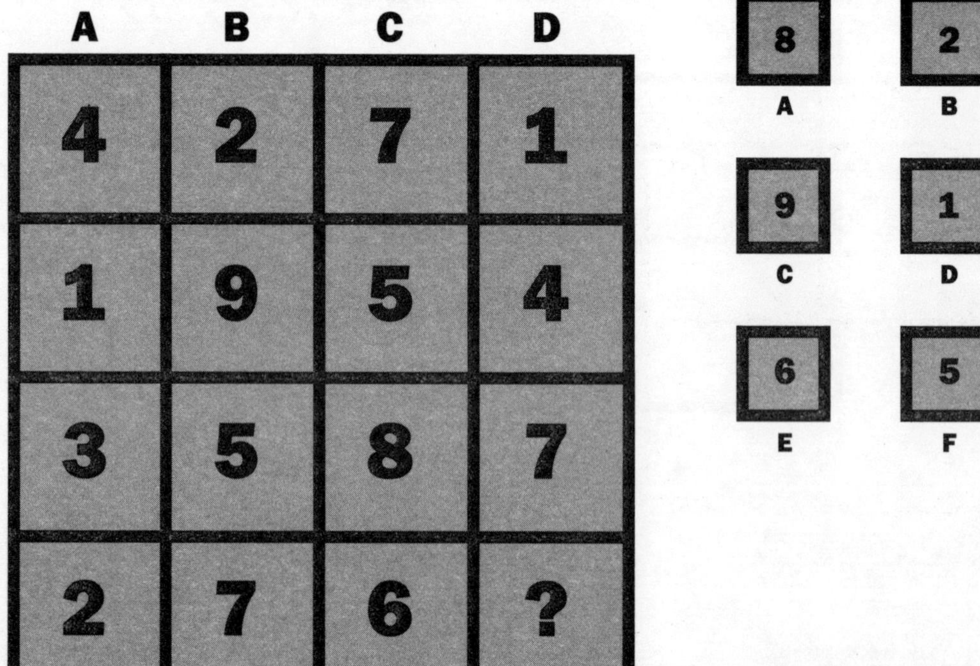

TEST 7 time limit 1 hour

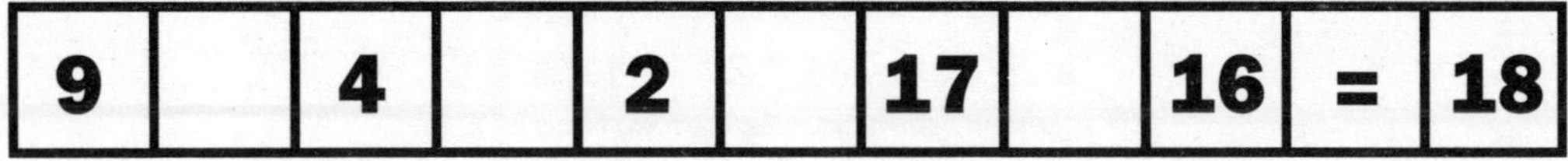

27 Insert the correct mathematical signs between each number in order to resolve the equation. What are the signs?

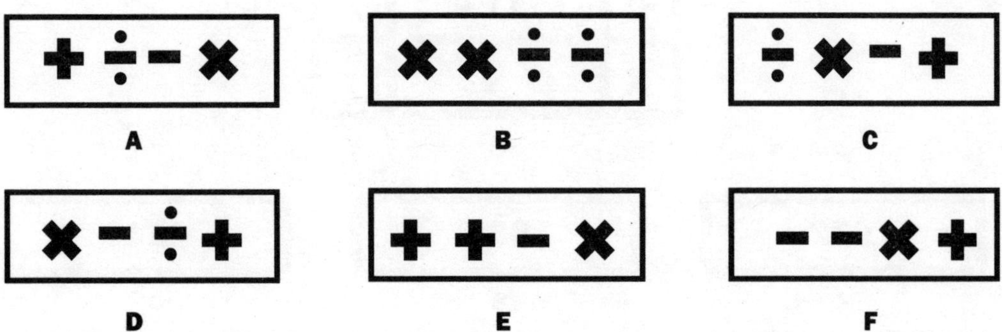

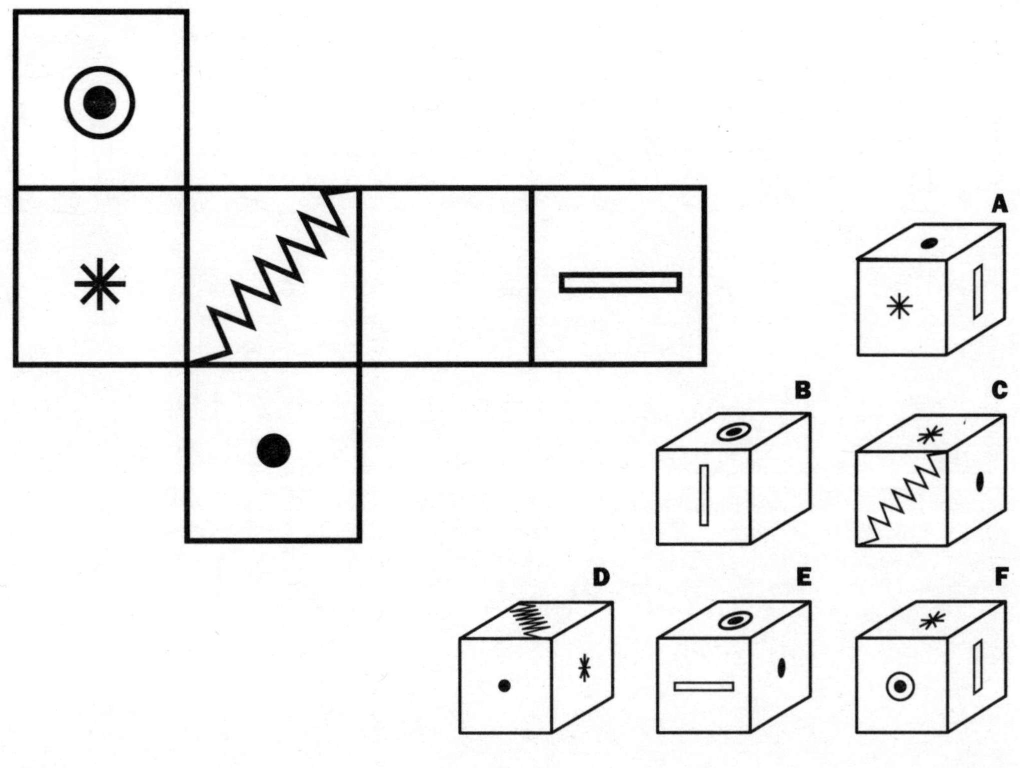

28 Which of the constructed boxes can be made from the pattern?

TEST 7 time limit 1 hour

TEST 7

29 Discover the connection between the letters and the numbers. Which number should replace the question mark?

F	136	M
U	421	D
H	178	Q
O	115	A
X	?	I

A	B	C
672	834	411

D	E	F
295	118	924

30 Which of the clocks continues this series?

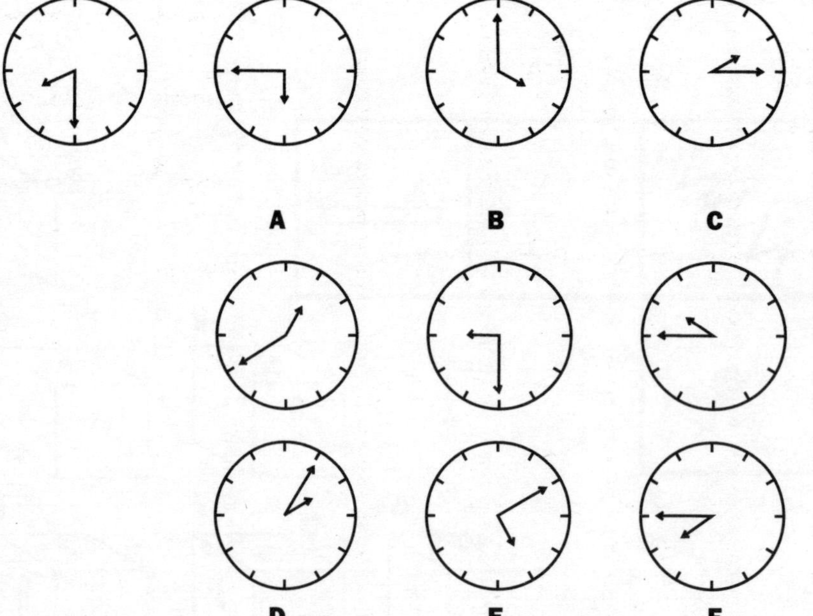

TEST 7 time limit 1 hour

TEST 8

1 Which of the numbers should logically replace the question mark in the octagon?

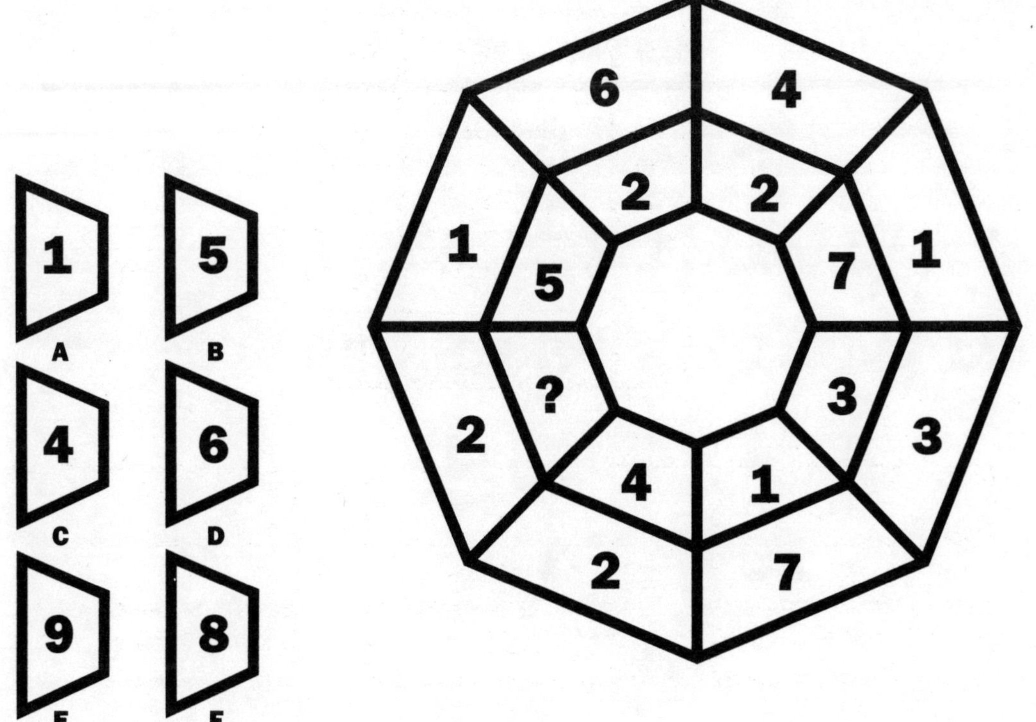

2 Complete the square using the five numbers shown. When completed no row, column or diagonal line will use the same number more than once. Which can logically replace the question mark?

5	2	4	3	
1				
		?		

5 A

2 B

1 C

3 D

4 E

TEST 8 time limit 1 hour

TEST 8

3 Start at 3 and move from circle to touching circle. Collect four numbers each time. How many different routes are there to collect 13? A reversed route counts twice.

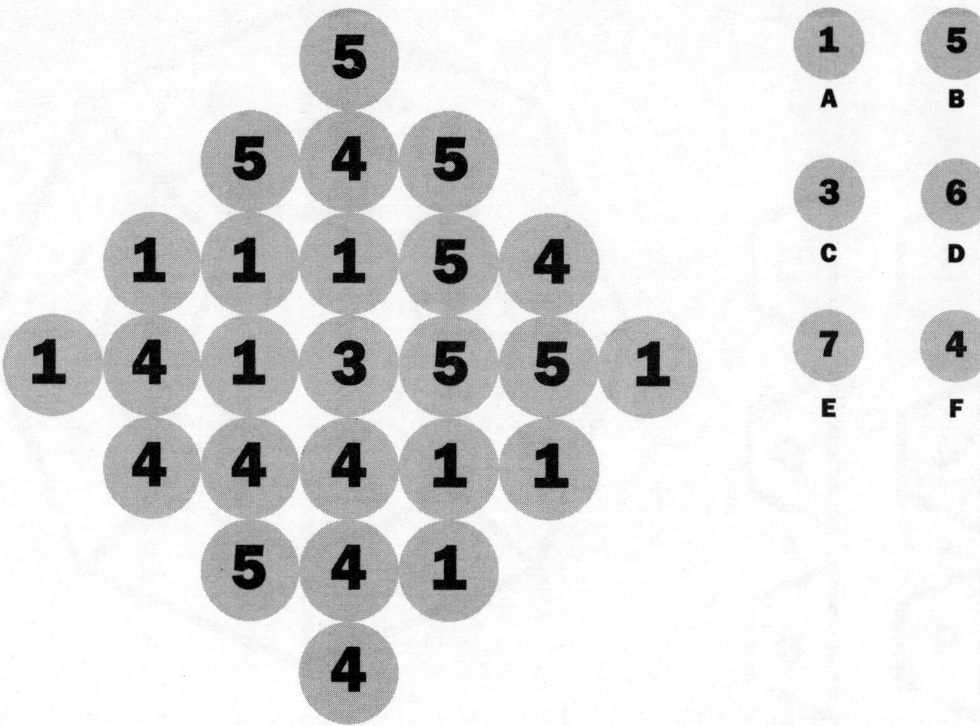

4 Which of the numbers should replace the question mark?

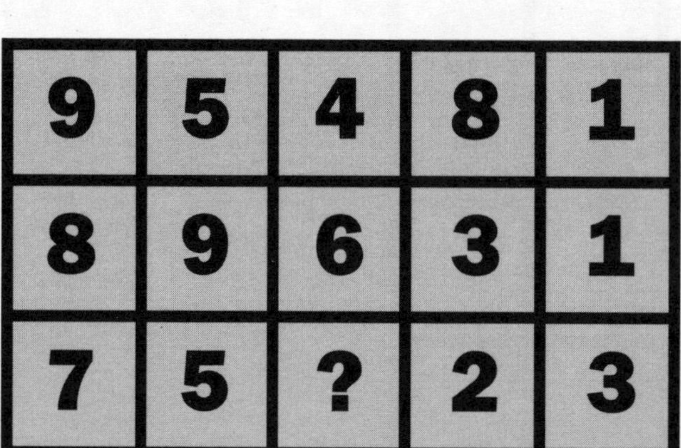

9	5	4	8	1
8	9	6	3	1
7	5	?	2	3

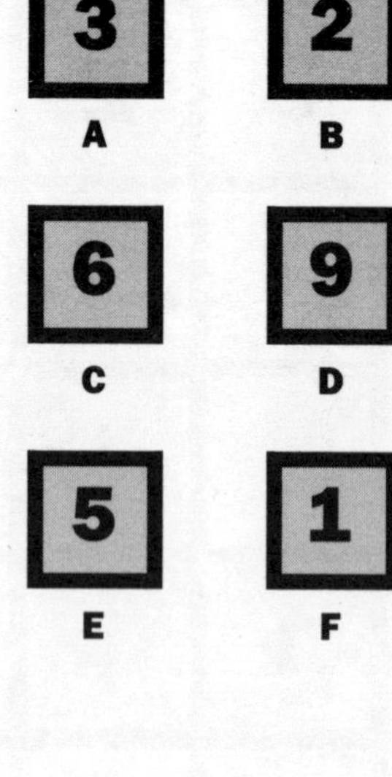

TEST 8 time limit 1 hour

TEST 8

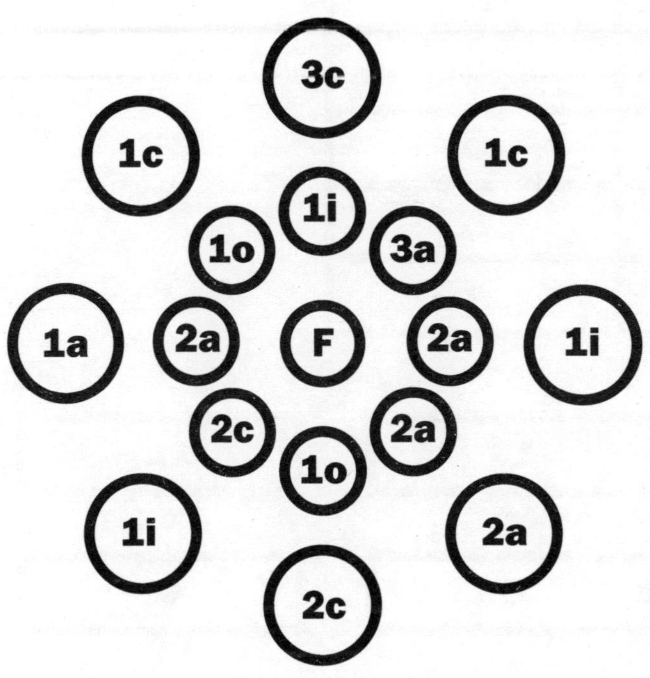

5 Here is an unusual safe. Each of the buttons must be pressed only once in the correct order to open it. The last button is marked F. The number of moves and the direction is marked on each button. Thus 1i would mean one move in, while 1o would mean one move out. 1c would mean one move clockwise and 1a would mean one move anti-clockwise. Which button is the first you must press?

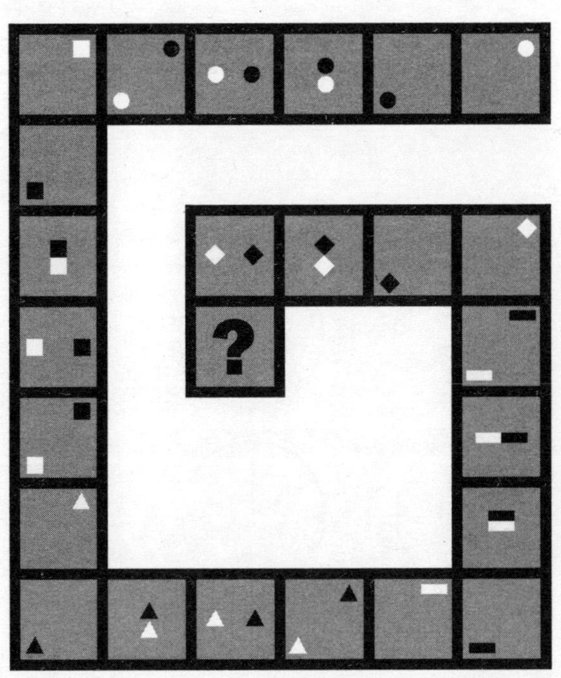

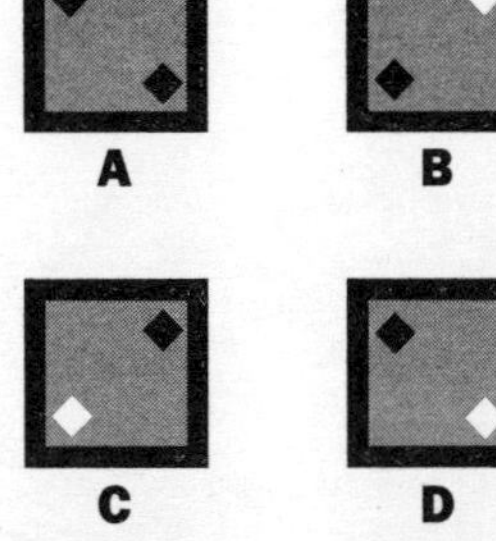

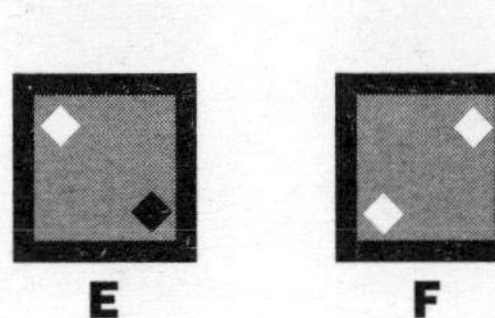

6 Which of the boxes should be used to replace the question mark?

TEST 8 time limit 1 hour

TEST 8

7 Discover the connection between the letters and the numbers. Which number should replace the question mark?

K	16
Y	2
P	11
E	22
L	?

15	13	11
A	B	C
18	**8**	**6**
D	E	F

8 Which of the clocks continues this series?

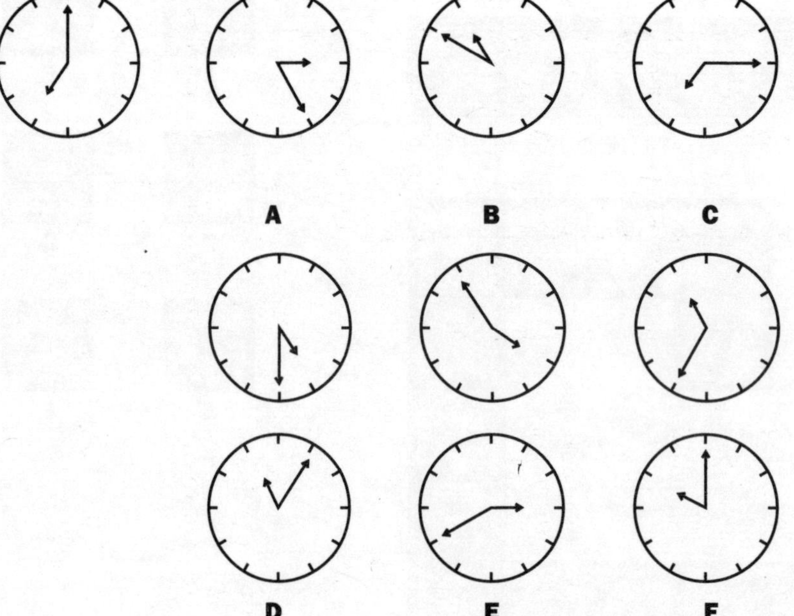

TEST 8 time limit 1 hour

TEST 8

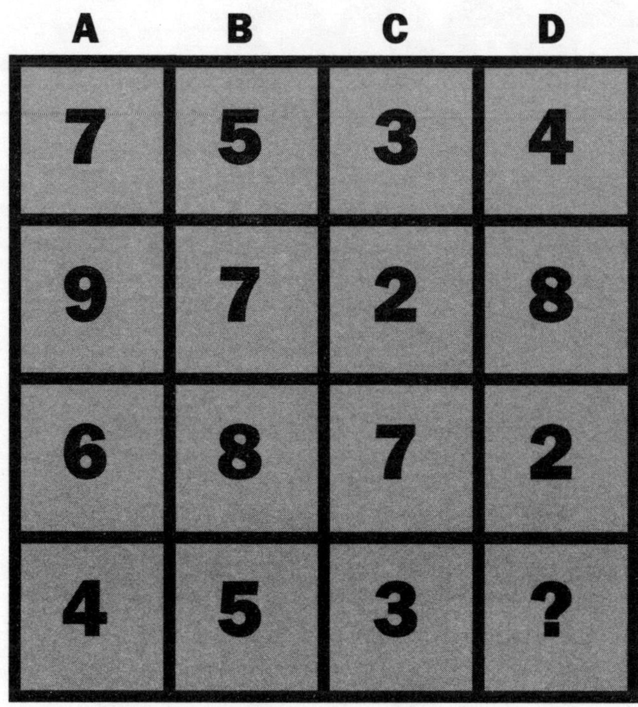

4	7
A	B
3	9
C	D
6	8
E	F

9 Which of the numbers should replace the question mark?

τ	ψ	η	φ	63
φ	η	ψ	ψ	
τ	τ	τ	ψ	85
η	φ	η	η	?
58	63	61		

33 A	30 B	38 C
31 D	36 E	34 F

10 Each same symbol has a value. Work out the logic and discover what should replace the question mark.

TEST 8 time limit 1 hour

TEST 8

11 Move from ring to touching ring, starting from the bottom left corner and finishing in the top right corner. Collect nine numbers and total them. Which is the highest possible total?

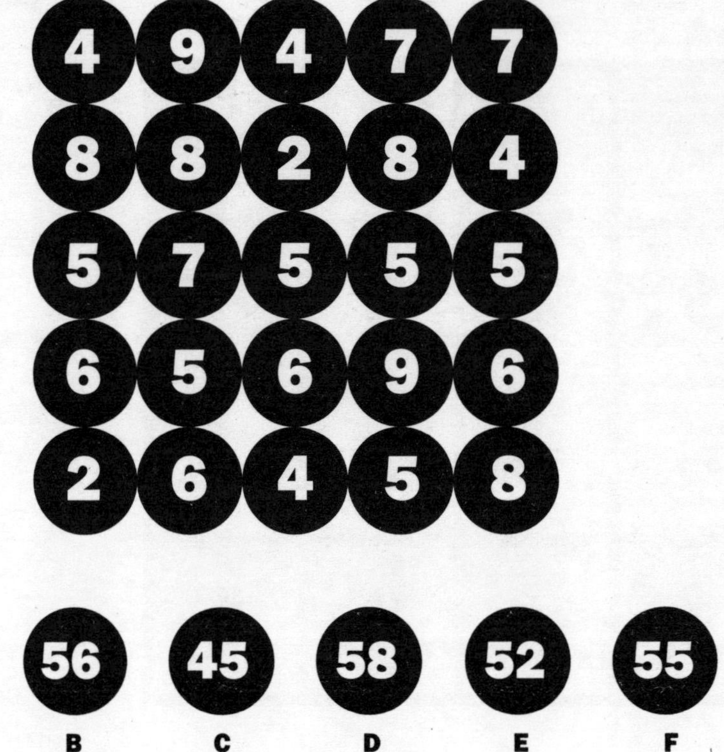

12 Scales one and two are in perfect balance. Which of these pans should replace the empty one?

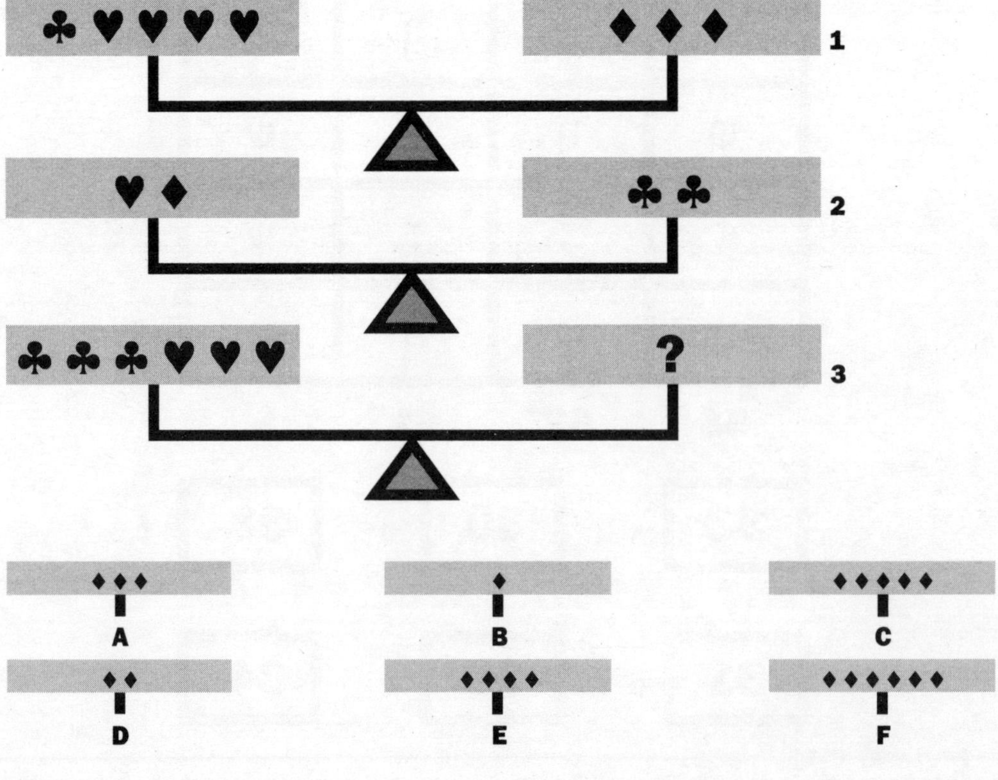

TEST 8 time limit 1 hour

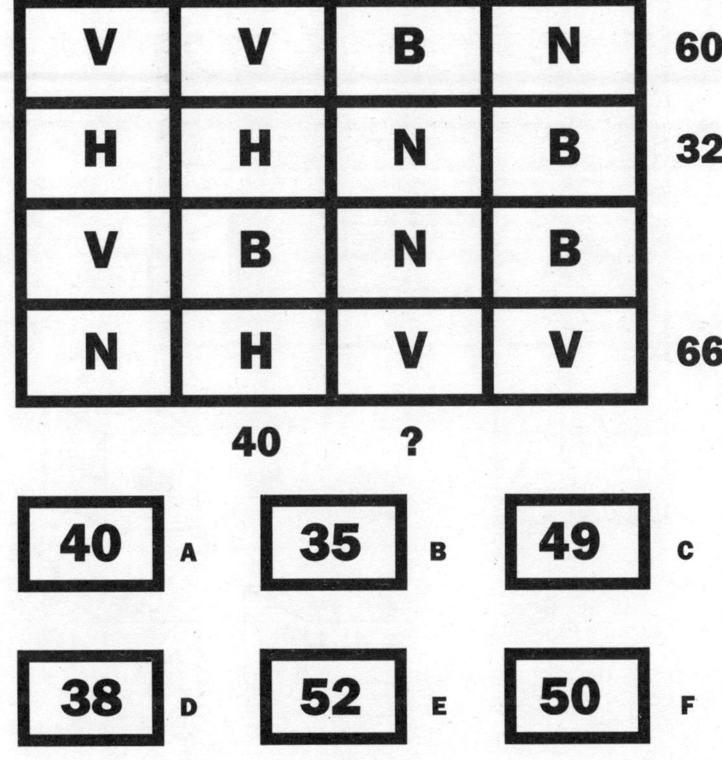

13 Each same letter has a value. Work out the logic and discover what should replace the question mark.

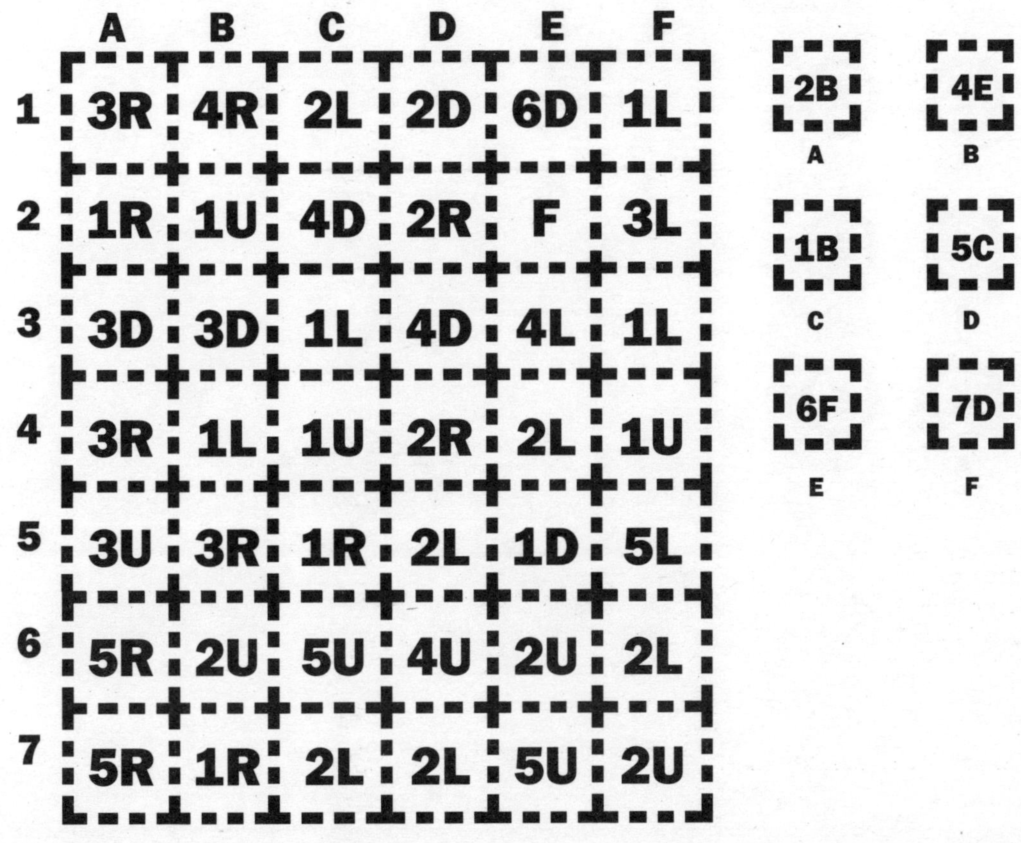

14 Here is an unusual safe. Each of the buttons must be pressed only once in the correct order to open it. The last button is marked F. The number of moves and the direction is marked on each button. Thus 1U would mean one move up, while 1L would mean one move to the left. Using the grid reference, which button is the first you must press?

TEST 8 time limit 1 hour

TEST 8

15 Which of the constructed boxes can be made from the pattern?

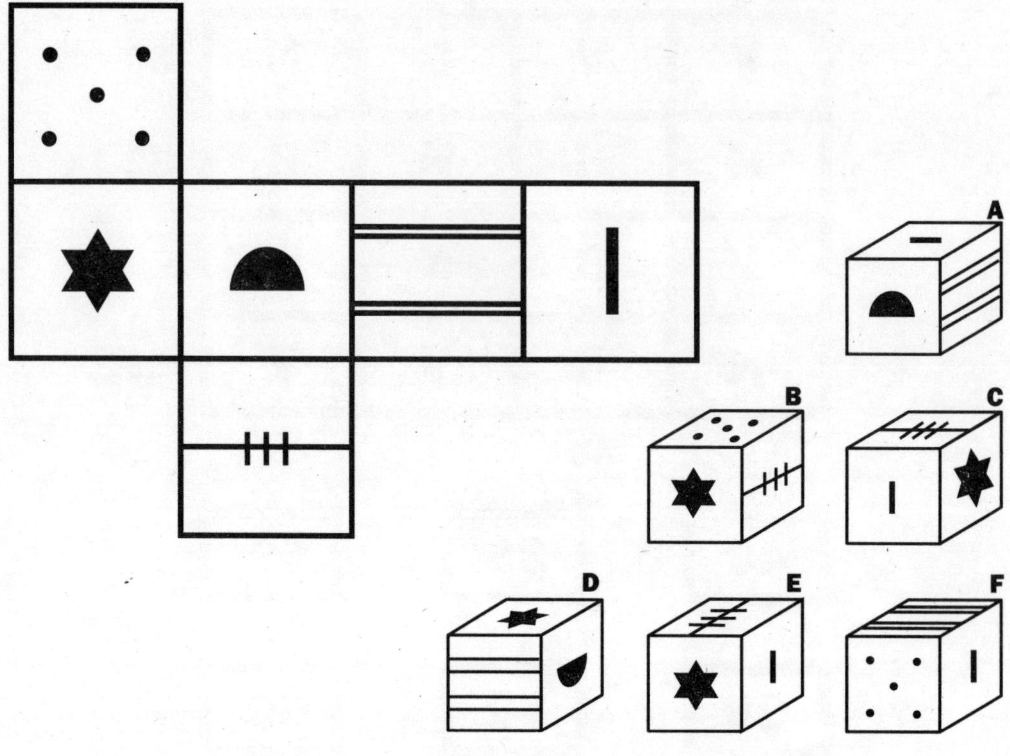

16 When rearranged the shapes will give a number. Which of the numbers is it?

TEST 8 time limit 1 hour

TEST 8

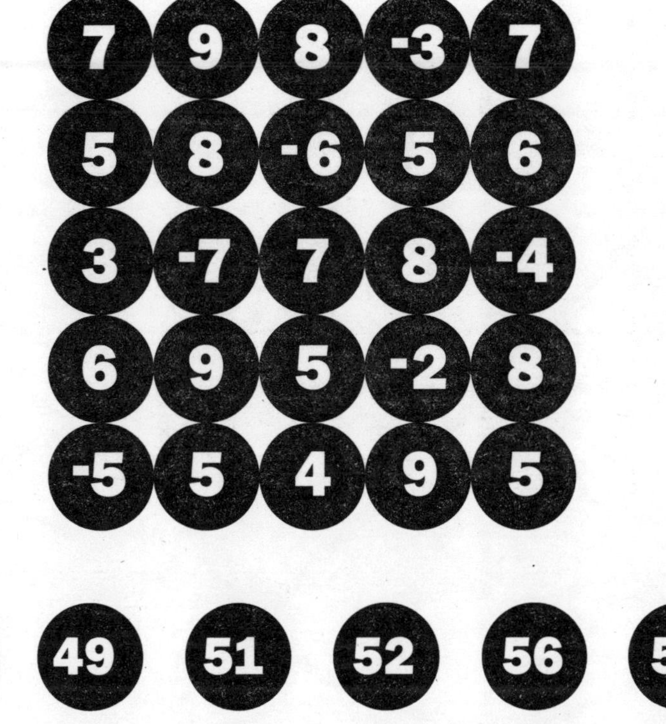

17 Move from ring to touching ring, starting from the bottom left corner and finishing in the top right corner. Collect nine numbers and total them. Which is the highest possible total?

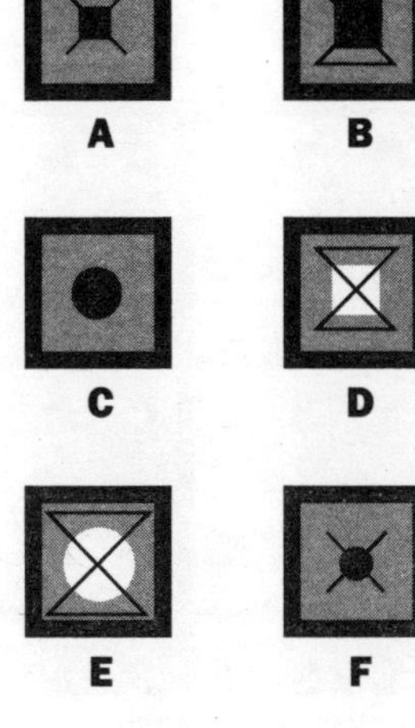

18 Which of the boxes should be used to replace the question mark?

TEST 8 time limit 1 hour

TEST 8

19 Which of the slices should be used to complete the cake so that the top half matches the bottom half?

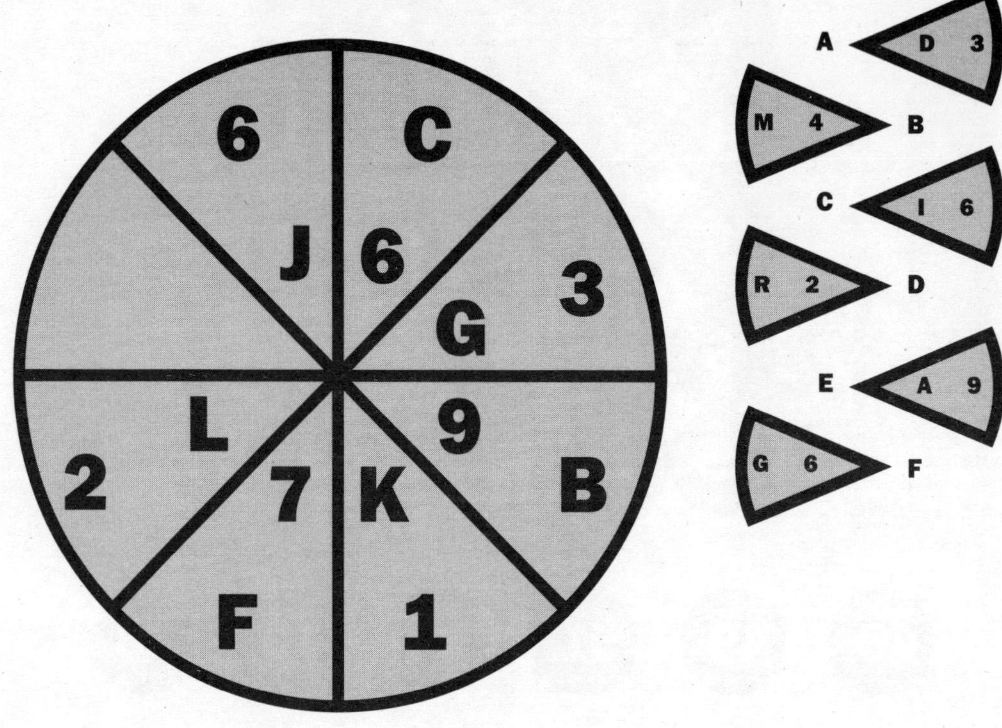

20 Which square's contents matches D2?

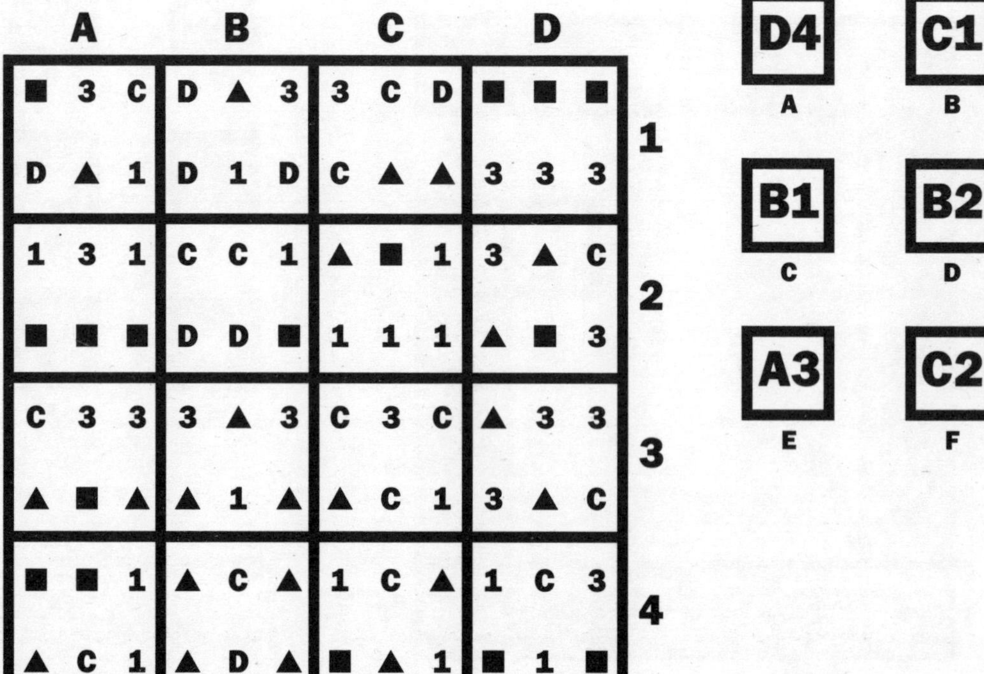

TEST 8 time limit 1 hour

TEST 8

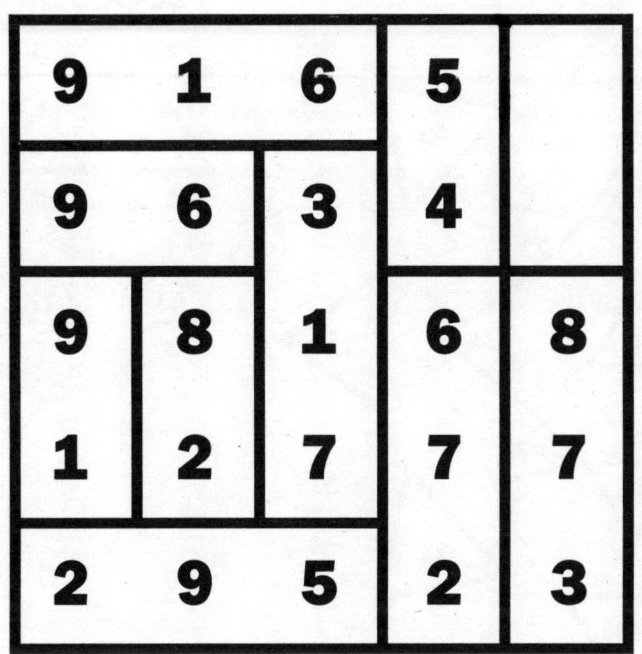

1	5
3	3
A	**B**

4	2
2	4
C	**D**

3	1
1	1
E	**F**

21 When the tiles in this square are rearranged a logical pattern will emerge. Which of the tiles should be used to complete the square?

W	4	S
J	6	D
O	3	L
R	10	H
V	?	K

22 Discover the connection between the letters and the numbers. Which number should replace the question mark?

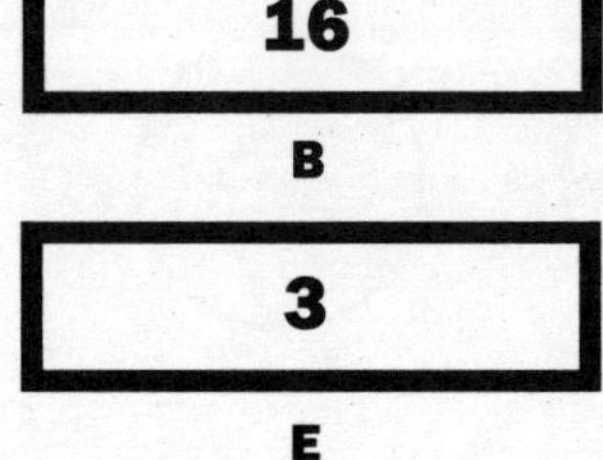

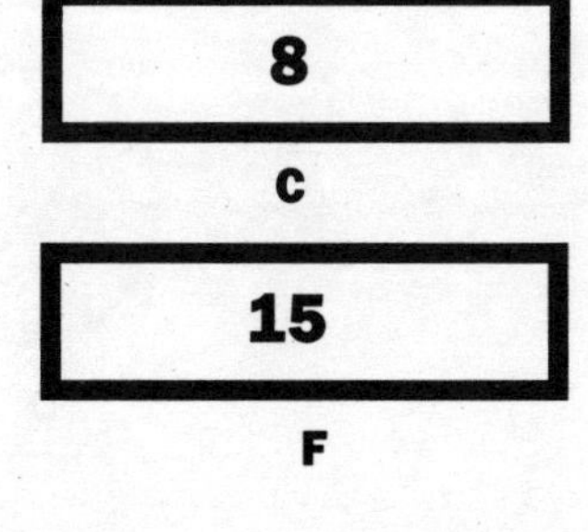

4	16	8
A	**B**	**C**
11	3	15
D	**E**	**F**

TEST 8 time limit 1 hour

TEST 8

23 Here is an unusual safe. Each of the buttons must be pressed only once in the correct order to open it. The last button is marked F. The number of moves and the direction is marked on each button. Thus 1i would mean one move in, while 1o would mean one move out. 1c would mean one move clockwise and 1a would mean one move anti-clockwise. Which button is the first you must press?

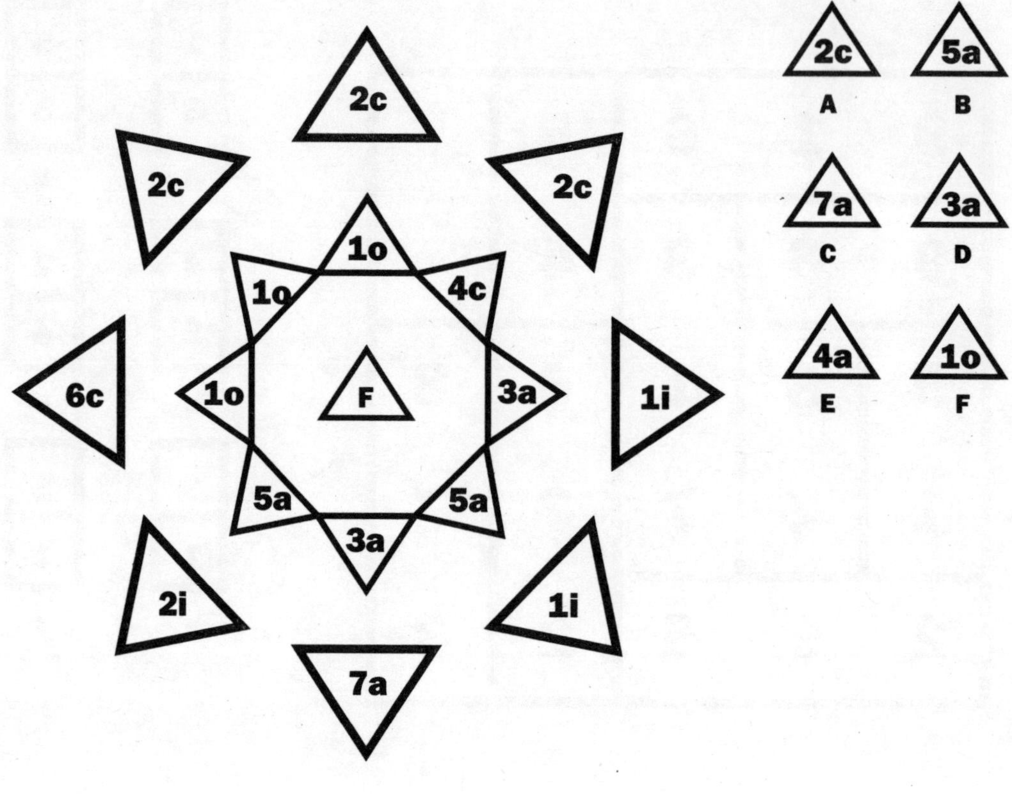

24 Which of the clocks continues this series?

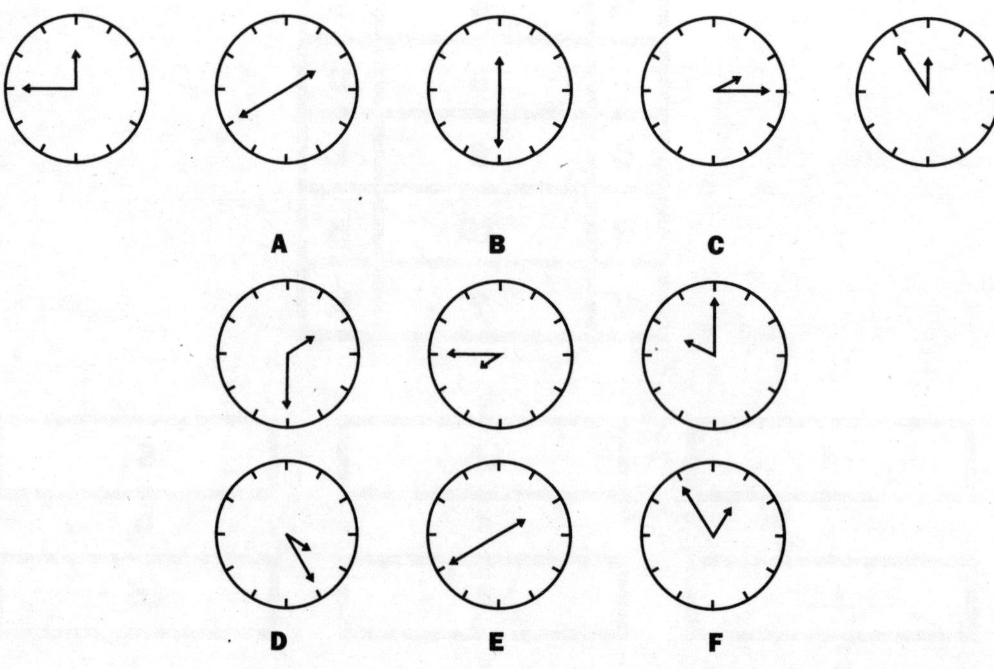

TEST 8 time limit 1 hour

TEST 8

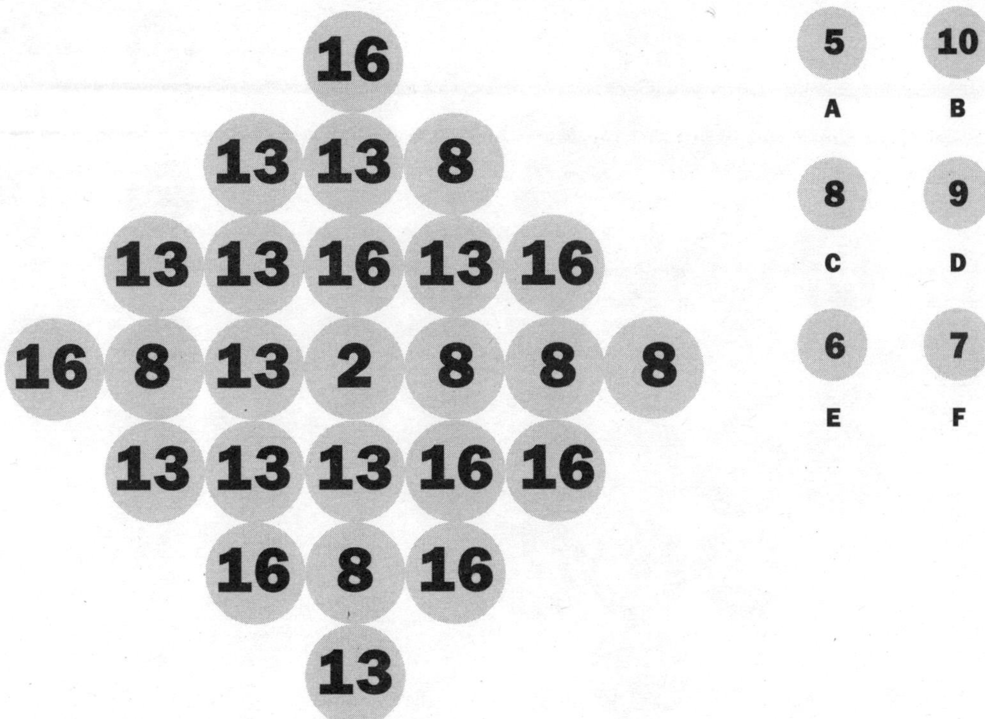

25 Start at 2 and move from circle to touching circle. Collect four numbers each time. How many different routes are there to collect 39? A reversed route counts twice.

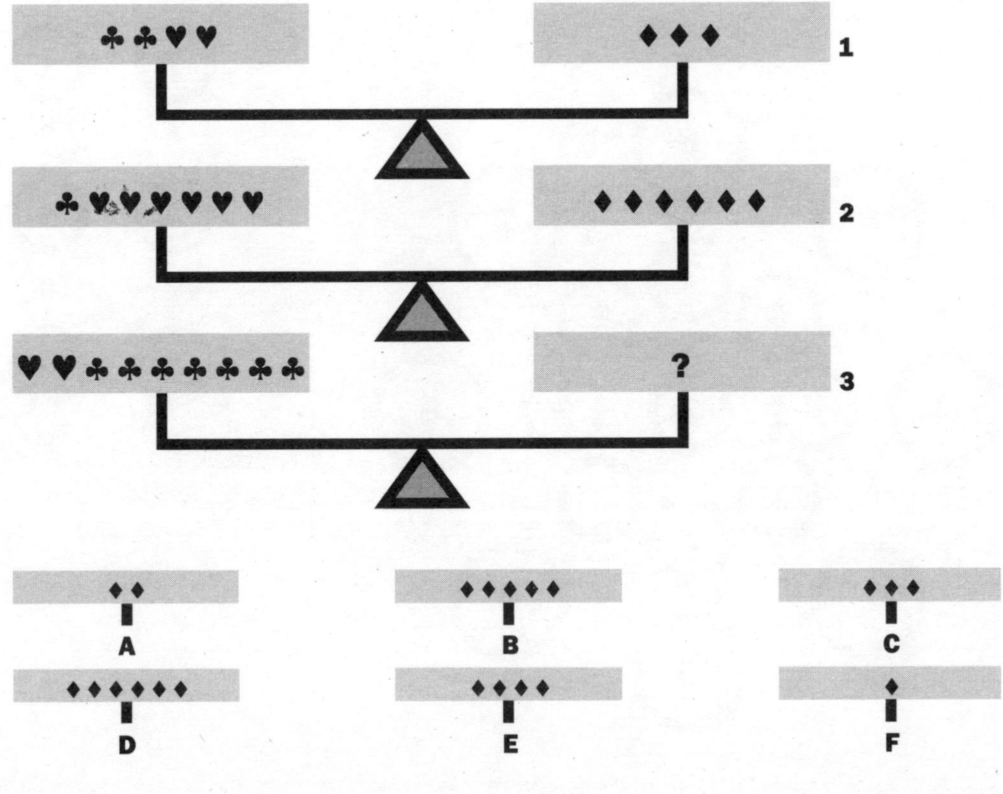

26 Scales one and two are in perfect balance. Which of these pans should replace the empty one?

TEST 8 time limit 1 hour

TEST 8

27 Which shape is missing from this series?

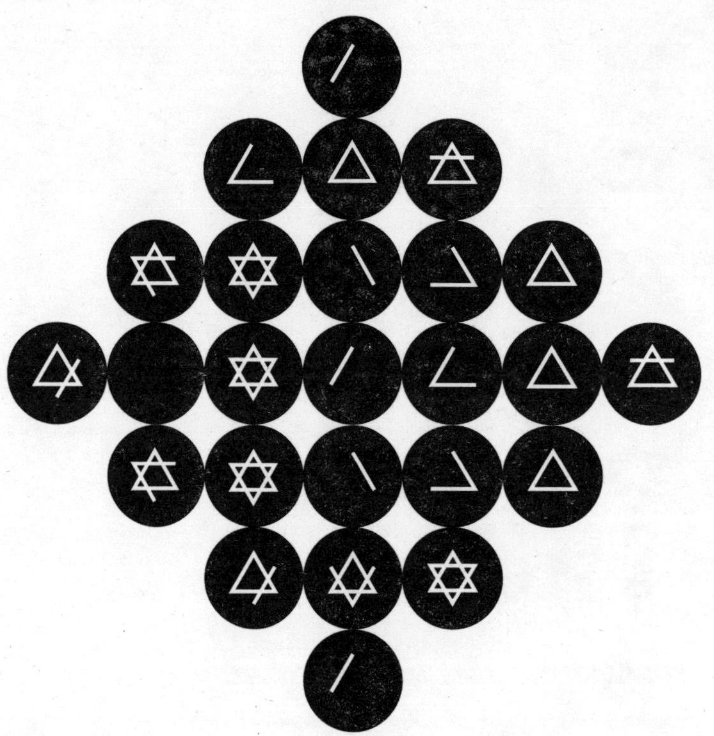

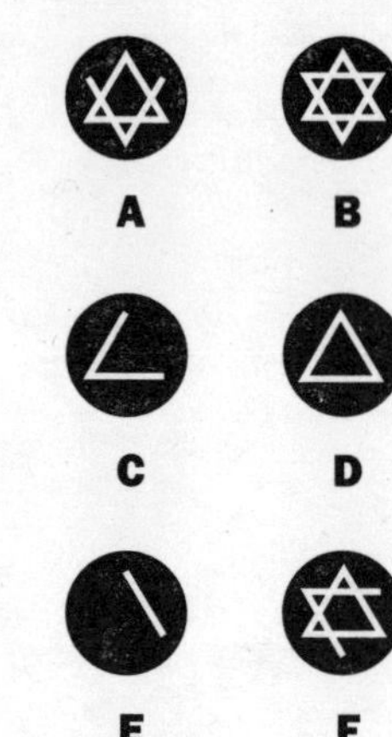

28 Which circle should replace the empty one?

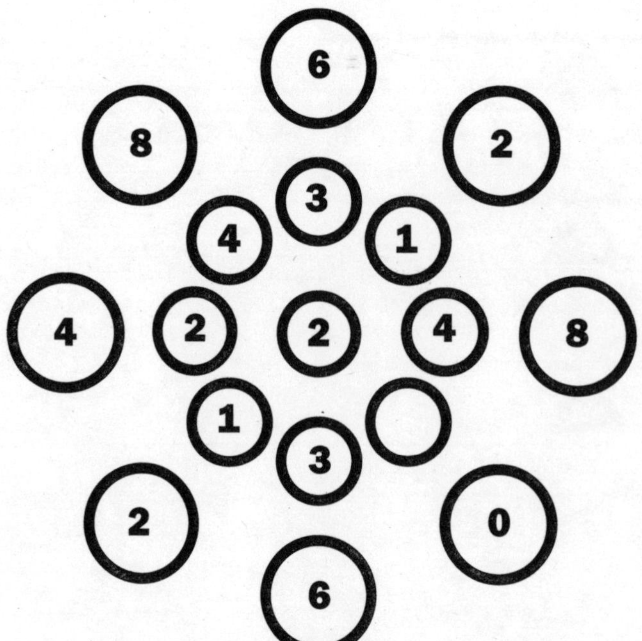

7 1
A B
8 4
C D
2 0
E F

TEST 8 time limit 1 hour

TEST 8

29 Which triangle continues this series?

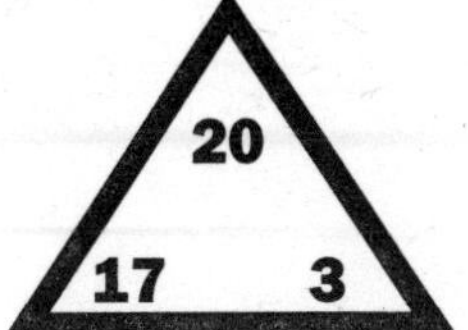

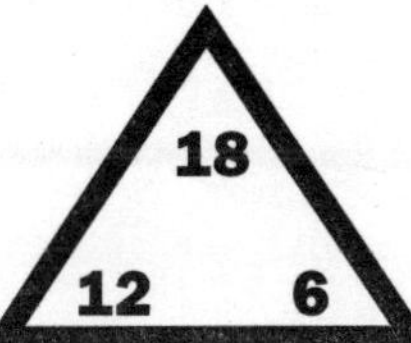

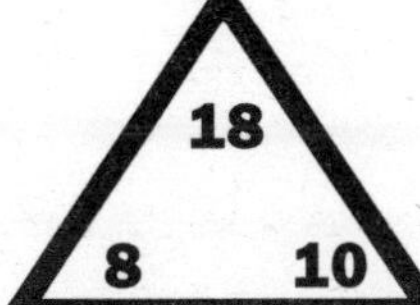

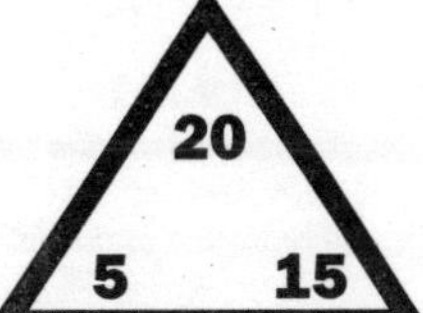

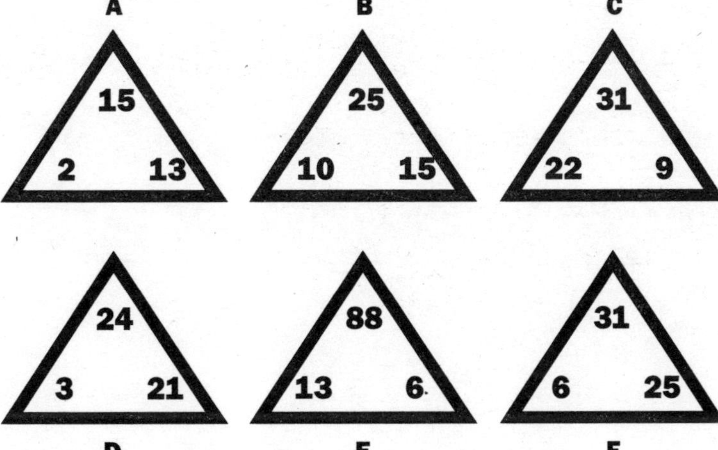

---

30 Insert the correct mathematical signs between each number in order to resolve the equation. What are the signs?

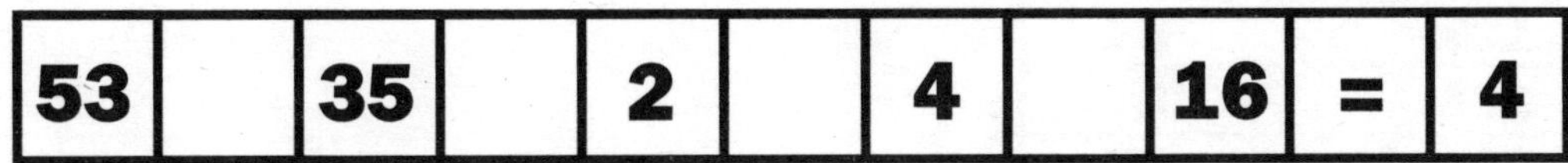

A

+ − × ×

B

C

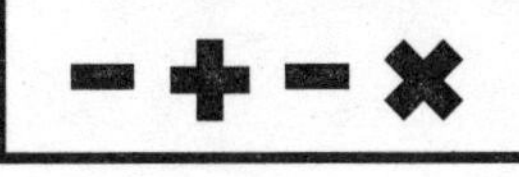

D

÷ × − −

E

F

TEST 8 time limit 1 hour

TEST 1 ANSWERS

1 F. On each row A + B + C = D.
2 D. Ω=5, Ξ=2, Ψ=4, Z=3.
3 F.
4 E.
5 B. The numbers in the first triangle total 3, the second 4 and so on.
6 B. The alphabetical value of each letter is placed next to it.
7 C.
8 C. Each row totals 10.
9 B. The hour hand moves forward two hours each time.
10 E.
11 F.
12 D. When completed the box reads the same both down and across.
13 C.
14 D.
15 F.

SCORE	I.Q.	PERCENTILE
15	130	90
14	125	85
13	122	80
12	117	75
11	115	70
10	112	65
9	108	60
8	105	55
7	100	50
6	95	45
5	90	40

TEST 2 ANSWERS

1 F.
2 A. ♣ = 6, ♥ = 5, ♦ = 2.
3 F.
4 E.
5 C. Each double section totals 10.
6 B. Two series lead from 1 to 16.
7 C.
8 D. Deduct row 2 from row 1 to give row 3.
9 C.
10 E.
11 E. On each row the two squares to the left total 9, as do the two to the right.
12 F. The numbers in the triangles total 4, 6, 8, 10 etc.
13 C.
14 A. The alphabetical value of each letter is placed next to it.
15 A.

SCORE	I.Q.	PERCENTILE
15	130	90
14	125	85
13	122	80
12	117	75
11	115	70
10	112	65
9	108	60
8	105	55
7	100	50
6	95	45
5	90	40

TEST 3 ANSWERS

1 C. α=4, β=7, χ=5, δ=8.
2 A. ♣ = 2, ♥ = 1, ♦ = 3.
3 E.
4 B. Each of the four columns of numbers totals 15.
5 C. 4a in the inner ring.
6 D. The numbers on each row total 9.
7 A. A large triangle added to the nearest small triangle will give the middle number.
8 E. Each double section is added together. Reading clockwise from 2 + 1, the totals increase by one each time.
9 B.
10 E.
11 D.
12 F. Each double section totals 13.
13 A. On each row the first figure minus the second figure plus the third figure gives the fourth.
14 E.
15 E. The first row plus the second row gives the third row.
16 C. The box now reads the same down and across.
17 B.
18 E.
19 E. ♣ = 8, ♥ = 6, ♦ = 7.
20 D. The hour hand moves forward two hours, then three hours, then four hours etc.

SCORE	I.Q.	PERCENTILE
20	138	95
19	136	94
18	134	93
17	132	92
16	131	91
15	130	90
14	125	85
13	122	80
12	117	75
11	115	70
10	112	65
9	108	60
8	105	55
7	100	50
6	95	45
5	90	40

TEST 4 ANSWERS

1 A.
2 B.
3 B. In each triangle the bottom two numbers, when added together, give the top number.
4 F. The hour hand moves back four hours each time.
5 C. On each row A + B - C = D.
6 E.
7 D.
8 A. When completed the box reads the same both down and across.
9 C.
10 C.
11 D.
12 D.
13 A. $\alpha=6$, $\beta=3$, $\chi=7$, $\delta=10$.
14 B.
15 D.
16 F. A large circle minus the nearest small circle will give the middle number.
17 A.
18 B. Reading clockwise, the numbers relate to the number of line forming the shape in the previous sector.
19 C. The first row plus the third row gives the second row. in the middle.
20 E. The alphabetical positions of the letters are placed together in the middle.

SCORE	I.Q.	PERCENTILE
20	138	95
19	136	94
18	134	93
17	132	92
16	131	91
15	130	90
14	125	85
13	122	80
12	117	75
11	115	70
10	112	65
9	108	60
8	105	55
7	100	50
6	95	45
5	90	40

TEST 5 ANSWERS

1 B. 2c in the inner ring.

2 B.

3 A. Reading clockwise, the number in the sector is the alphabetical value of the letter in the previous sector.

4 F.

5 F.

6 C. Each column totals 8.

7 E.

8 B. From the 1, the numbers increase in a spiral by missing out one number, then two numbers, then three numbers and so on.

9 C.

10 F.

11 B. Each double section is added together. These totals increase by two each time.

12 F. When completed the box reads the same both down and across.

13 D. The value of individual letters is irrelevant. The total of the row of numbers must match the total of the column of numbers.

14 E.

15 A.

16 E. On each row A - B - C = D.

17 B.

18 C. ♣ = 4, ♥ = 3, ♦ = 1.

19 D. 1o in the inner ring, between another 1o and 5a.

20 F.

21 A. The left number plus the top number gives the right number in each triangle.

22 C. The alphabetical values of the letters are added to give the number in the middle space.

23 B. The minute hand moves forward ten minutes and the hour hand one hour on each clock.

24 F. Divide the square into four 2 x 2 blocks. The four numbers in each block total 20.

25 D.

26 A.

27 D.

28 A.

29 A.

30 E.

SCORE	I.Q.	PERCENTILE
30	161	99
29	160	99
28	157	99
27	155	99
26	154	98
25	152	98
24	150	98
23	148	98*
22	143	97
21	140	96
20	138	95
19	136	94
18	134	93
17	132	92
16	131	91
15	130	90
14	125	85
13	122	80
12	117	75
11	115	70
10	112	65
9	108	60
8	105	55
7	100	50
6	95	45
5	90	40

*** MENSA LEVEL**
You should attempt to join
– see front page for details.

TEST 6 ANSWERS

1 E. The sectors in the bottom half total one higher than their opposite in the top half.
2 C.
3 F.
4 B.
5 F. 2c in the inner ring with 2c on either side, and 2c outside.
6 D. ♣ = 5, ♥ = 7, ♦ = 4.
7 F.
8 F. The third row plus the second row gives the first row.
9 A. Start in the extreme left circle. The series of arrows zigzags up and down with the arrows pointing as follows: up, down, right, left, down. This repeats.
10 D.
11 B. When completed the box shows the same pattern both down and across.
12 F.
13 C.
14 A. Each double section is added together. This double and its opposite have the same total.
15 E. The middle circle and the two rings of circles all total 24.
16 D.
17 E. The alphabetical positions of the letters are found and the smaller is taken from the larger.
18 C. In each triangle the bottom two numbers are multiplied to give the top.
19 B. K=11, Λ=12, O=15, Π=16.
20 D. On each row A x B + C = D.
21 E. The hour hand moves forward one hour and the minute hand moves five minutes back each time.
22 E.
23 B. Opposite sectors total the same.
24 D.
25 B.
26 B.
27 C.
28 D.
29 C. Start in the top circle. The series of arrows zigzags across in a downward direction with the arrows pointing as follows: right, left, up, up, down, left. This repeats.
30 E.

SCORE	I.Q.	PERCENTILE
30	161	99
29	160	99
28	157	99
27	155	99
26	154	98
25	152	98
24	150	98
23	148	98*
22	143	97
21	140	96
20	138	95
19	136	94
18	134	93
17	132	92
16	131	91
15	130	90
14	125	85
13	122	80
12	117	75
11	115	70
10	112	65
9	108	60
8	105	55
7	100	50
6	95	45
5	90	40

*** MENSA LEVEL**
You should attempt to join – see front page for details.

TEST 7 ANSWERS

1 D. The left number divided by the top number gives the right number in each triangle.
2 A.
3 E. The first row plus the second row gives the third row.
4 C. Each double section is added together. All double sections total 9.
5 E.
6 D.
7 D.
8 A. Reverse each row of numbers. Add the second row to the third to give the first row.
9 B.
10 D. When completed the box reads the same both down and across.
11 C.
12 C.
13 F.
14 A. All straight lines of five triangles total 22.
15 E.
16 D.
17 E. In each triangle the left number increases by four, the right number decreases by three and the number at the top doubles each time.
18 D.
19 E.
20 A. 2a in the inner ring, between 1o and 1i.
21 C. ϕ=6, γ=7, η=8, τ=20.
22 E. When completed the box shows the same pattern both down and across.
23 D.
24 C. ♣ = 1, ♥ = 8, ♦ = 11.
25 E.
26 A. On each row A x B - C = D.
27 D.
28 F.
29 F. The alphabetical values of the letters are placed on opposite sides in the middle space.
30 C. The minute hand moves forward fifteen minutes and the hour hand moves back two hours on each clock.

SCORE	I.Q.	PERCENTILE
30	161	99
29	160	99
28	157	99
27	155	99
26	154	98
25	152	98
24	150	98
23	148	98*
22	143	97
21	140	96
20	138	95
19	136	94
18	134	93
17	132	92
16	131	91
15	130	90
14	125	85
13	122	80
12	117	75
11	115	70
10	112	65
9	108	60
8	105	55
7	100	50
6	95	45
5	90	40

*** MENSA LEVEL**
You should attempt to join – see front page for details.

TEST 8 ANSWERS

1 D. Each double section is added together. Totals of opposite sections are equal.
2 C.
3 E.
4 F. Reverse each row of numbers. Add the first row to the second to give the third row.
5 C. 2a in the inner ring between 2a and 1o.
6 C.
7 A. Reverse the alphabet and give each letter its value. For example A=26, B = 25.
8 D. The minute hand moves forward twenty-five minutes and the hour hand moves back four hours on each clock.
9 C. On each row A + B ÷ C = D.
10 F. η=8, φ=10, τ=20, ψ=25.
11 B.
12 E. ♣ = 7, ♥ = 5, ♦ = 9.
13 E. B=2, H=8, N=14, V=22.
14 D.
15 E.
16 B.
17 A.
18 E.
19 C. Give the letters their value in the alphabet and add them to the numbers. The top half of the circle will total 50, as will the bottom half.
20 E.
21 C. When completed the box reads the same both down and across.
22 D. The alphabetical value of the letters to the right are subtracted from the left to give the number in the middle space.
23 D. 3a in the inner ring, with 5a on both sides.
24 A. The minute hand moves back five minutes, then ten minutes then fifteen and so on. The hour hand moves two forward, two back, two forward and so on.
25 B.
26 D.♣ = 6, ♥ = 9, ♦ = 10.
27 A.
28 F. The number in the middle circle multiplied by the adjacent small circle gives the value in the large outer circle.
29 D. In each triangle the left number decreases by five, four, three, two and so on. The right number increases by three, four, five, six and so on. The number at the top is left plus right.
30 C.

SCORE	I.Q.	PERCENTILE
30	161	99
29	160	99
28	157	99
27	155	99
26	154	98
25	152	98
24	150	98
23	148	98*
22	143	97
21	140	96
20	138	95
19	136	94
18	134	93
17	132	92
16	131	91
15	130	90
14	125	85
13	122	80
12	117	75
11	115	70
10	112	65
9	108	60
8	105	55
7	100	50
6	95	45
5	90	40

*** MENSA LEVEL**
You should attempt to join – see front page for details.

INTRODUCTION

Human fascination with mazes is almost as old as civilization itself. The story of Theseus slaying the Minotaur in the labyrinth at Knossos is a prime example of the way in which a tangle of dark passages can inflame the human imagination. People only have to look briefly at a complicated pattern in order to imagine hidden horrors, buried treasure and lurking monsters. There is certainly something about such patterns, a hint of magic maybe, which seems to promise the answer to untold mysteries. Most cultures have been attracted to constructing involved patterns and then, quite often, turning them into puzzles with some sort of goal hidden within.

TO THE MAZES

These mazes are the product of unknown artists from different eras in a number of quite disparate cultures. We have included the delicate bamboo groves of Japan, the formal symmetry of Chinese lattice work, the knots and mythical monsters of the Celtic culture, and the wonderfully intricate geometric patterns of the Middle East. We must thank the Dover Pictorial Archive for making this material available to researchers such as myself, thus ensuring that these treasures of design continue to be used to enrich our lives.

FINISH
START

START

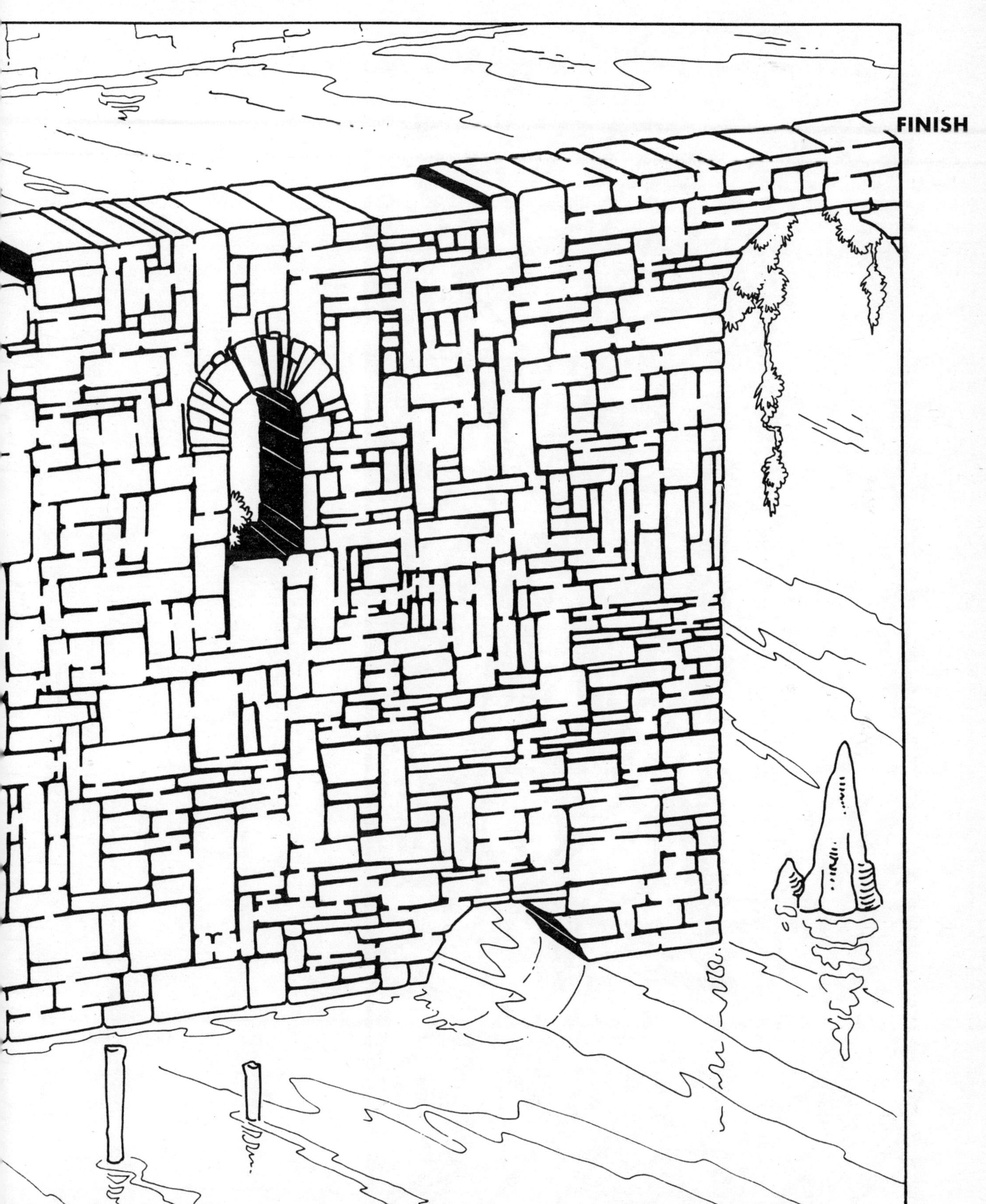
FINISH

FINISH
START

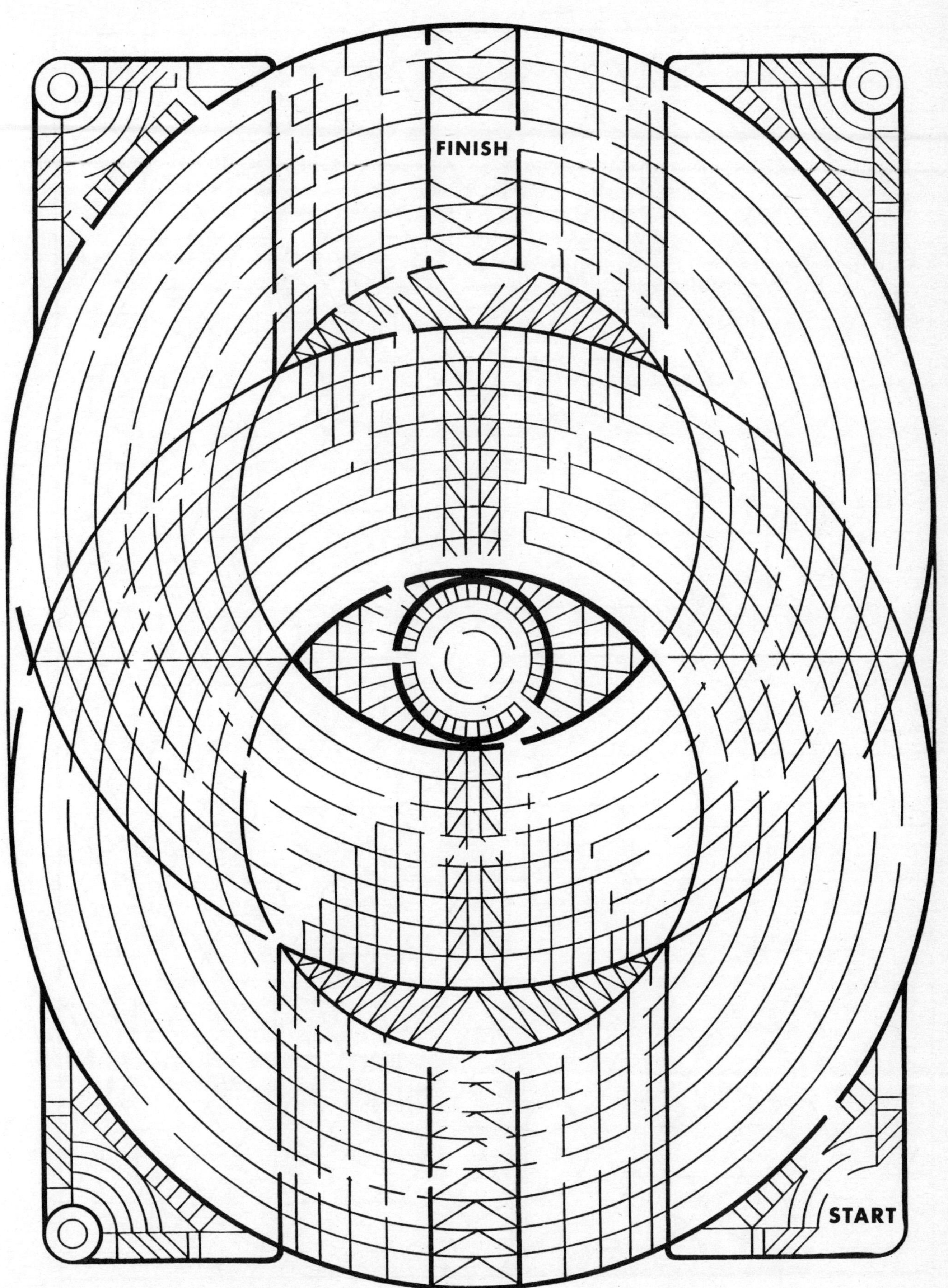
FINISH
START

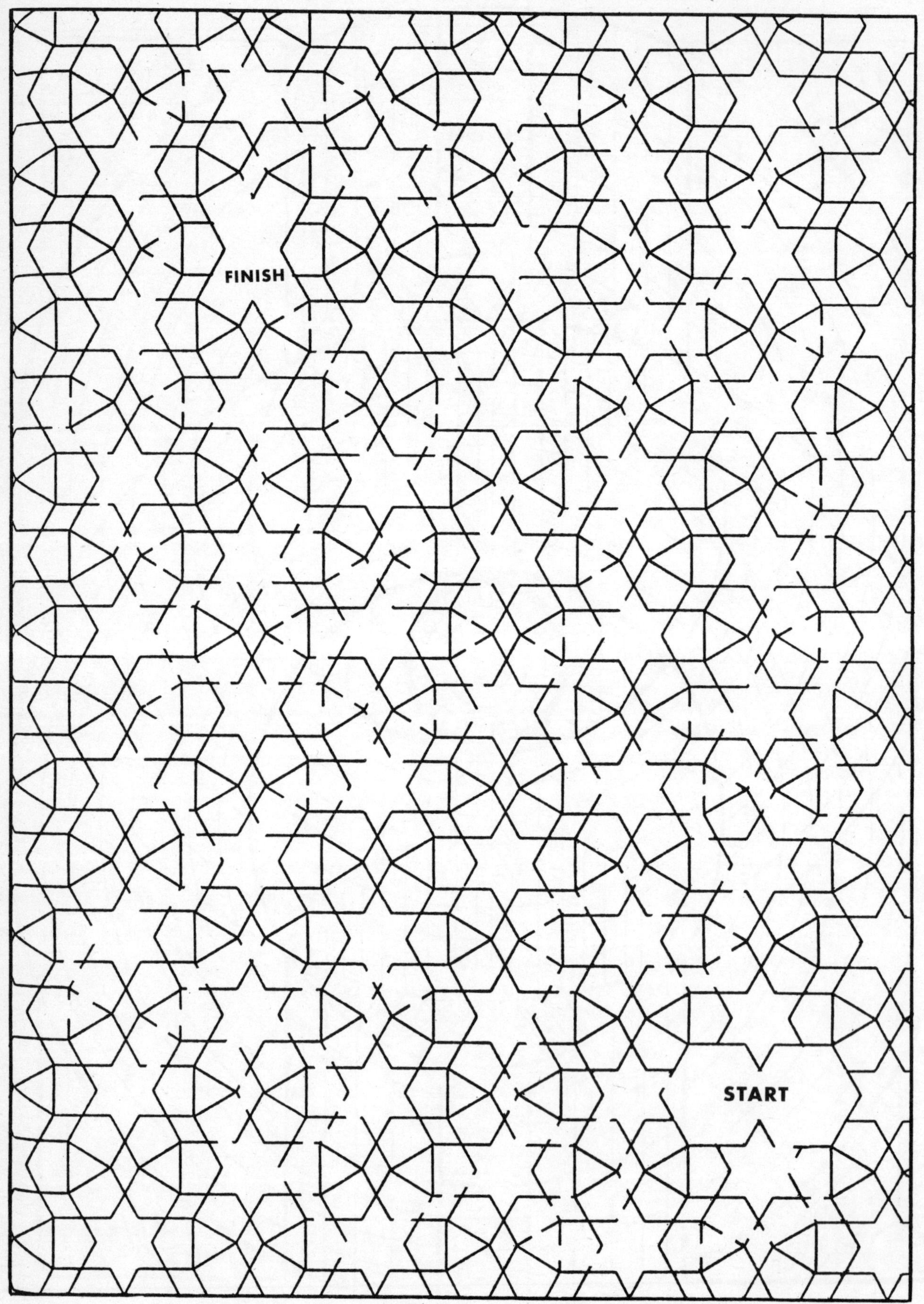
FINISH
START

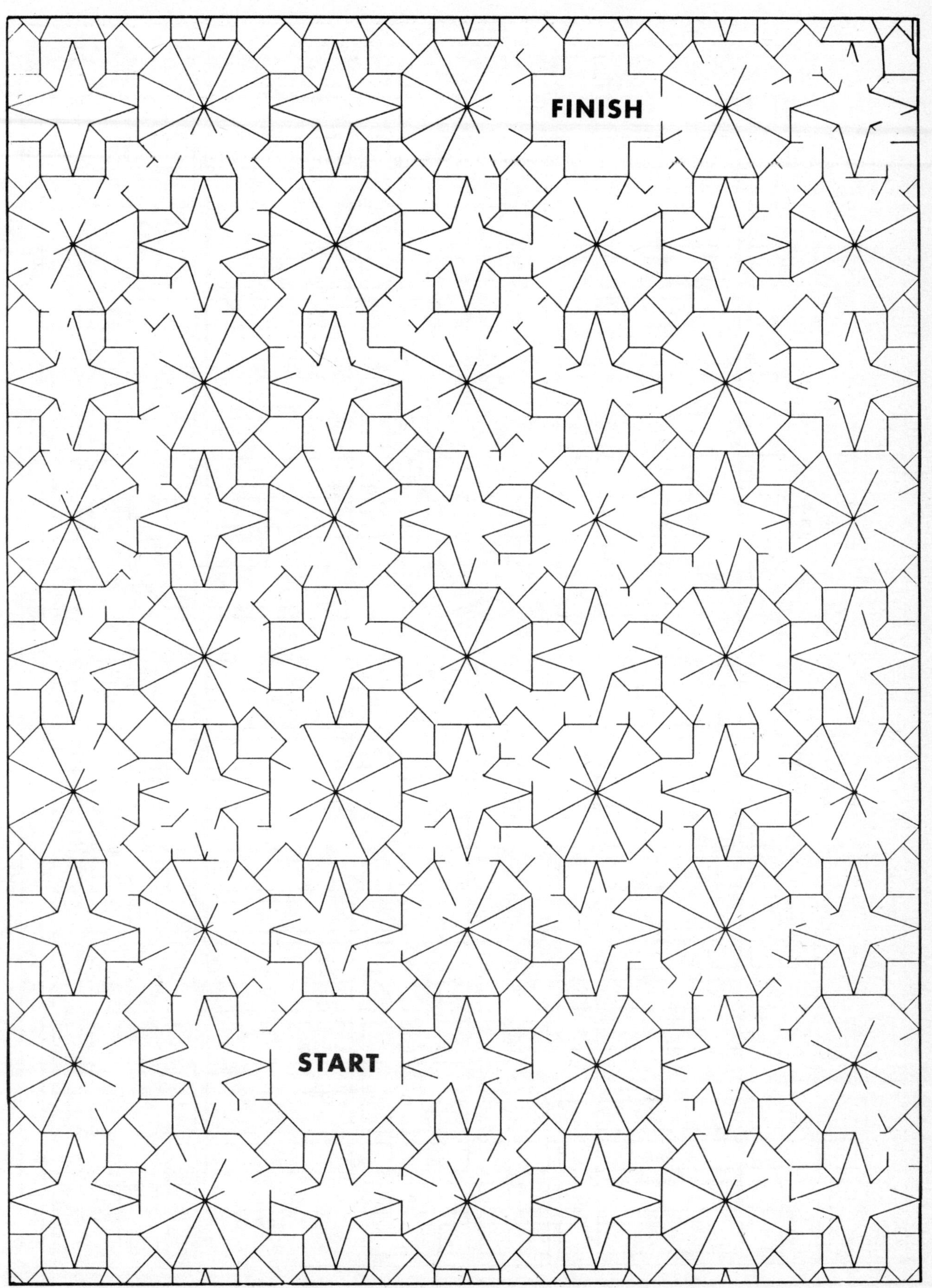
FINISH
START

START
FINISH

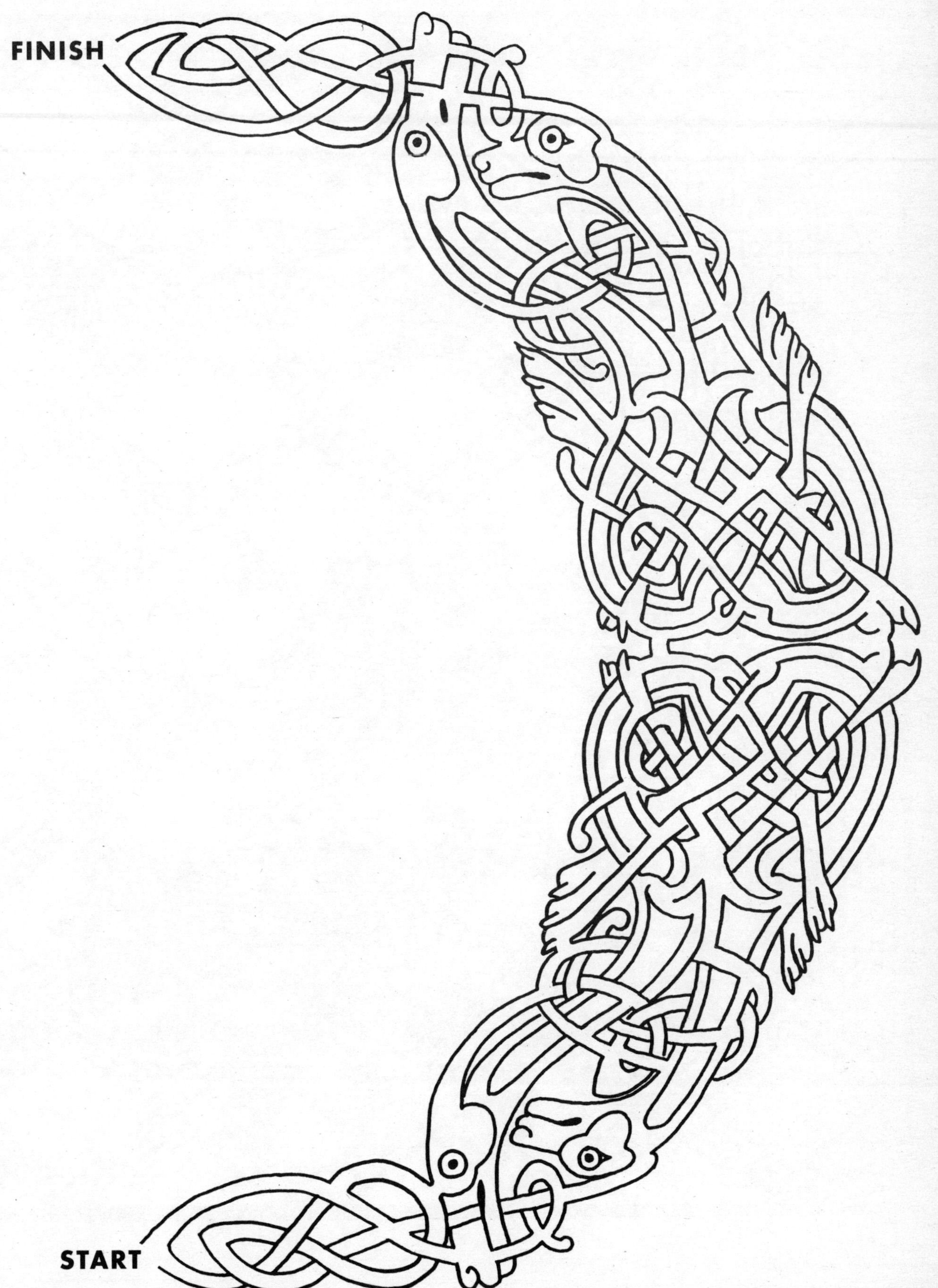
FINISH
START

FINISH
START

START
FINISH

FINISH
START

FINISH
START

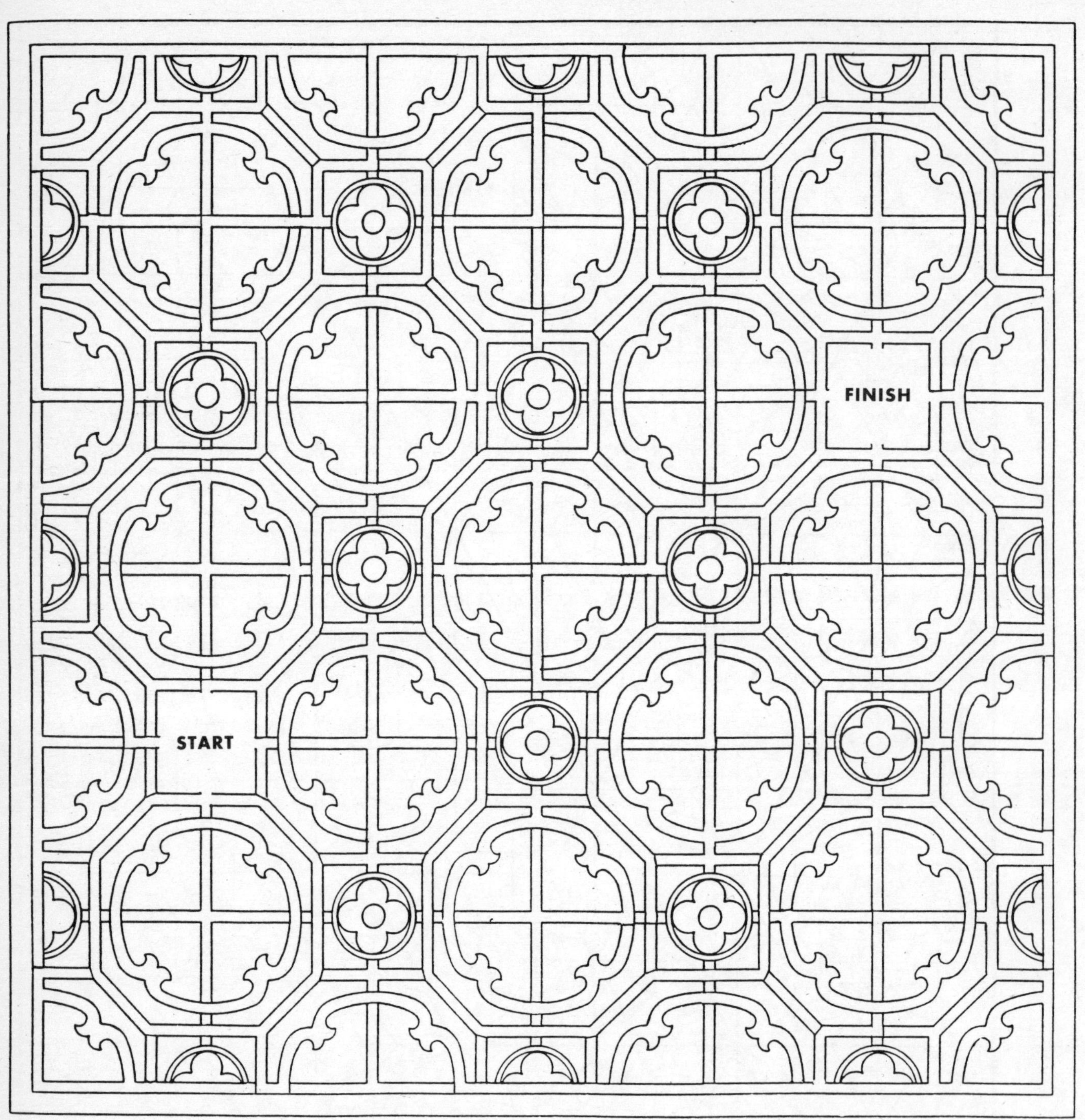
FINISH
START

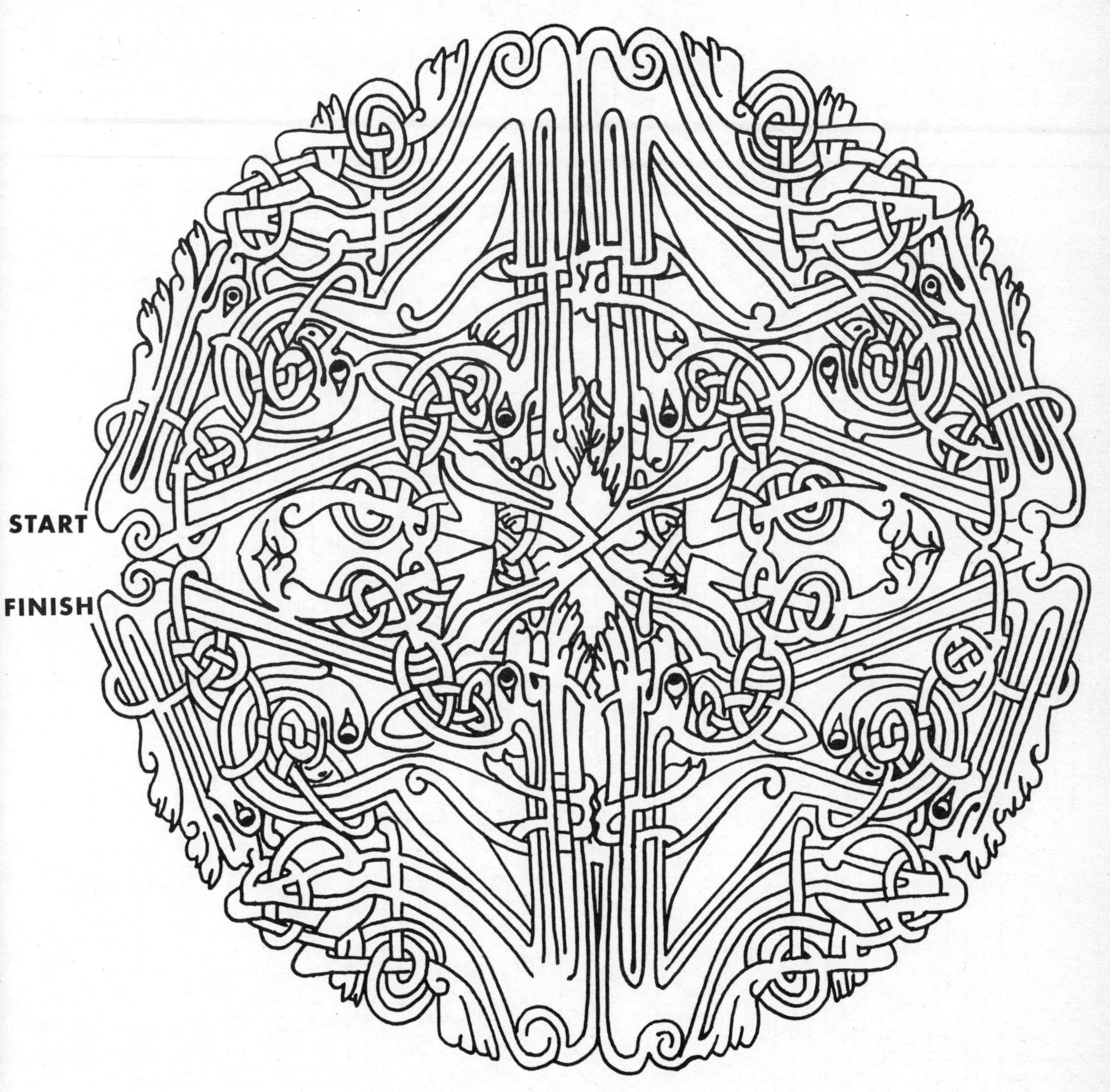
START
FINISH

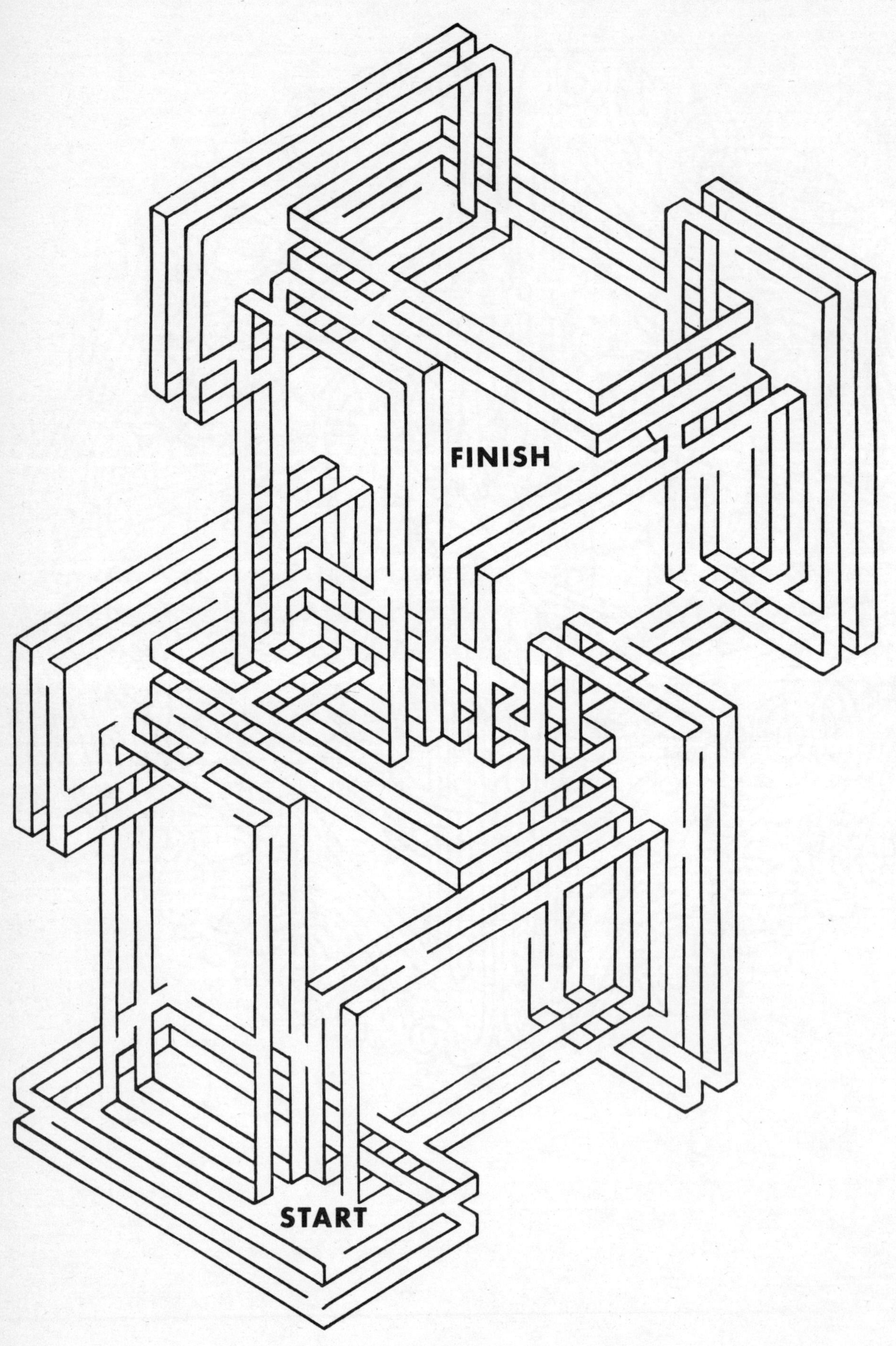
FINISH
START

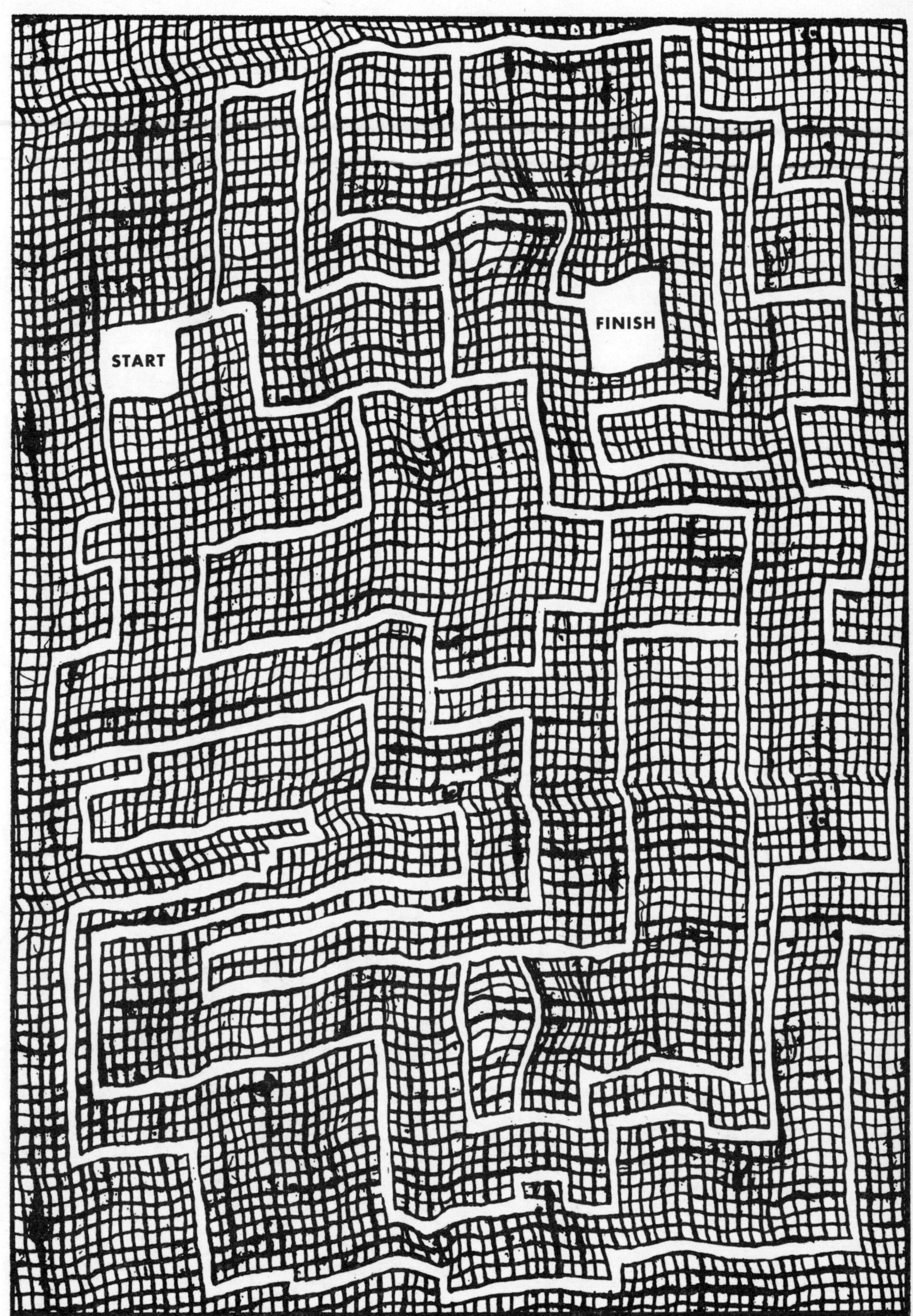
START
FINISH

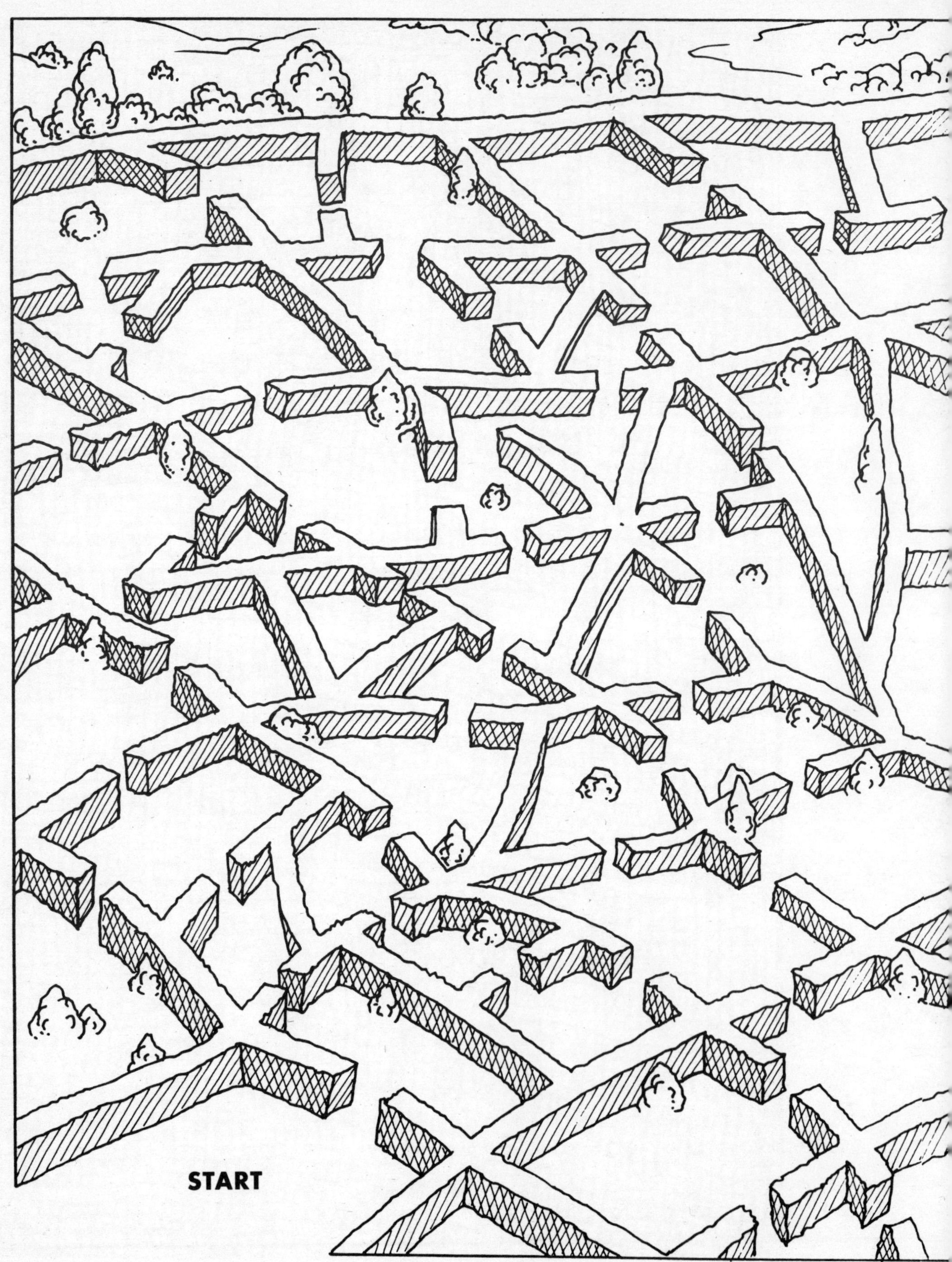
START

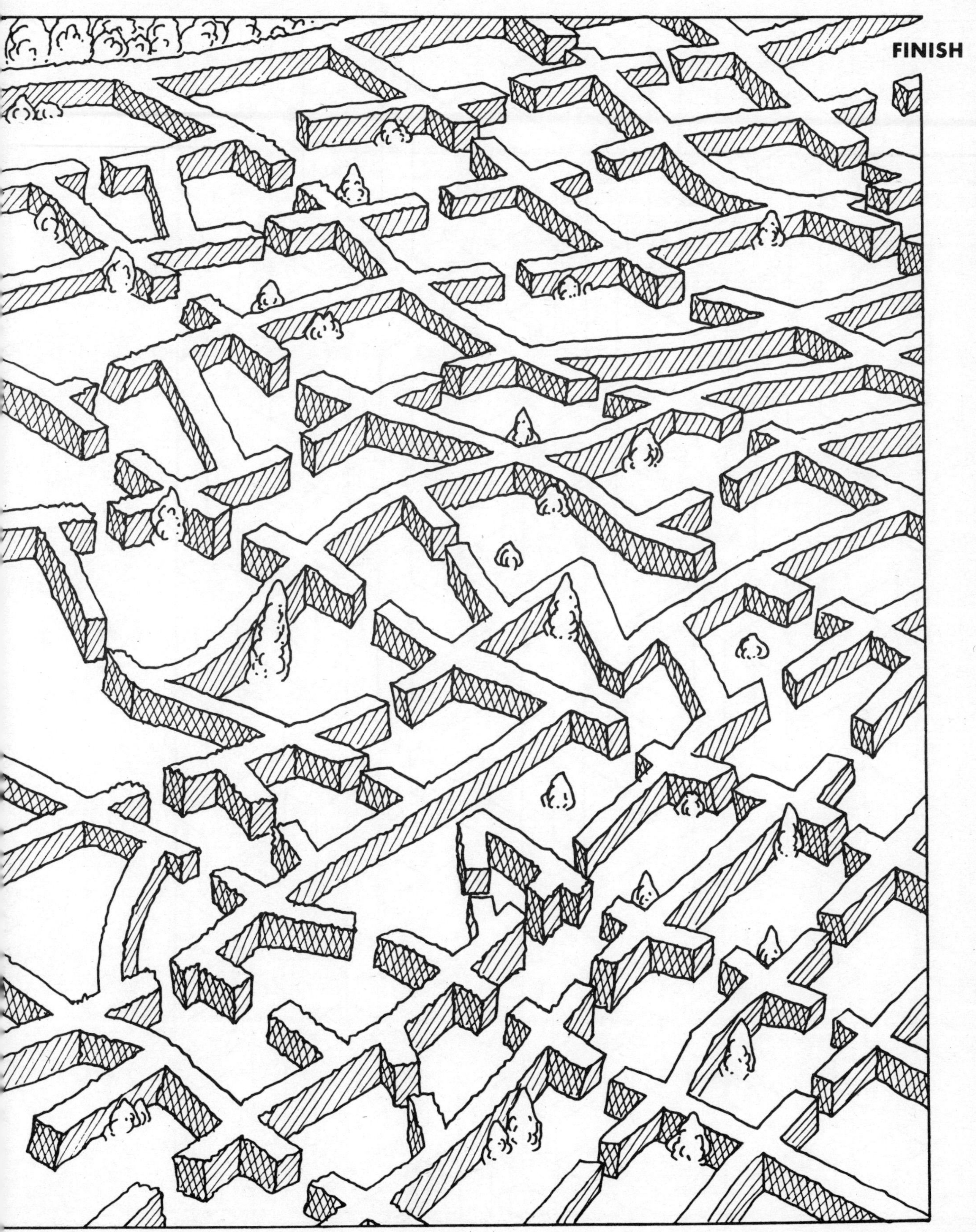
FINISH

FINISH
START

FINISH
START

FINISH
START

FINISH
START

FINISH
START

FINISH
START

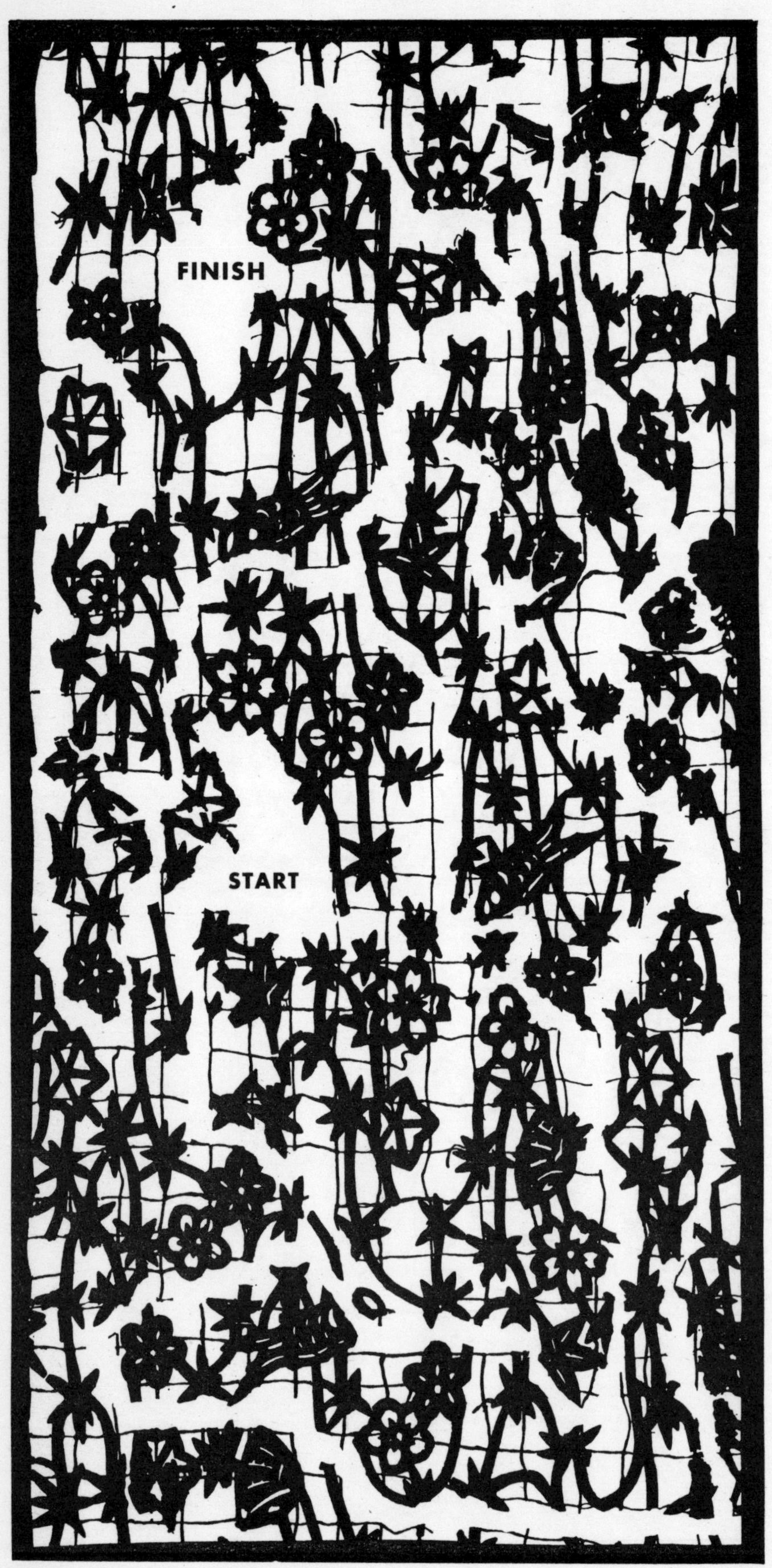
FINISH
START

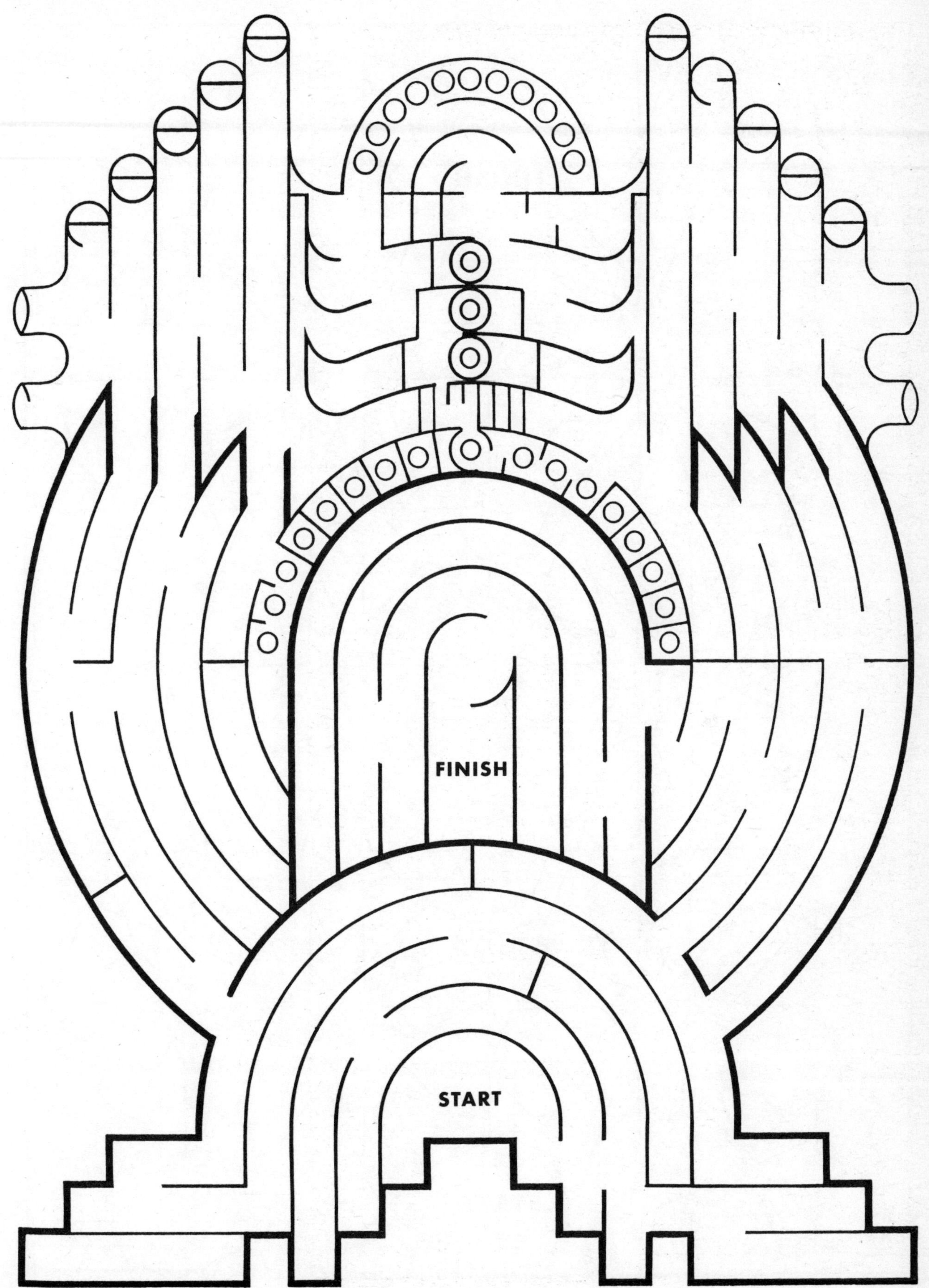
FINISH
START

FINISH
START

FINISH
START

FINISH
START

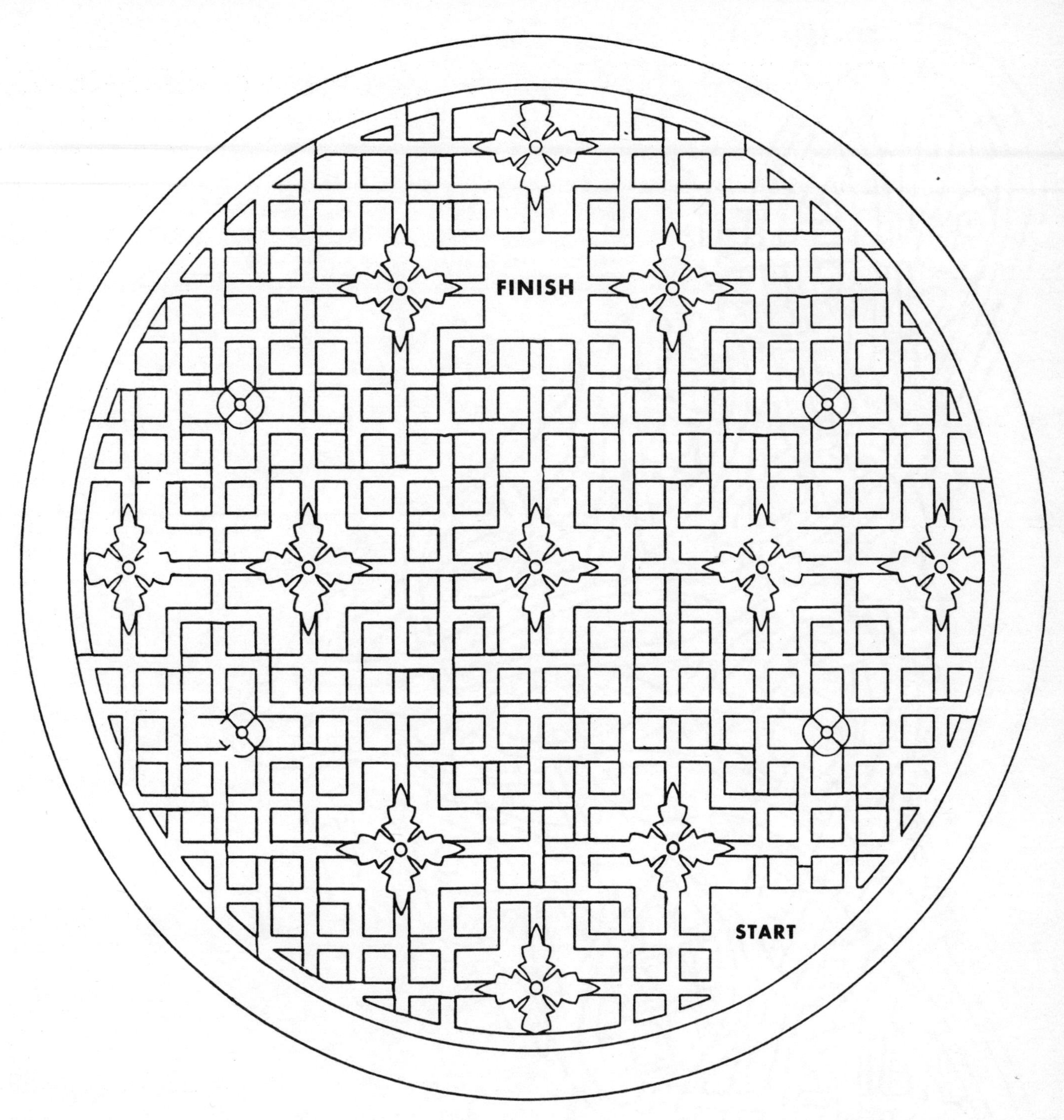
FINISH
START

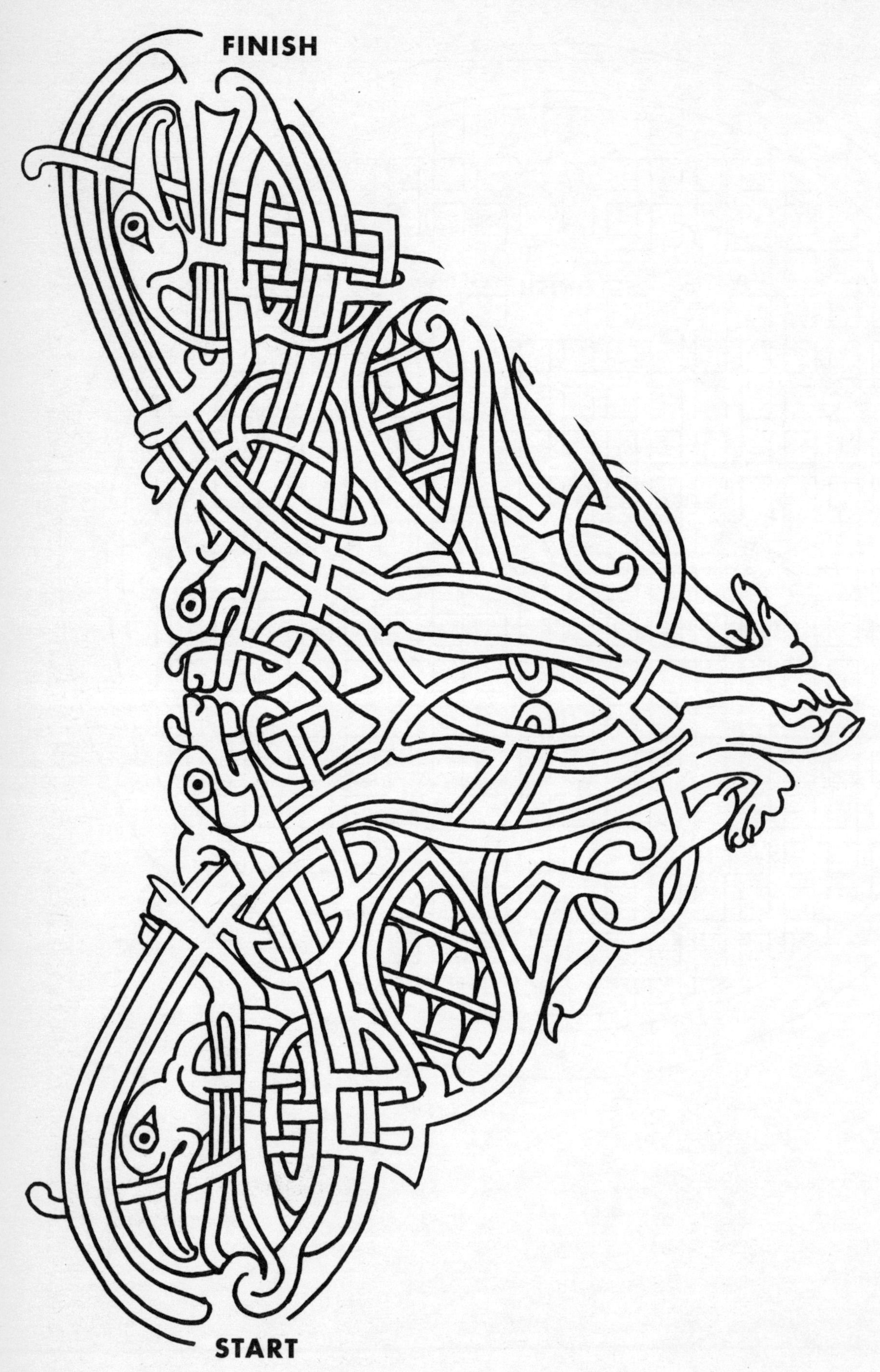
FINISH
START

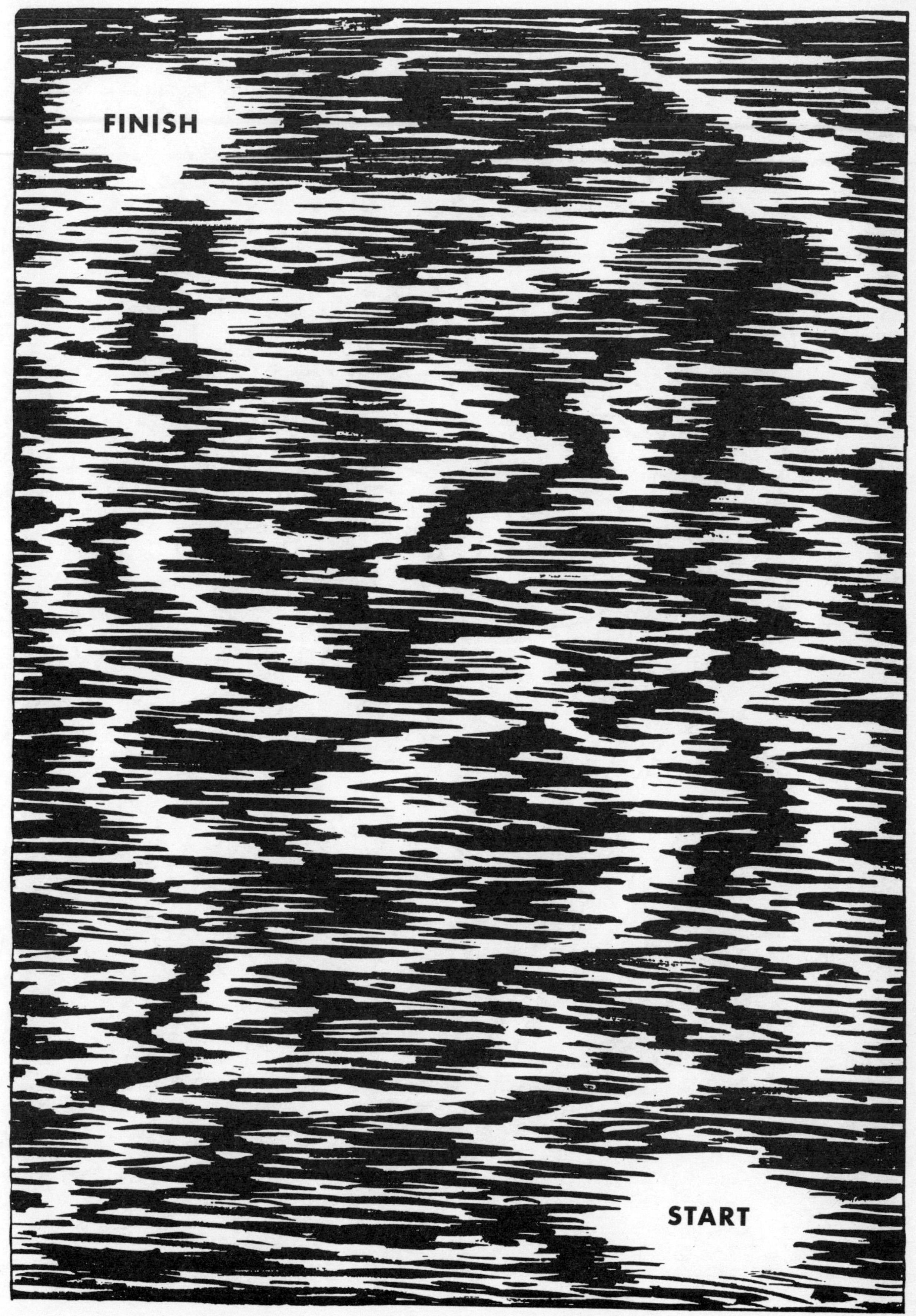
FINISH
START

FINISH

START

FINISH
START

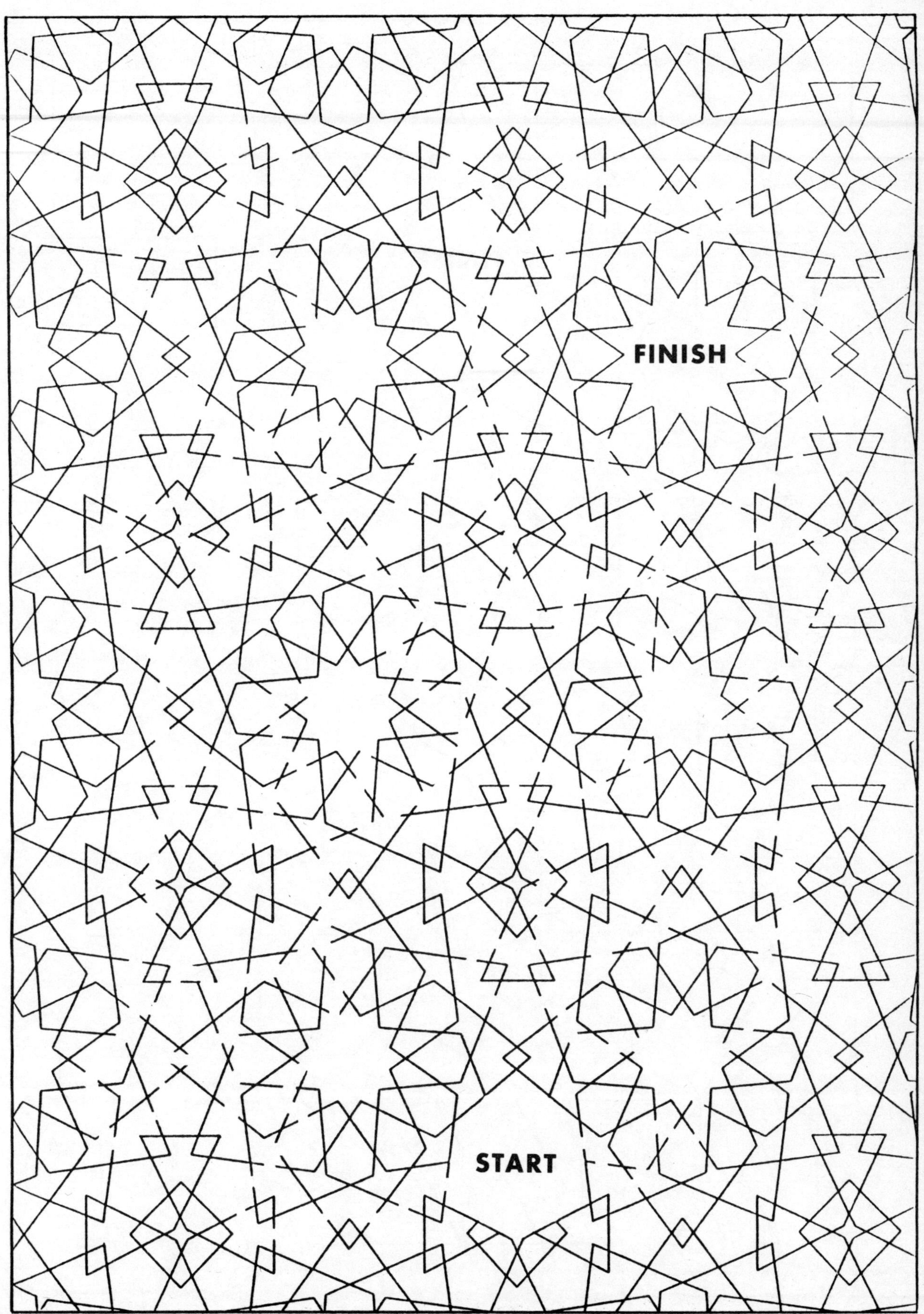
FINISH
START

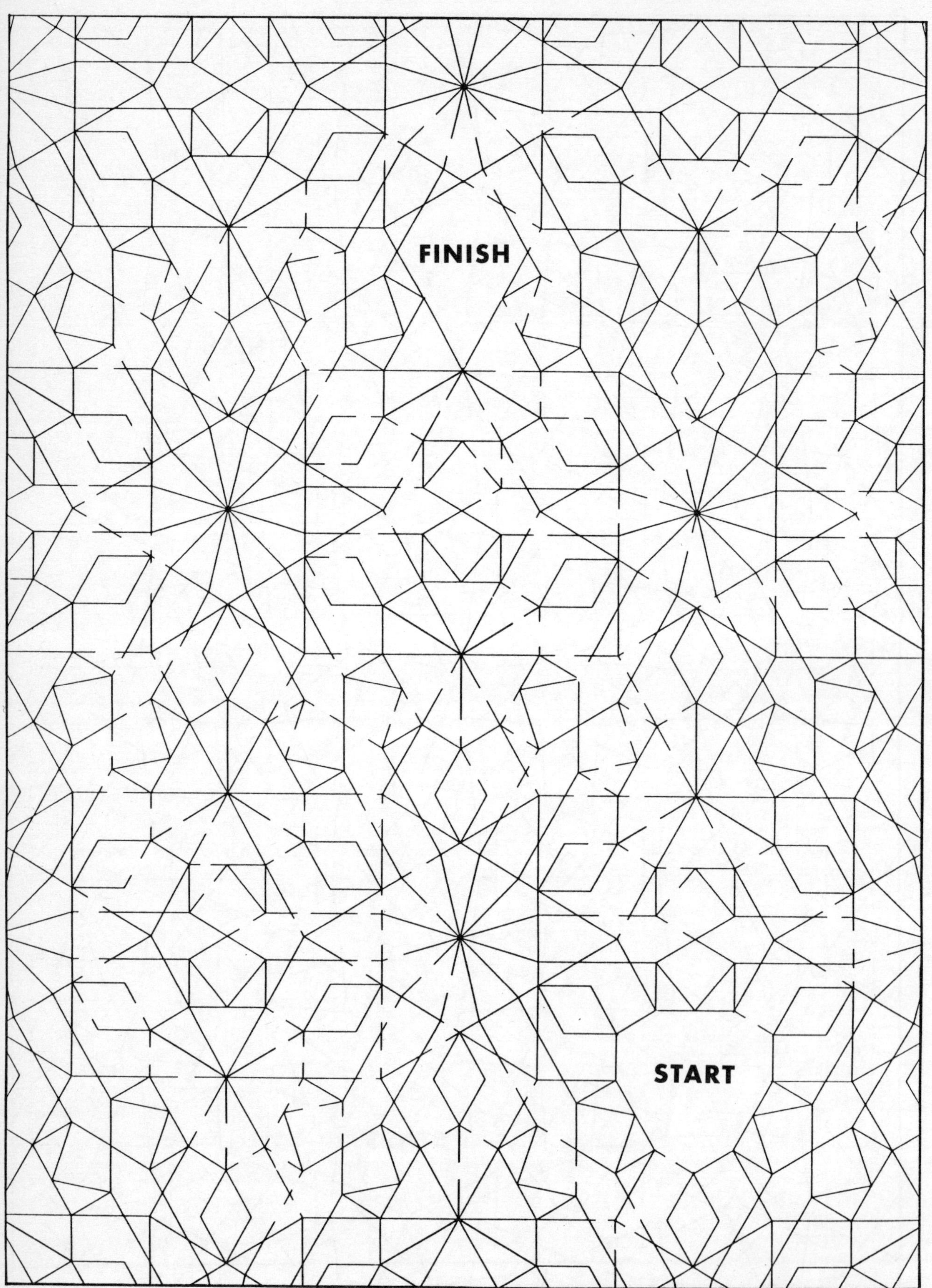
FINISH
START

3
2
END
4
1

START
FINISH

FINISH
START

FINISH
START

START
FINISH

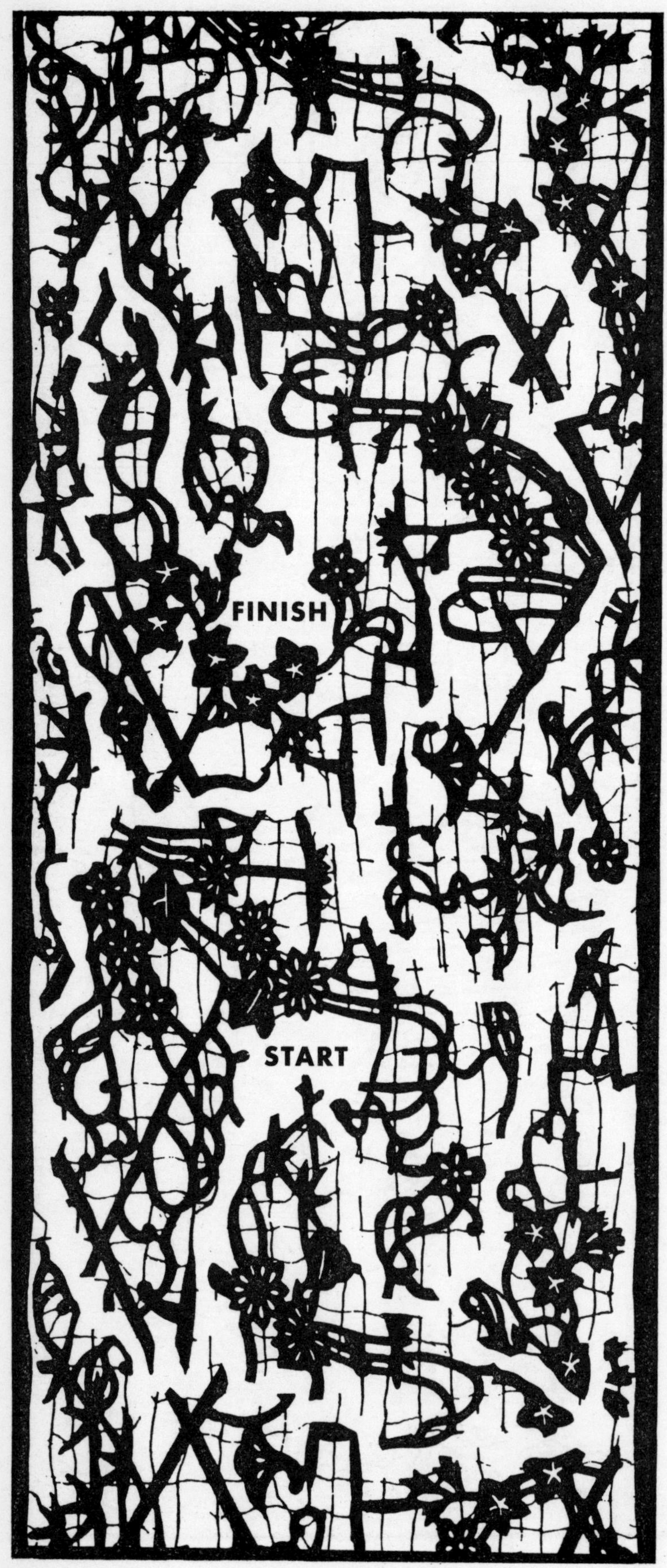
FINISH
START

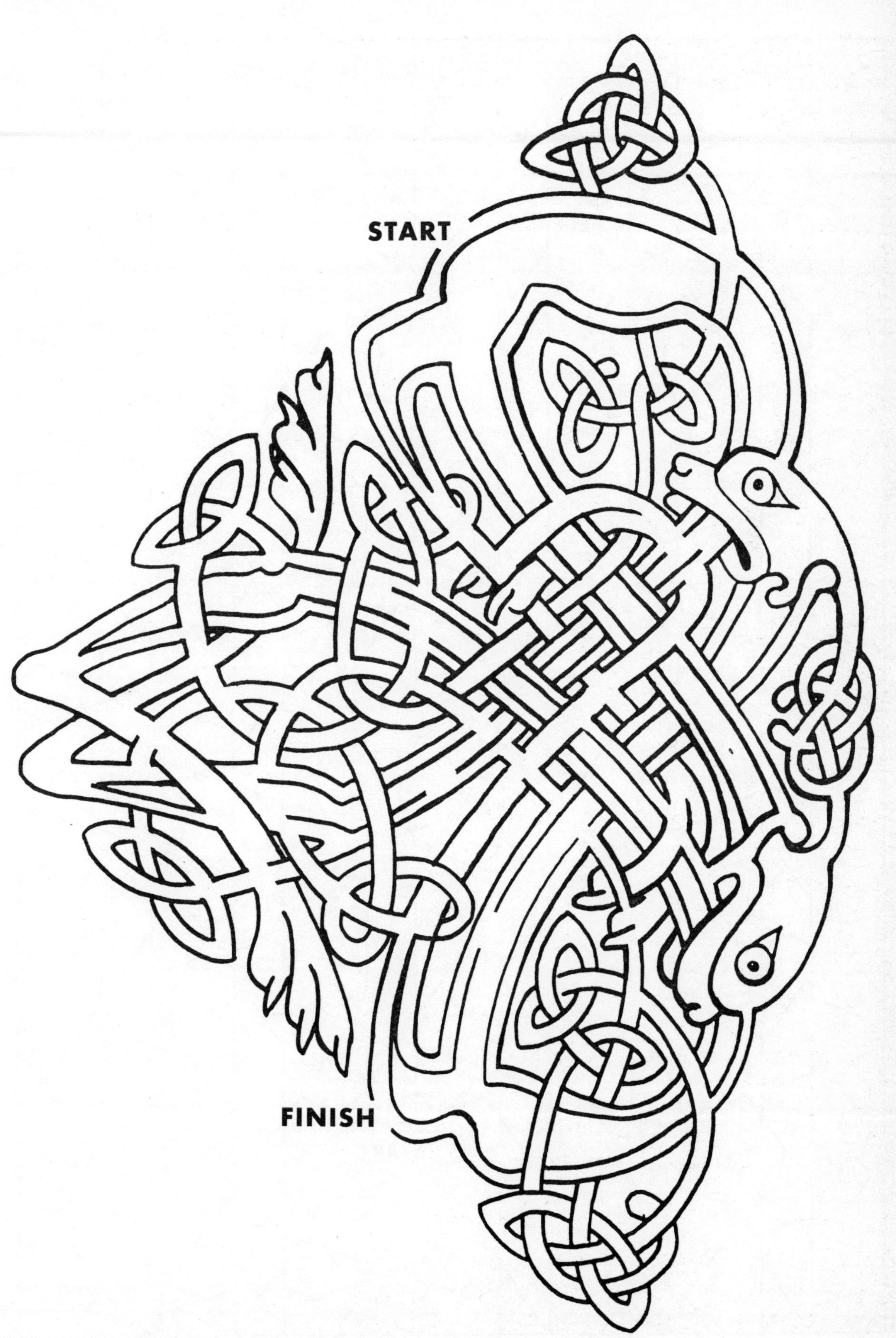
START
FINISH

FINISH
START

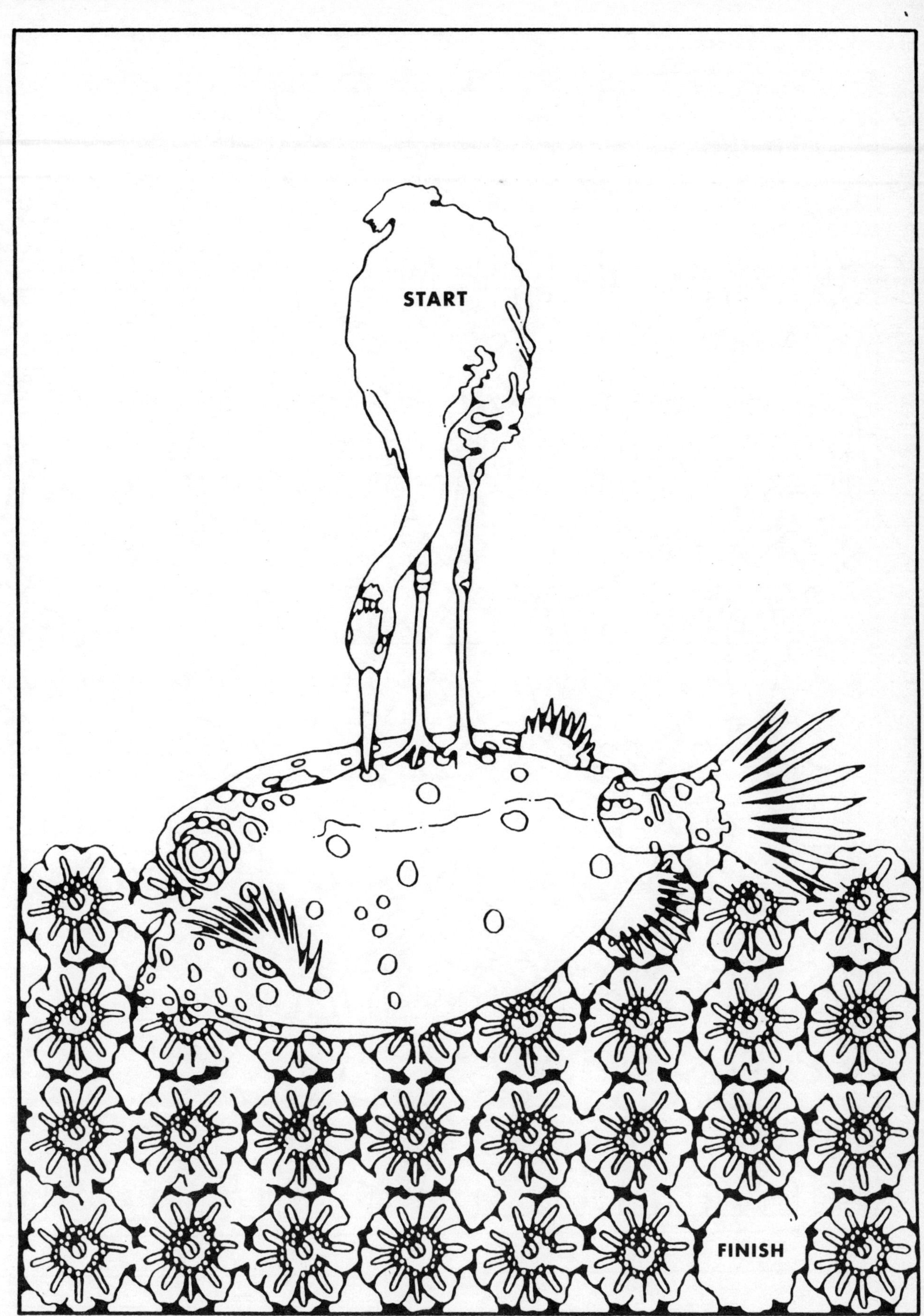
START
FINISH

FINISH
START

FINISH
START

START

FINISH

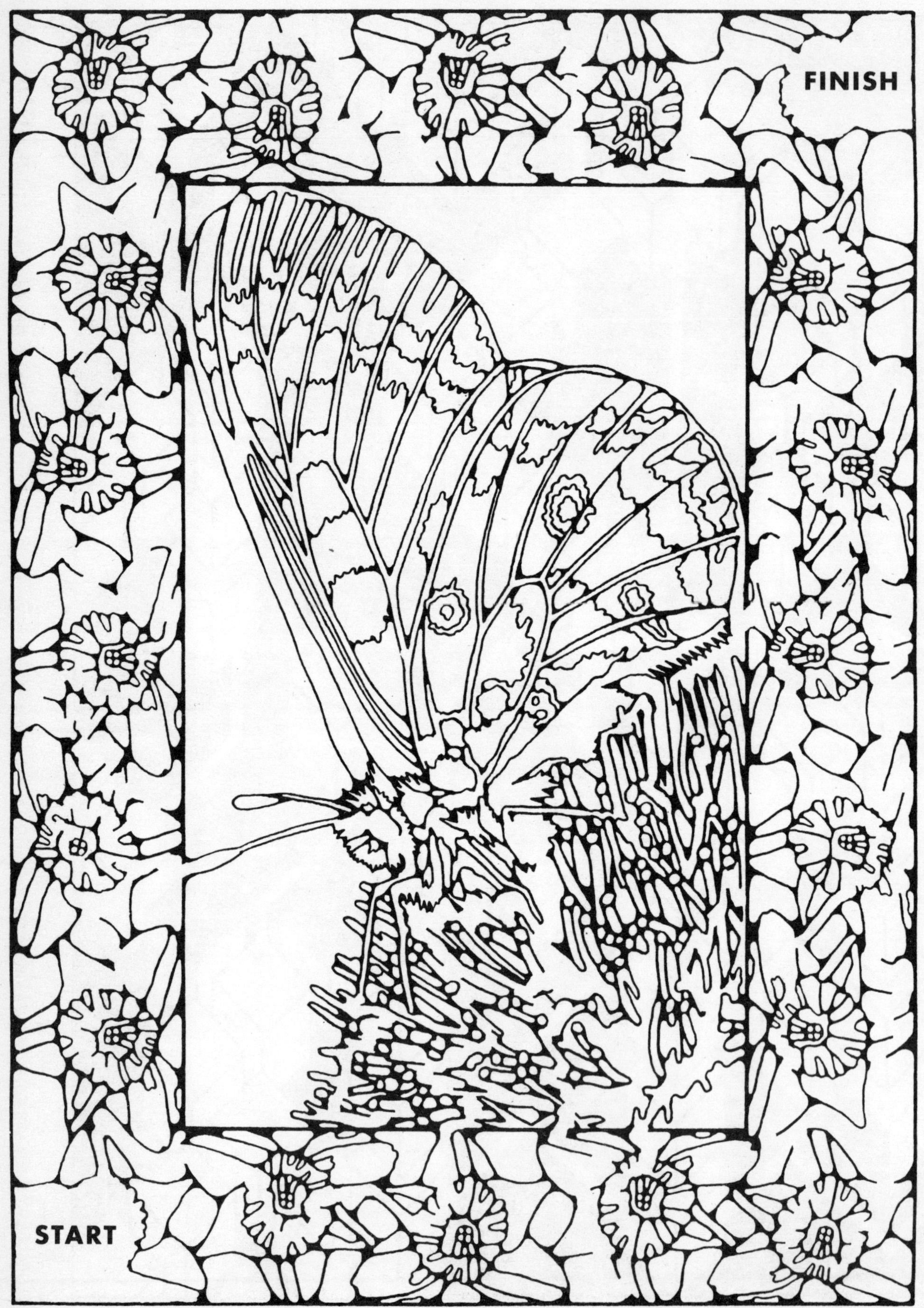
FINISH
START

START
FINISH

FINISH
START

FINISH
START

FINISH
START

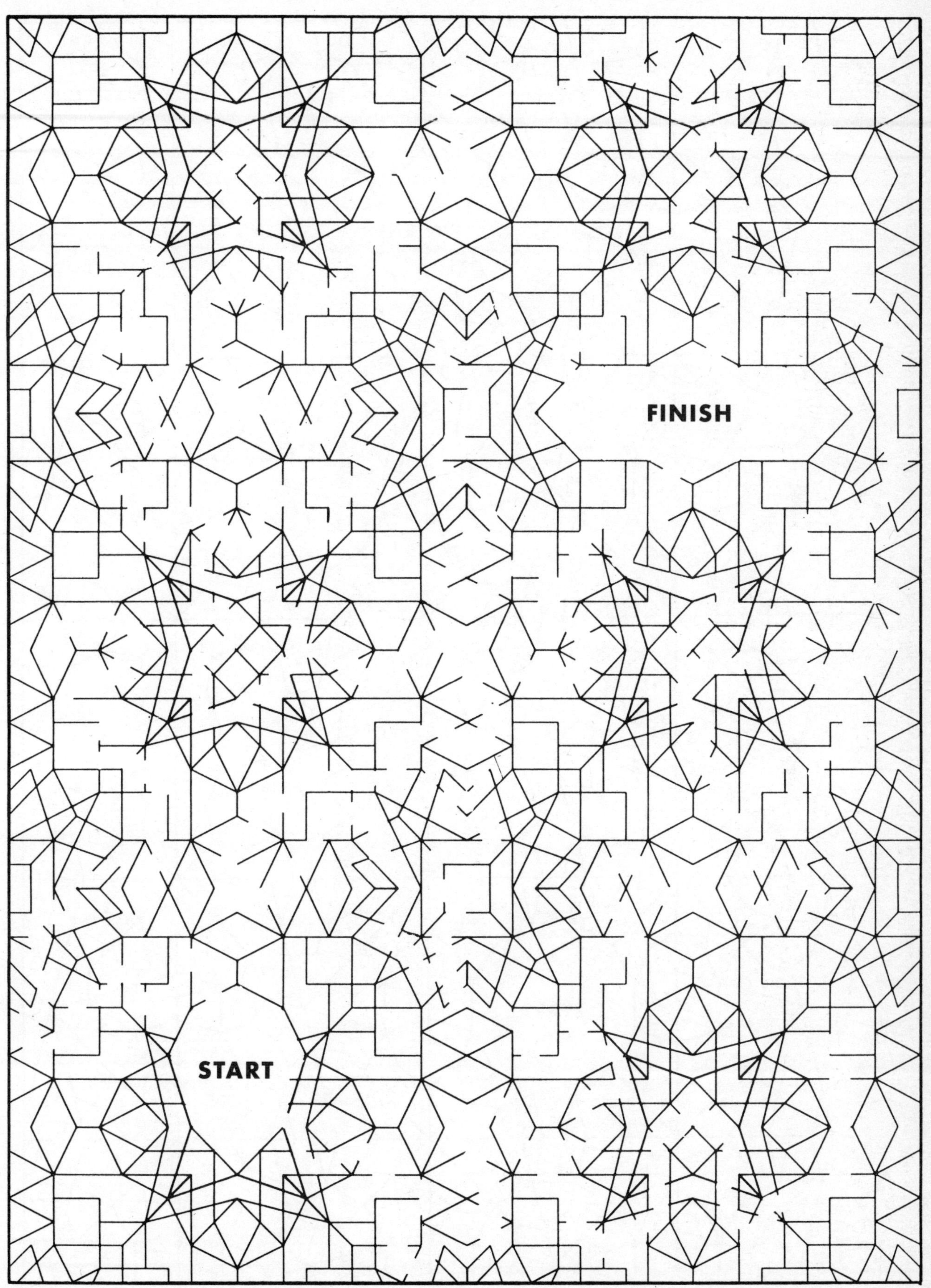
FINISH
START

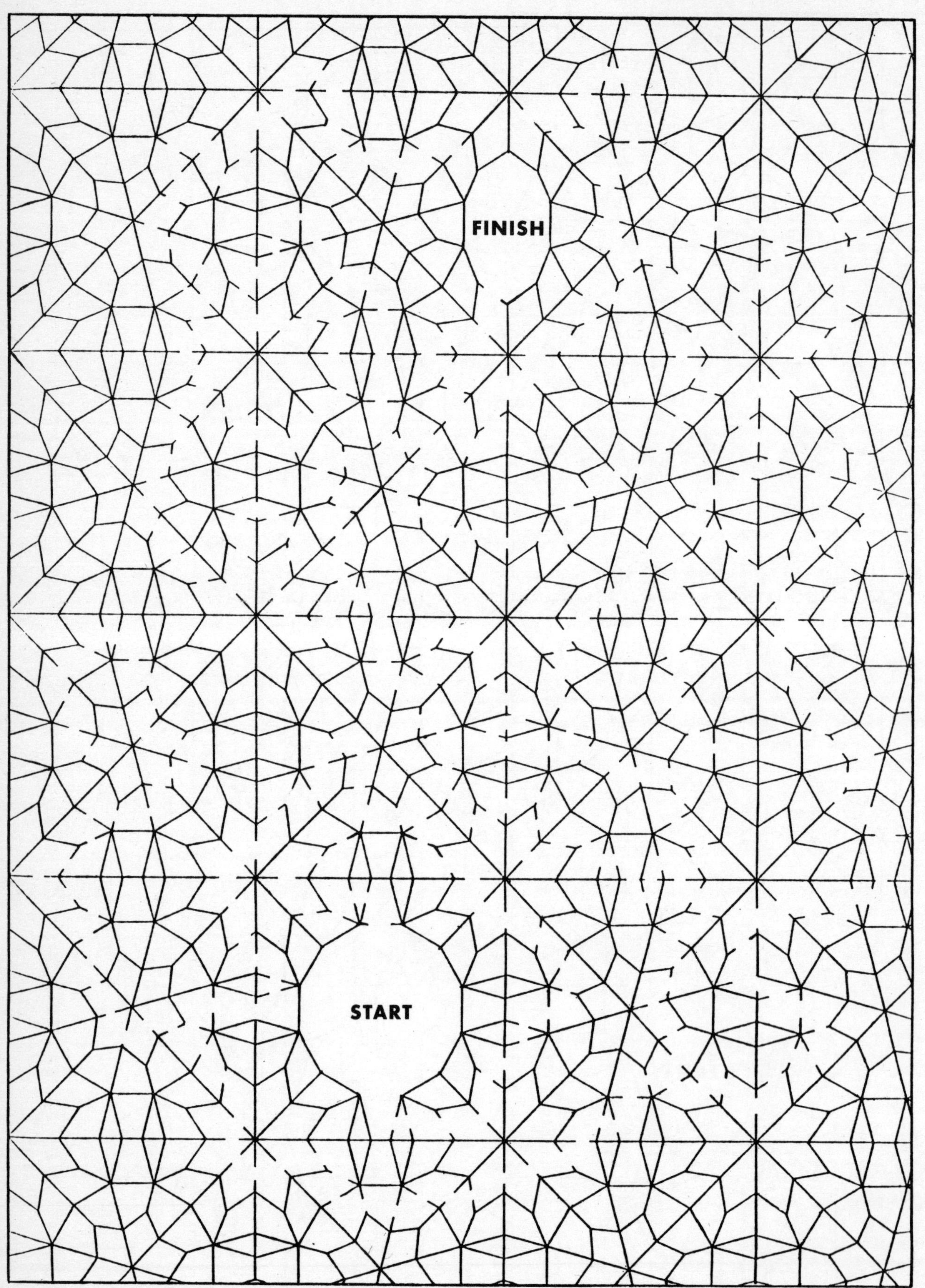
FINISH
START

FINISH
START

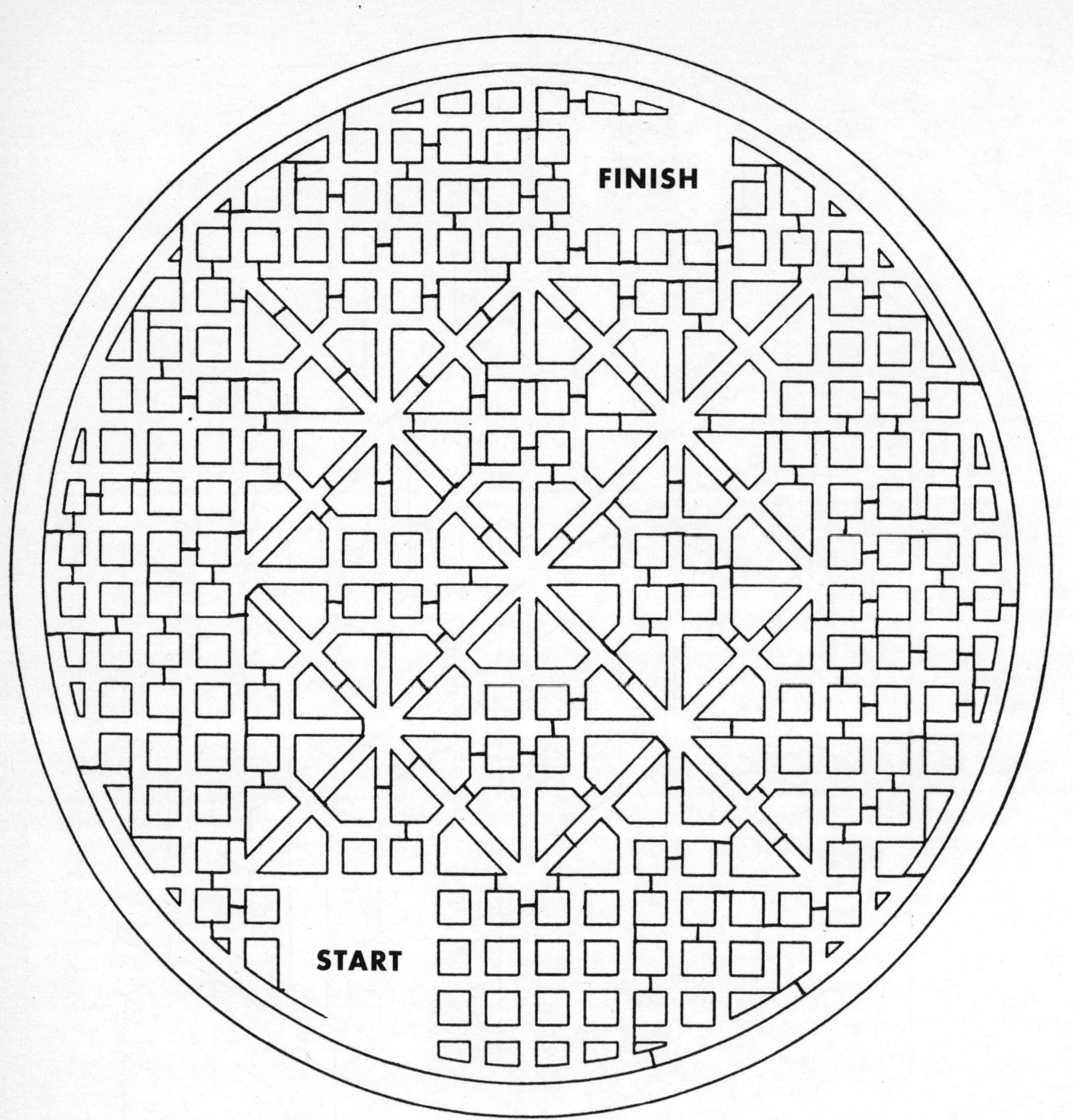
FINISH
START

FINISH
START

FINISH
START

FINISH
START

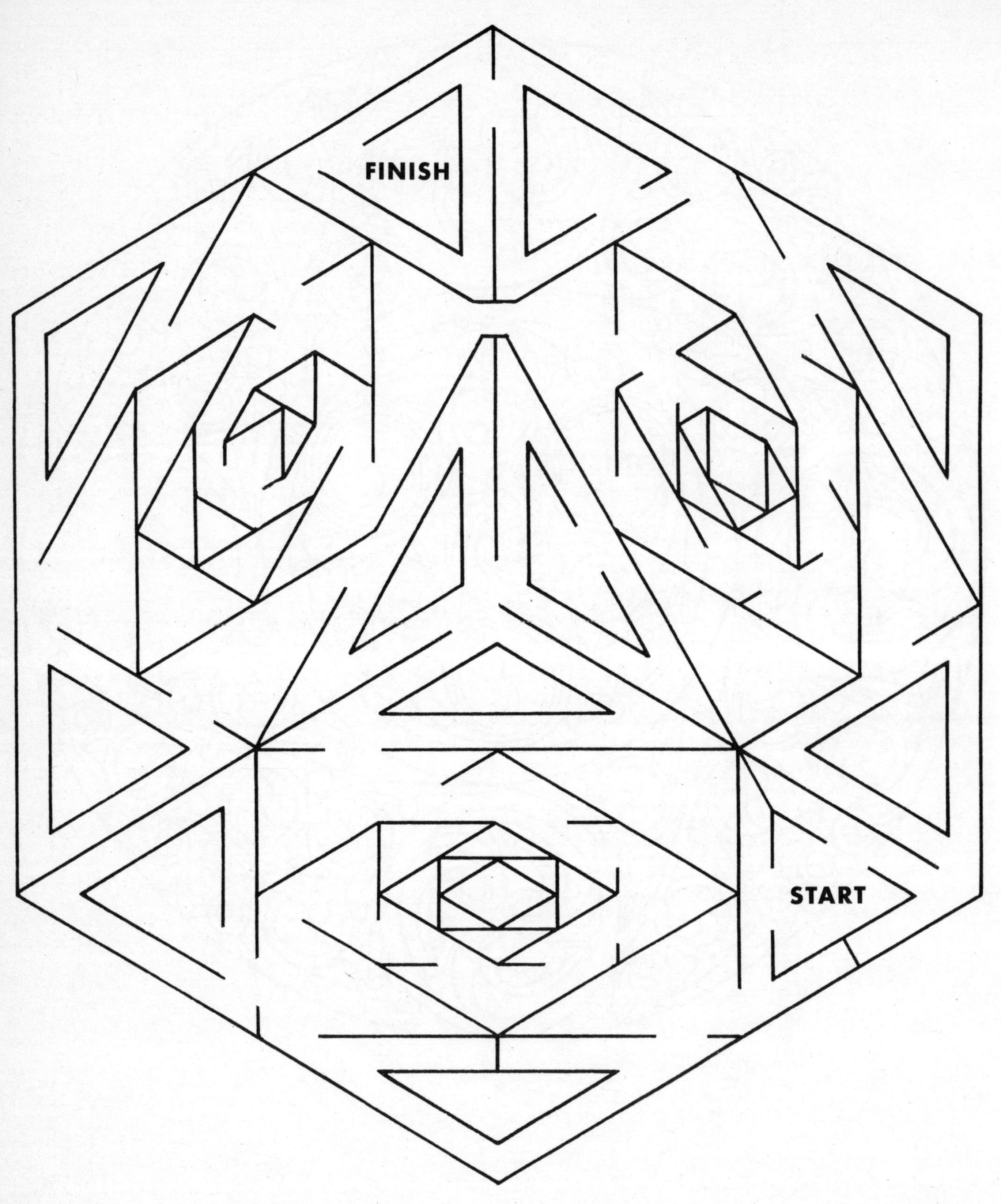
FINISH
START

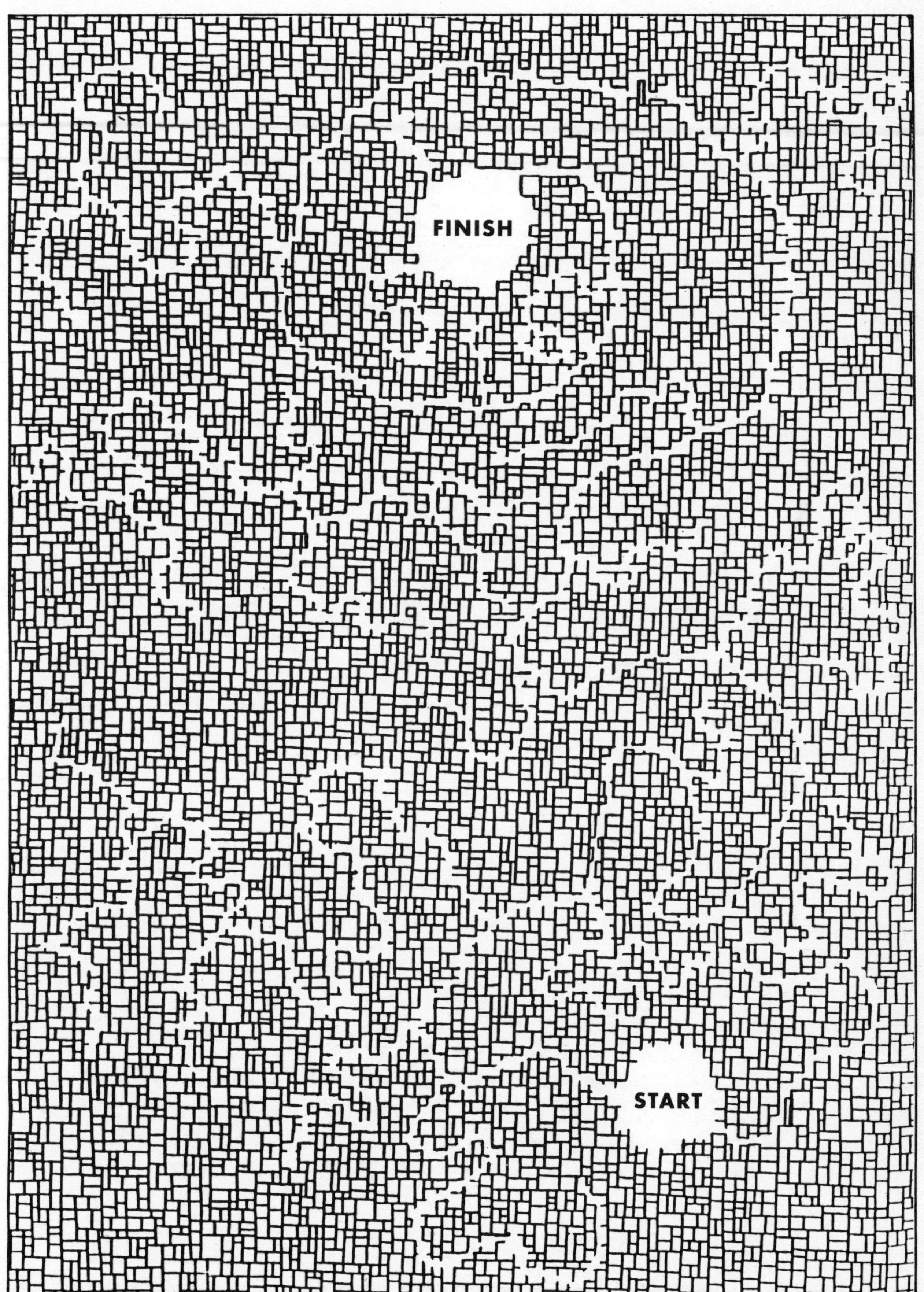
FINISH
START

START

FINISH

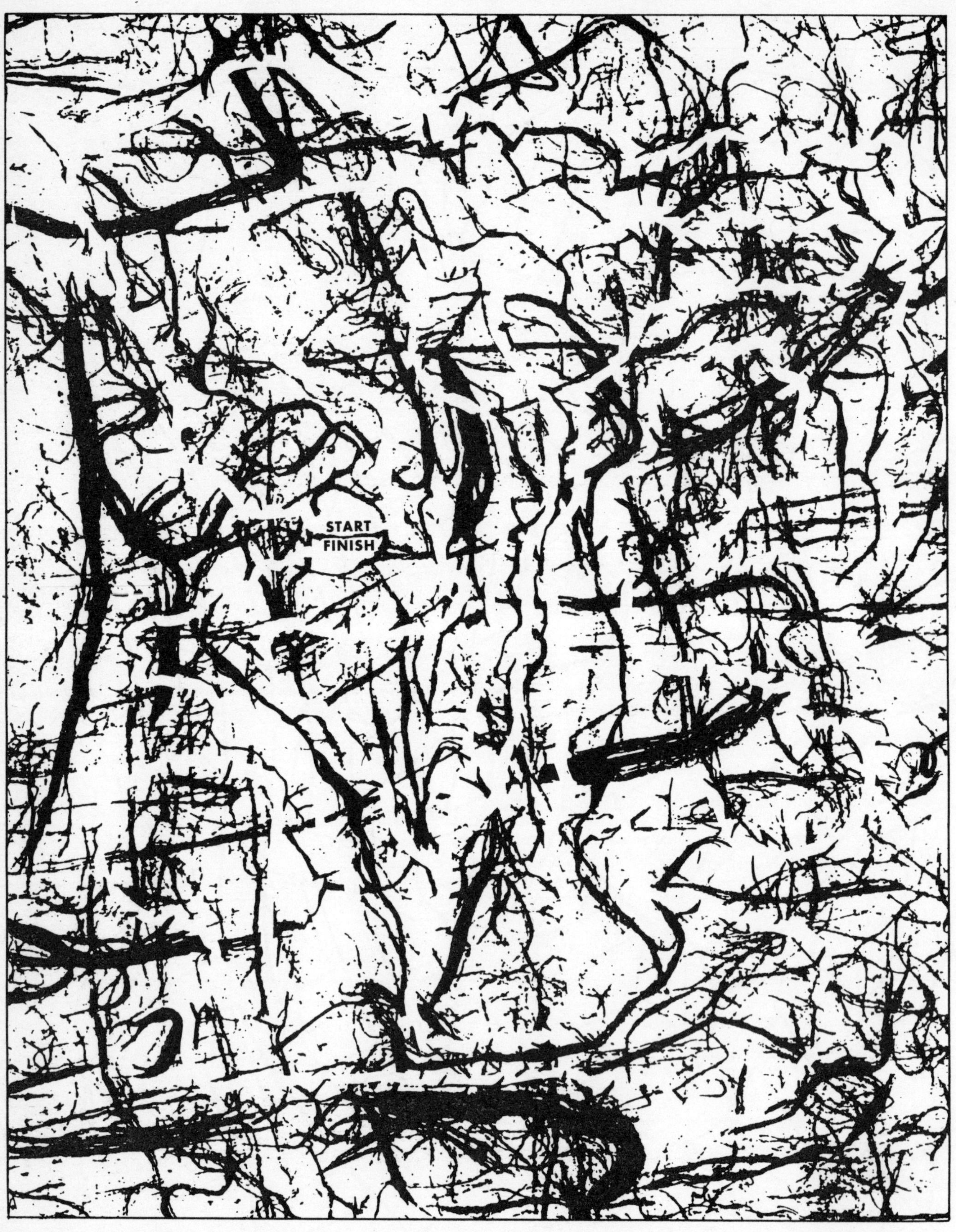
START
FINISH

FINISH
START

FINISH
START

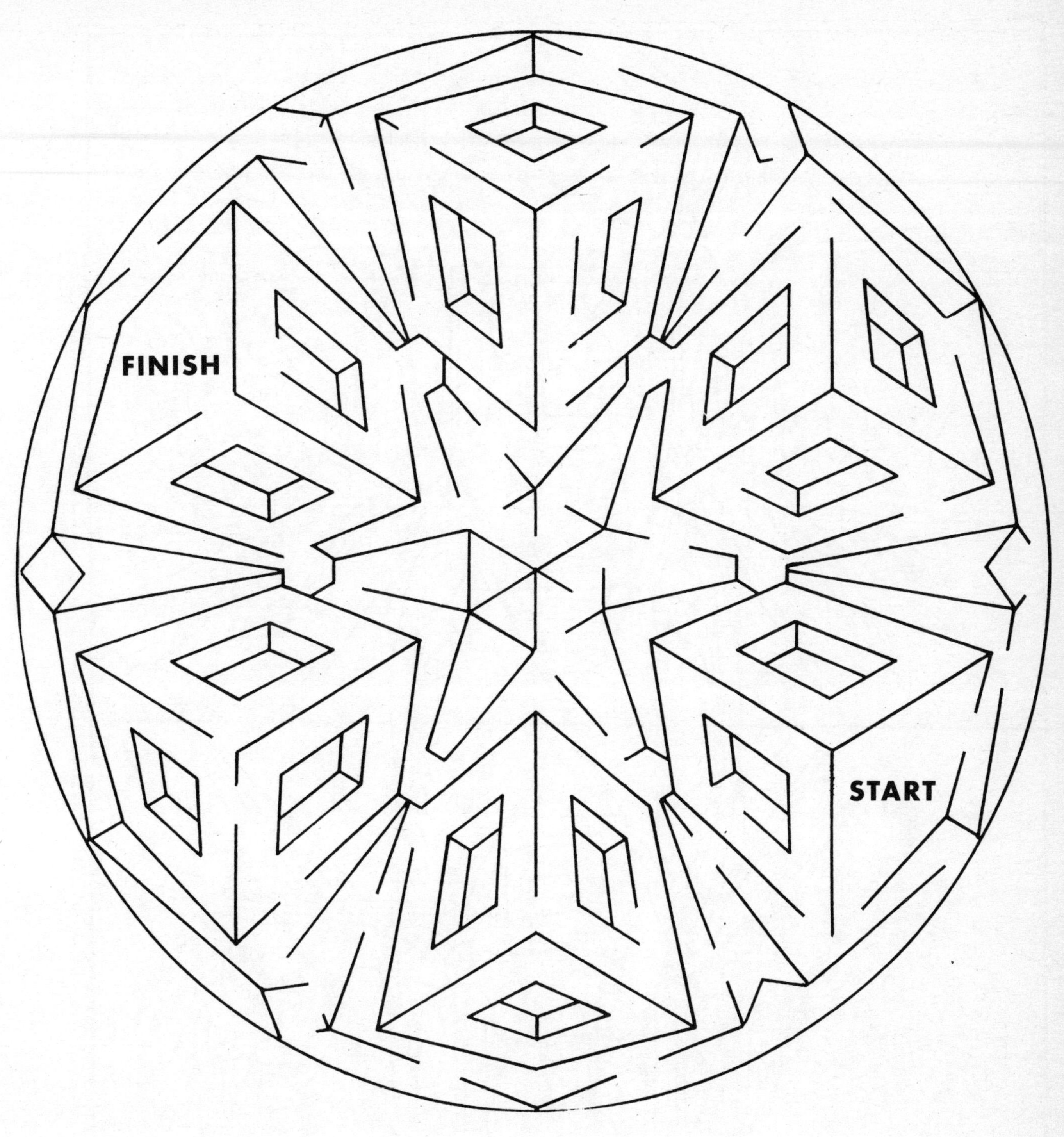
FINISH
START

FINISH
START

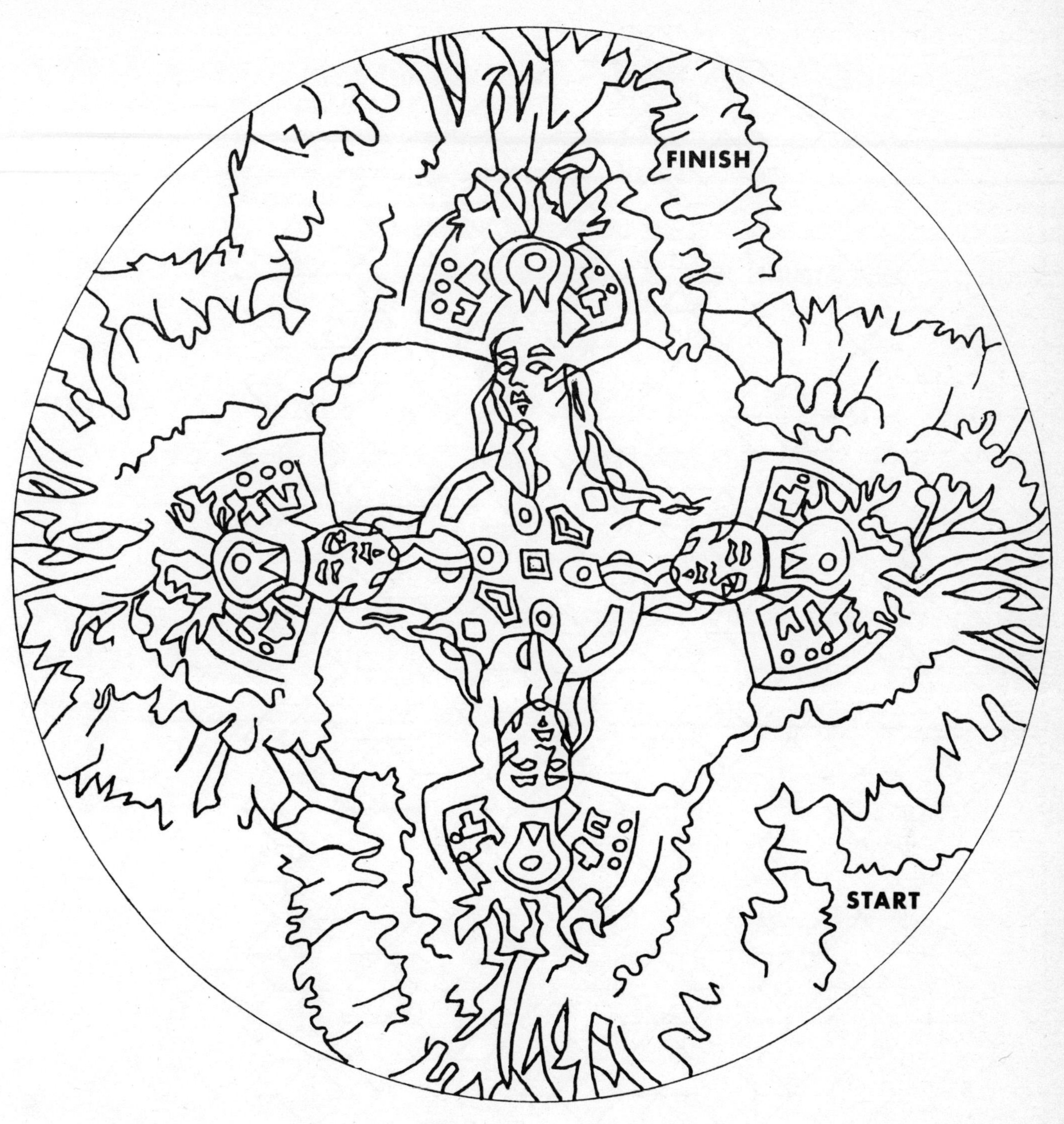
FINISH
START

FINISH
START

FINISH
START

FINISH
START

START
FINISH

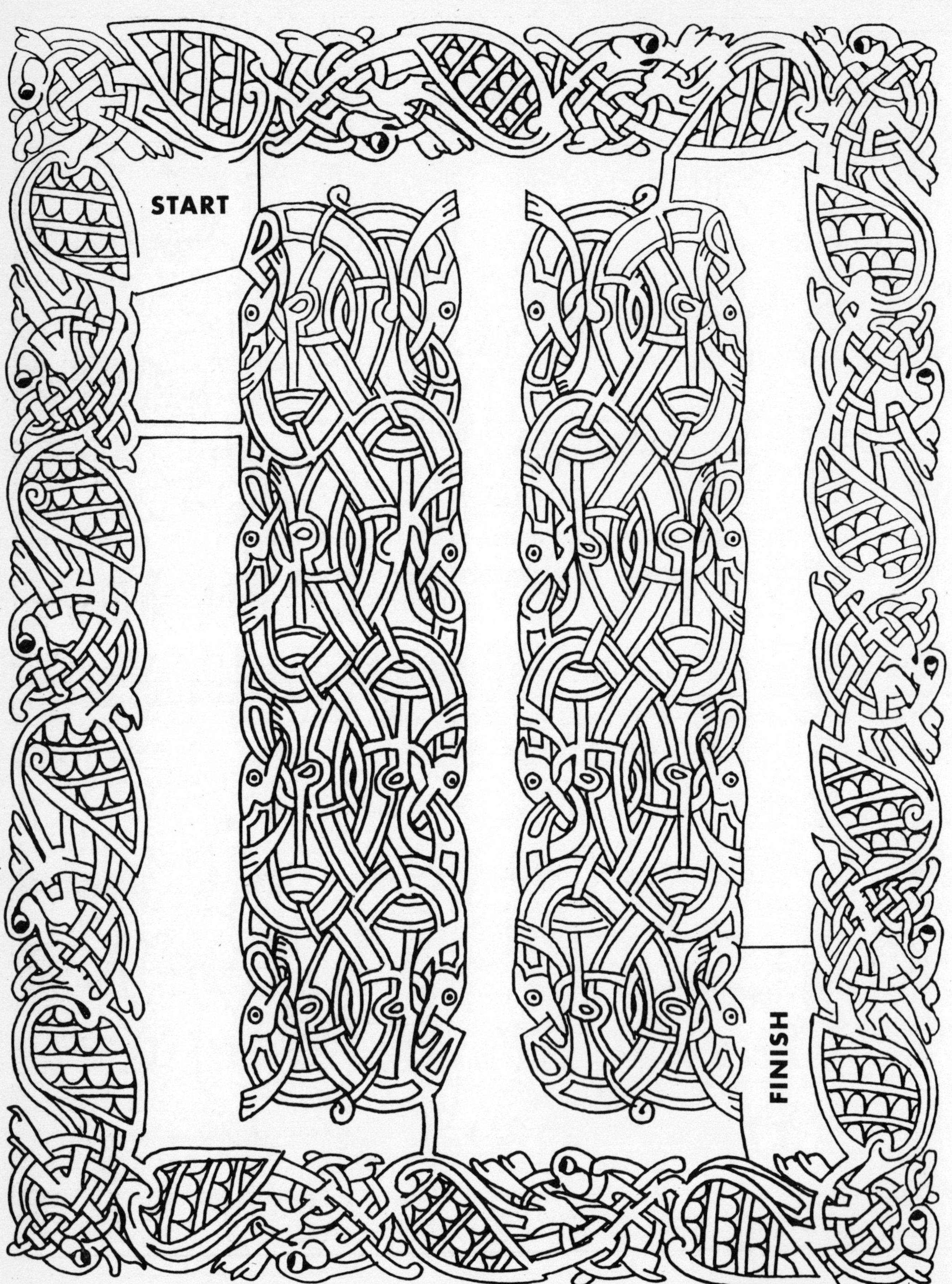
START
FINISH

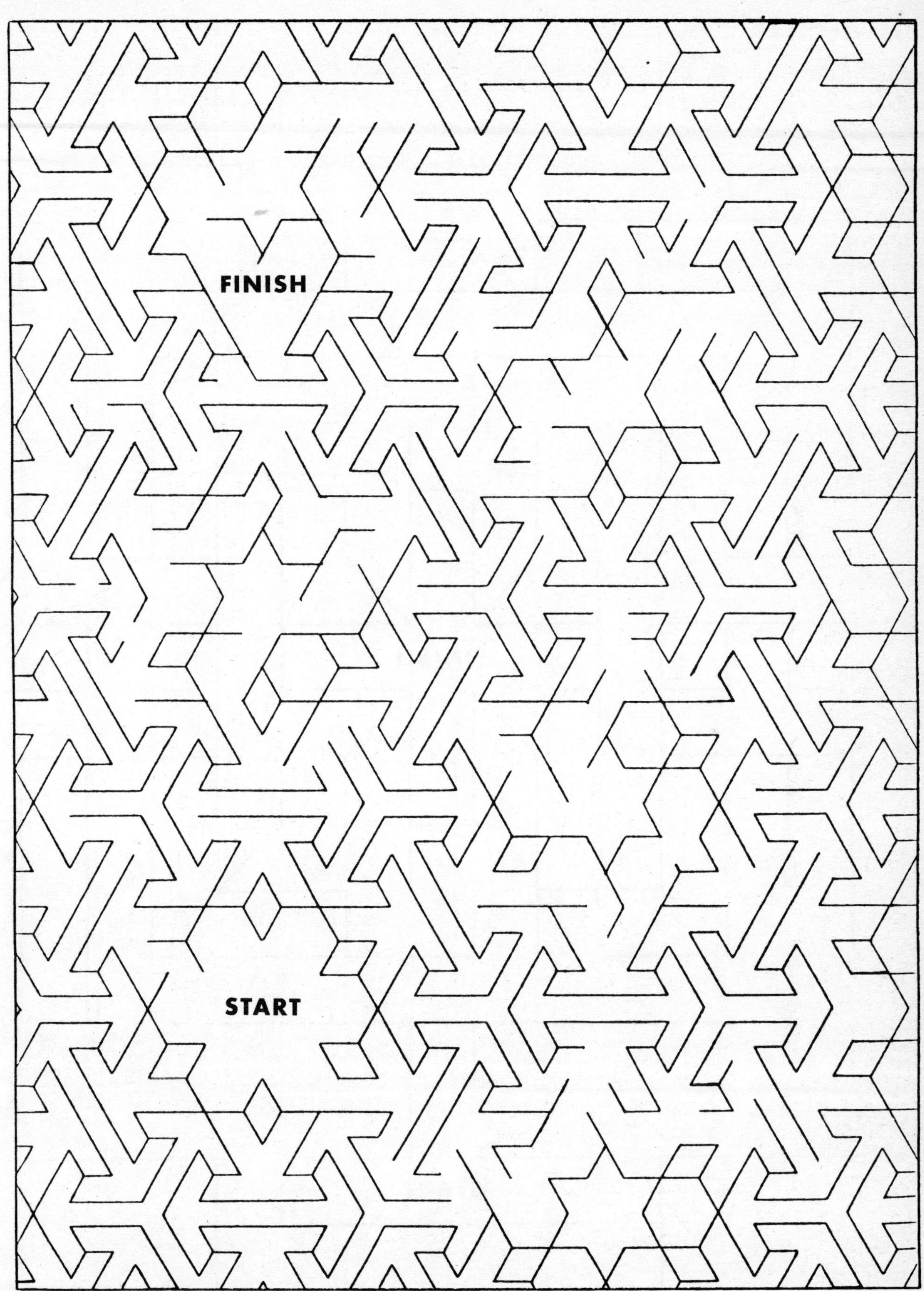
FINISH
START

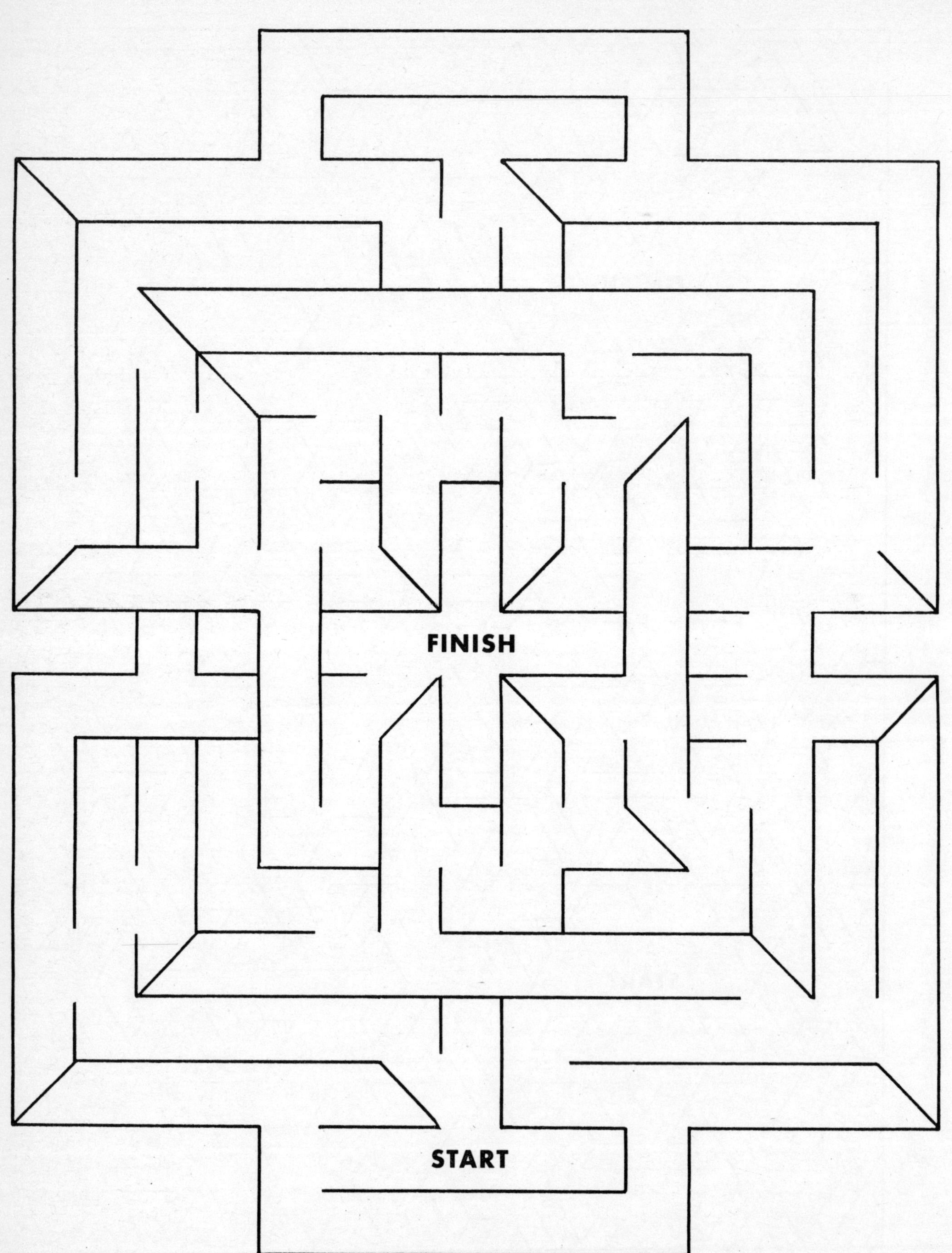
FINISH
START

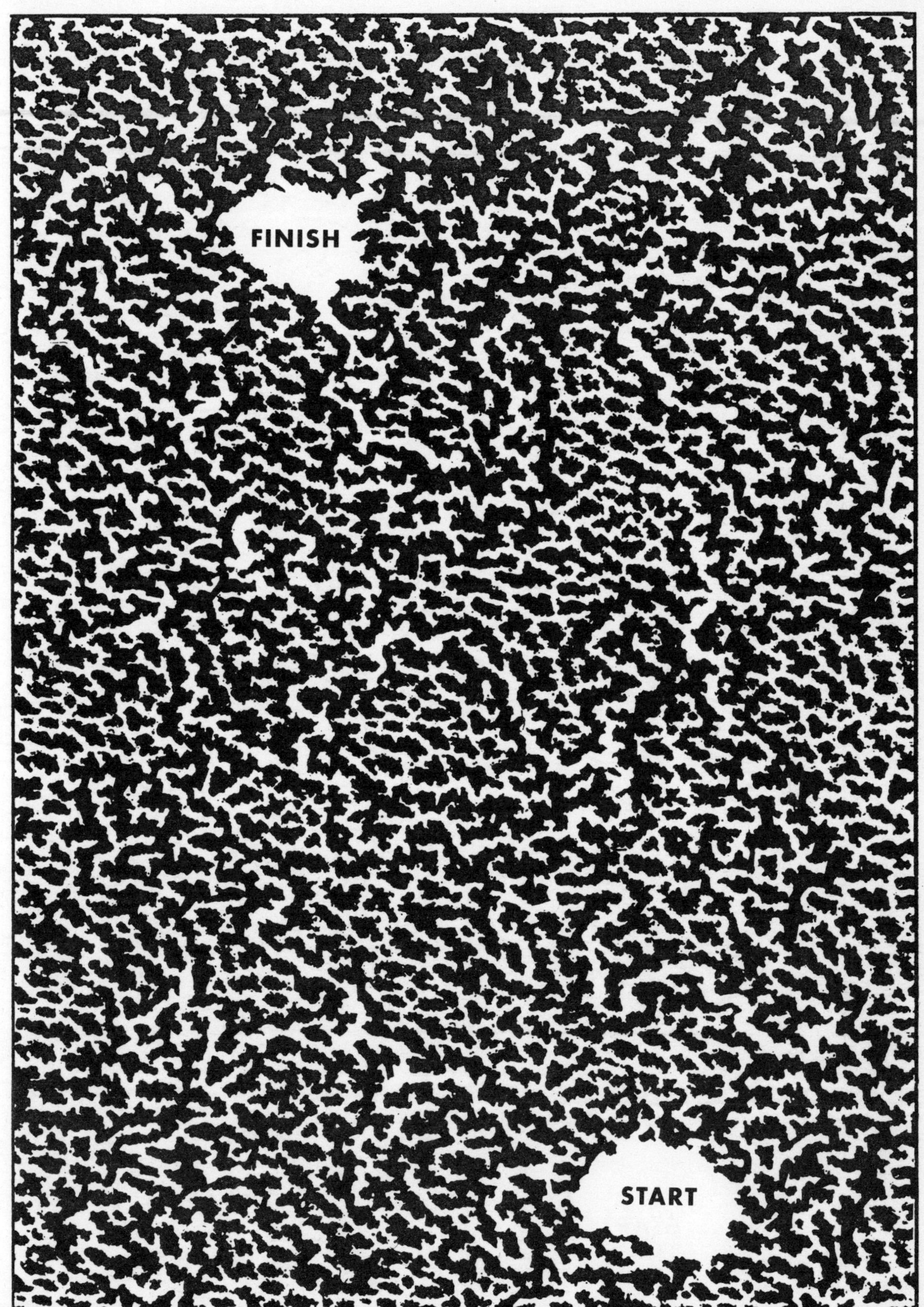
FINISH
START

START

FINISH

FINISH
START

SOLUTIONS

117

118/119

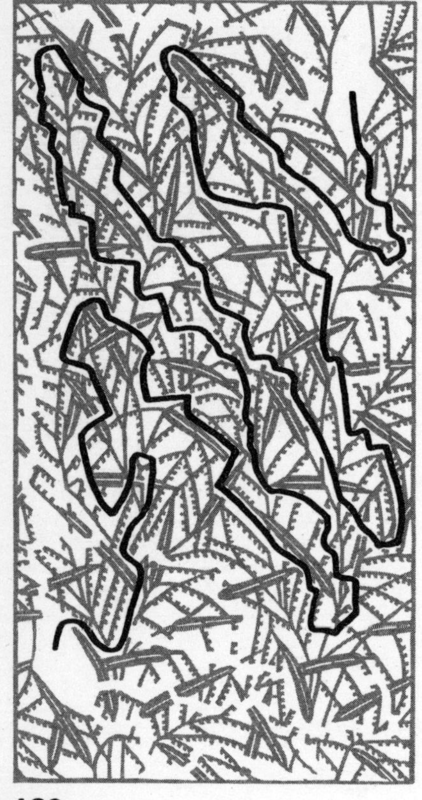
120

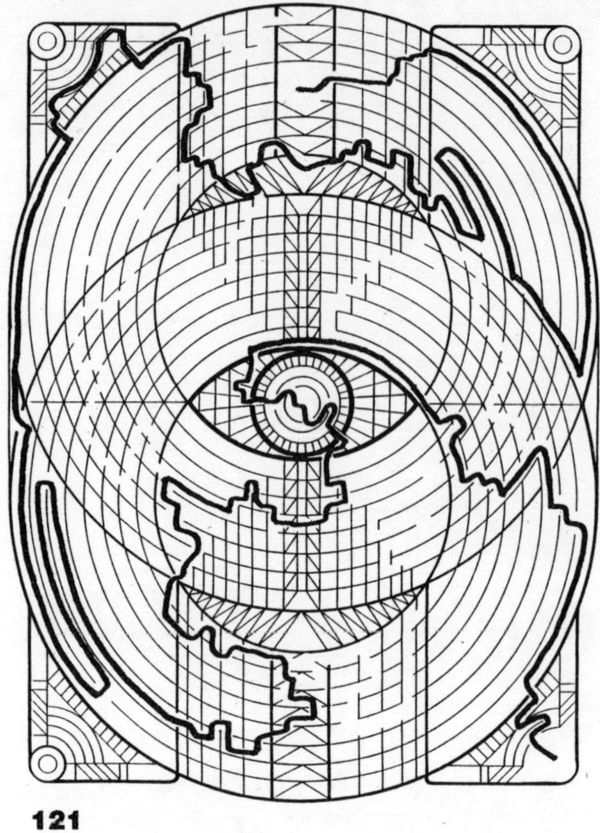
121

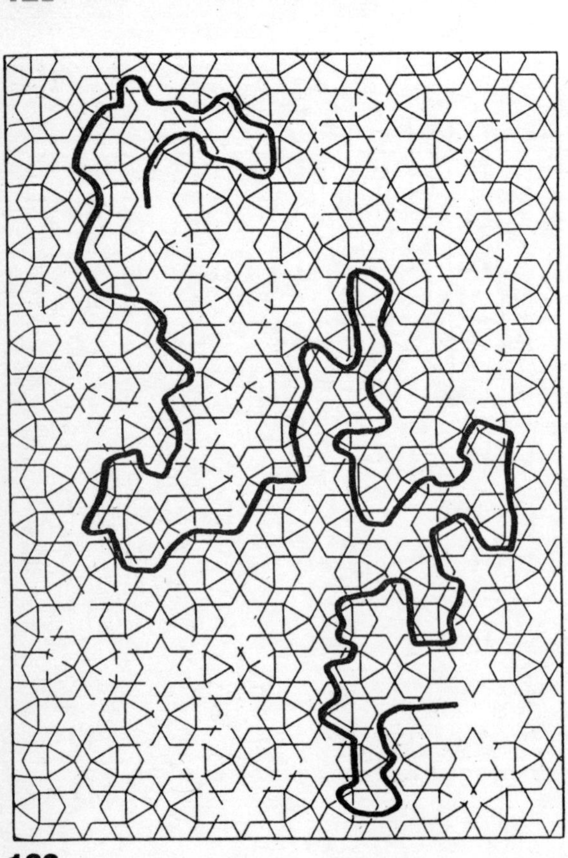
122

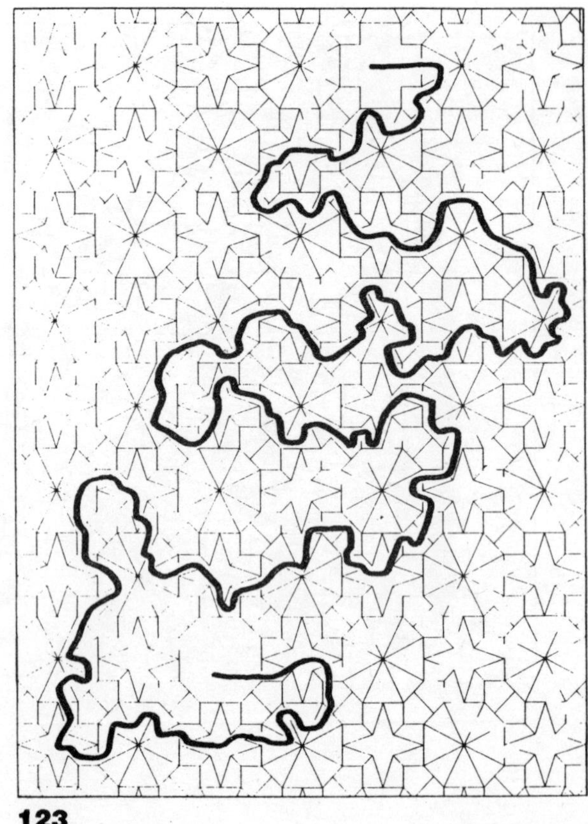
123

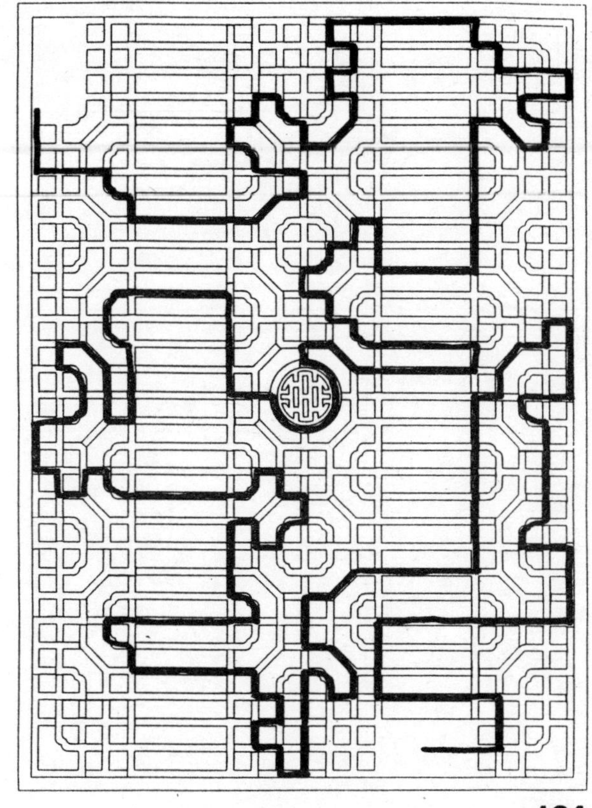

124

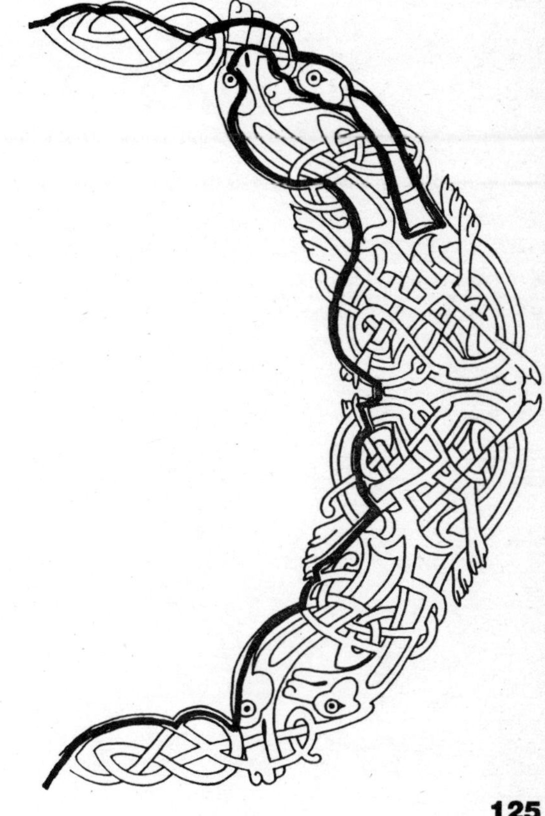

125

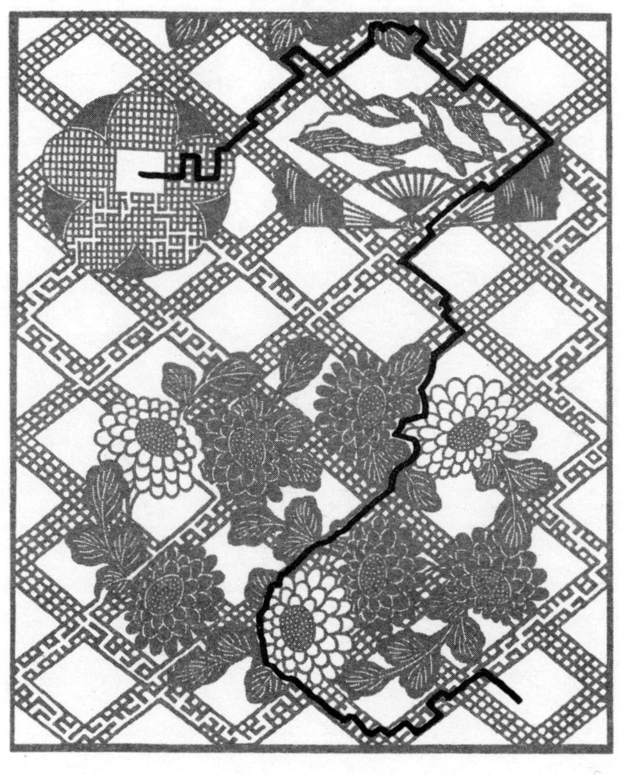

126

127

128

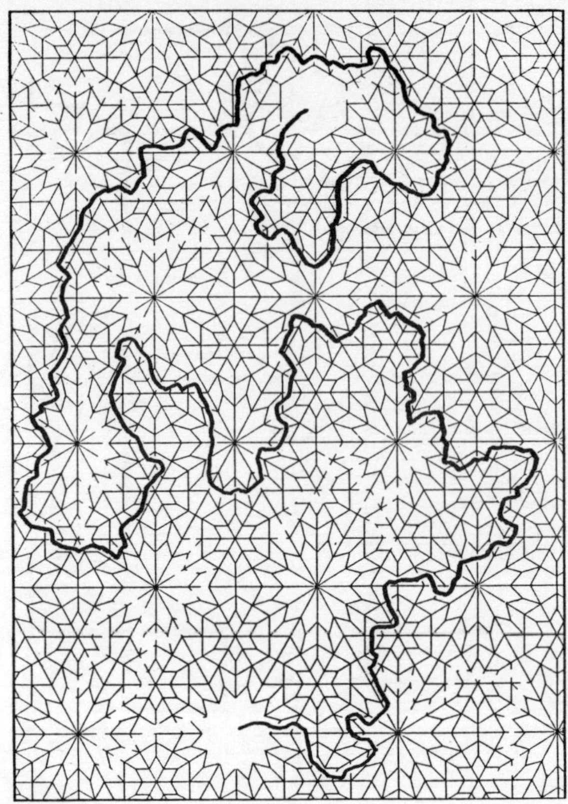

129

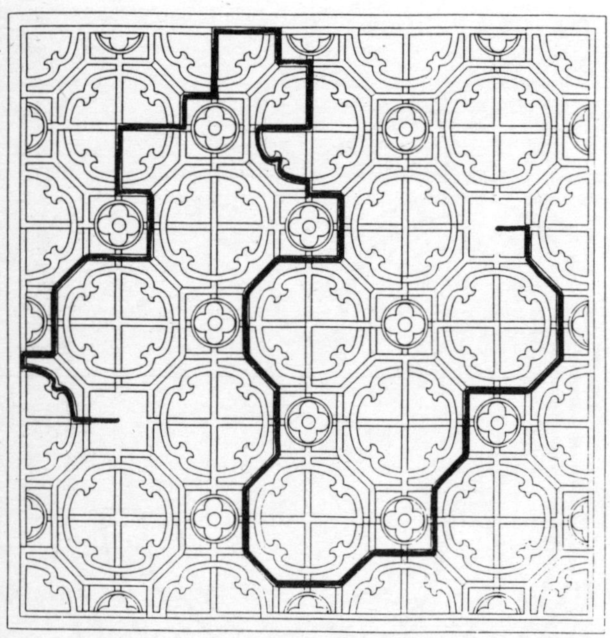

130

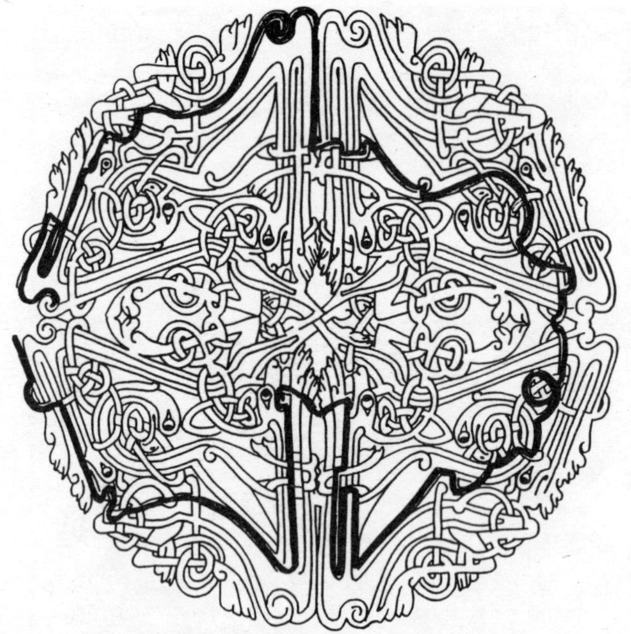

131

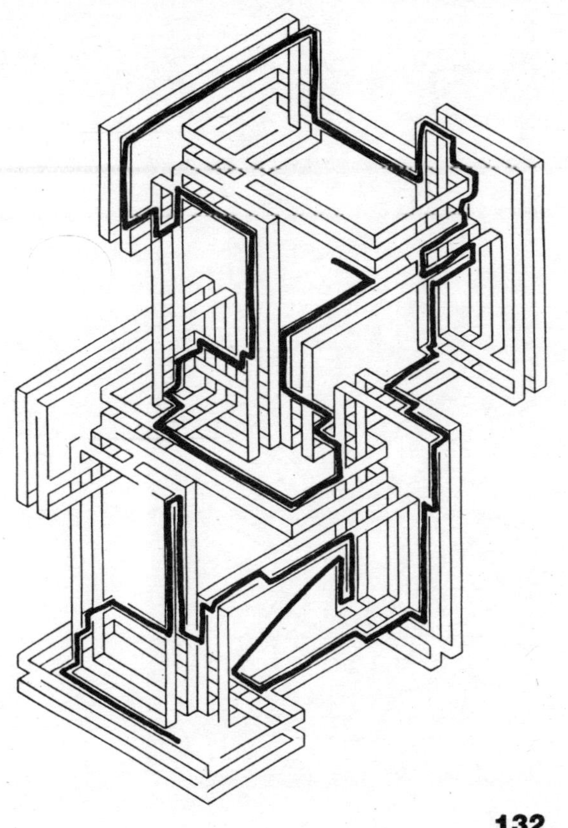

132

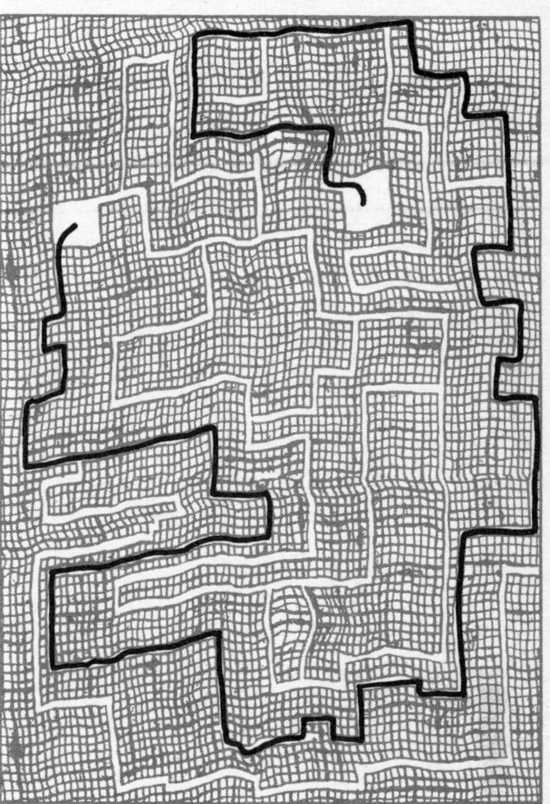

133

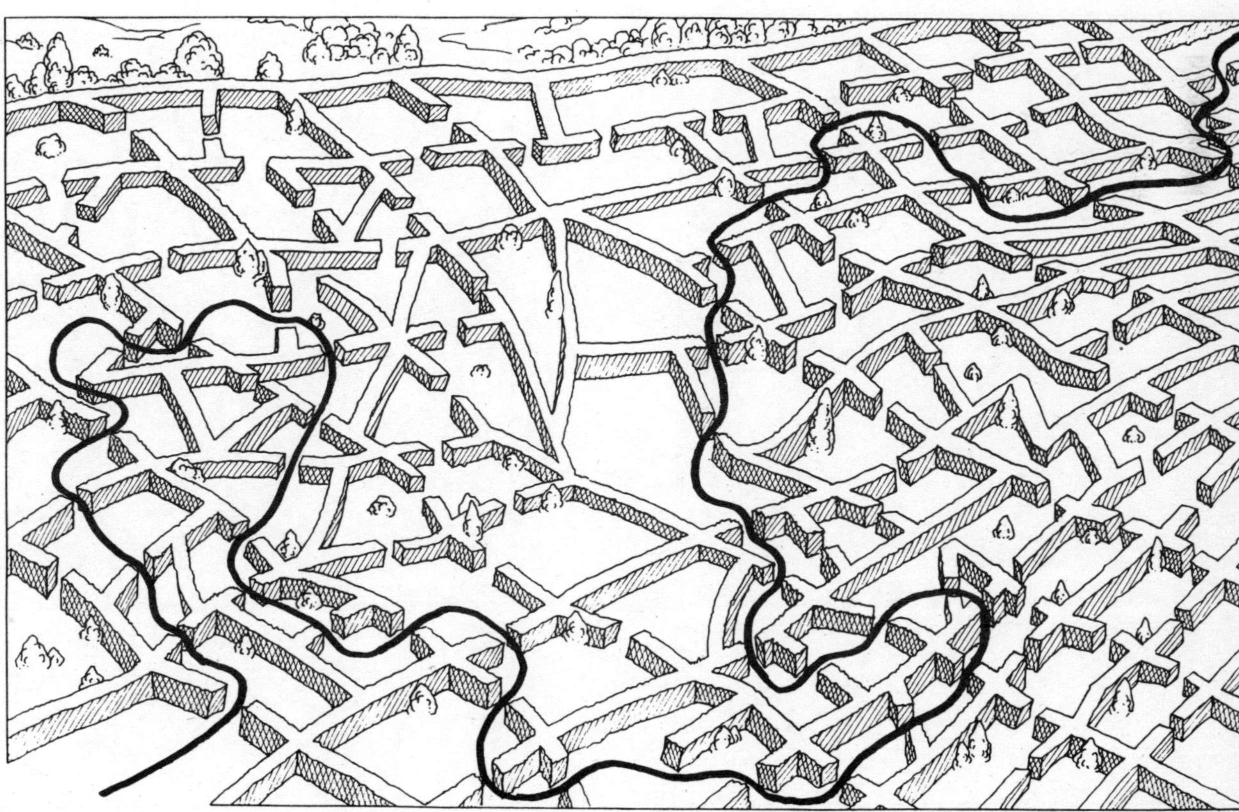

134/135

136

137

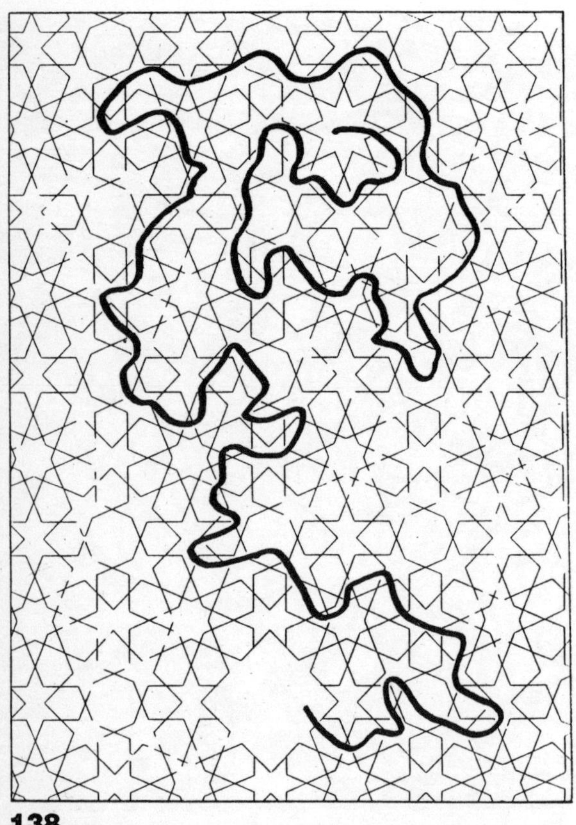

138

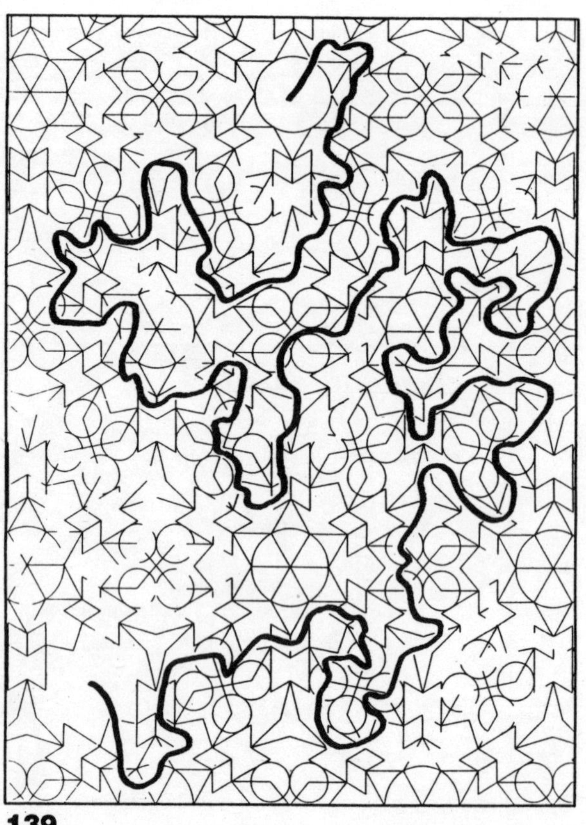

139

140

141

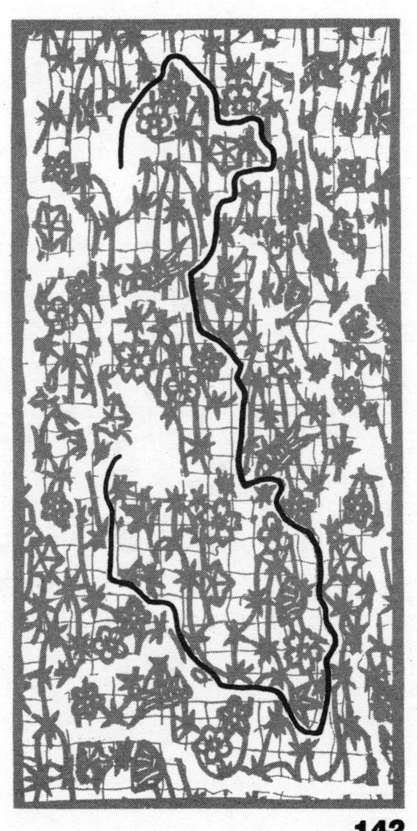
142

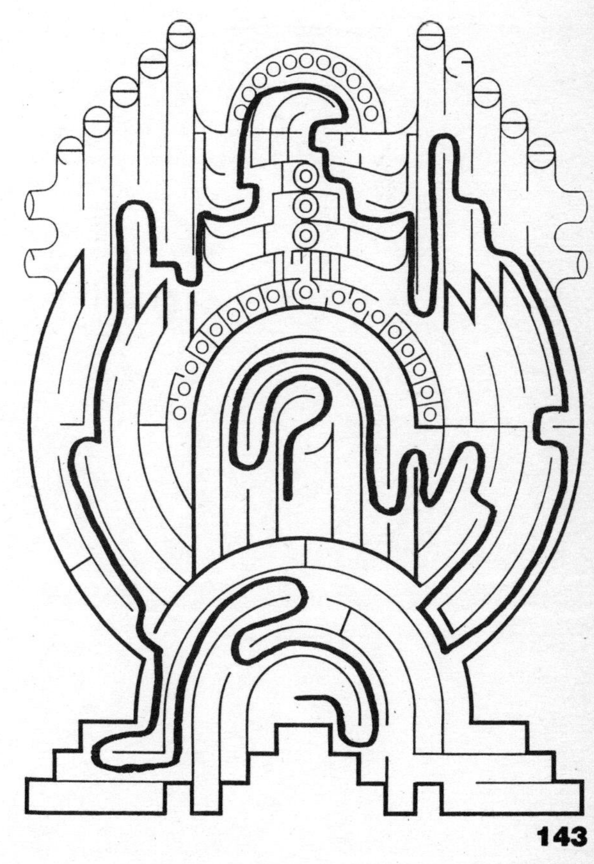
143

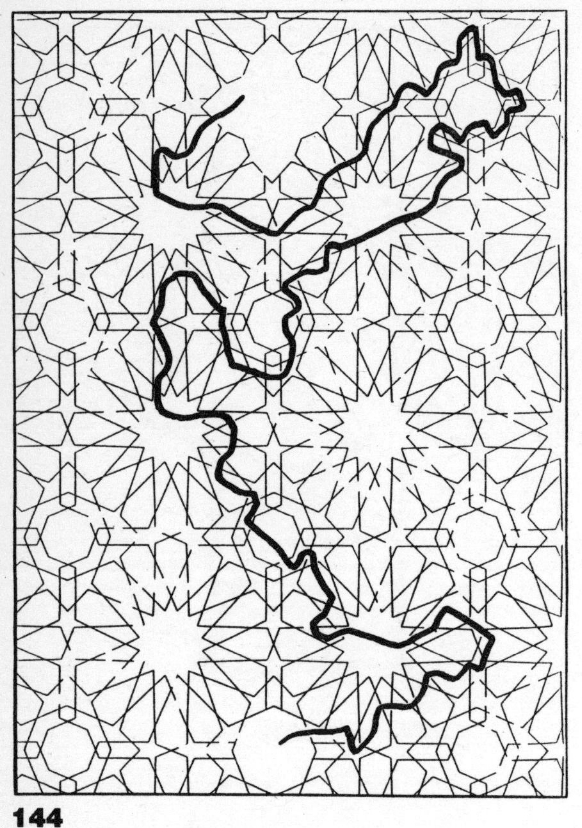

144

145

146

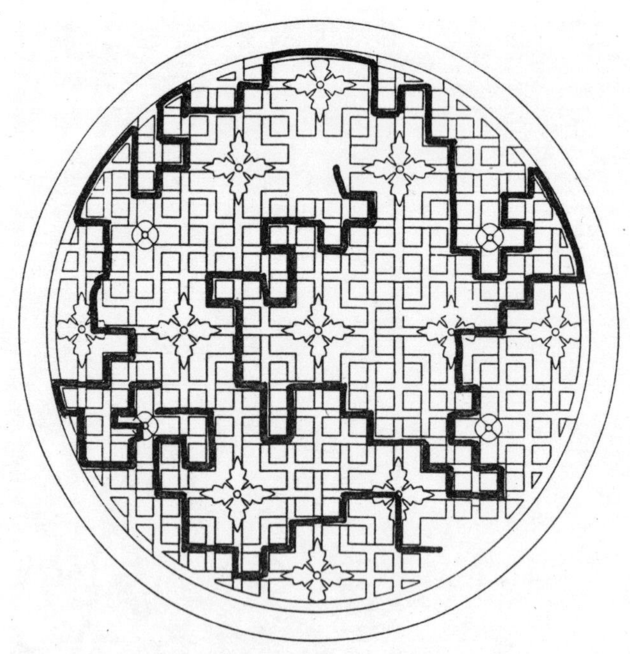

147

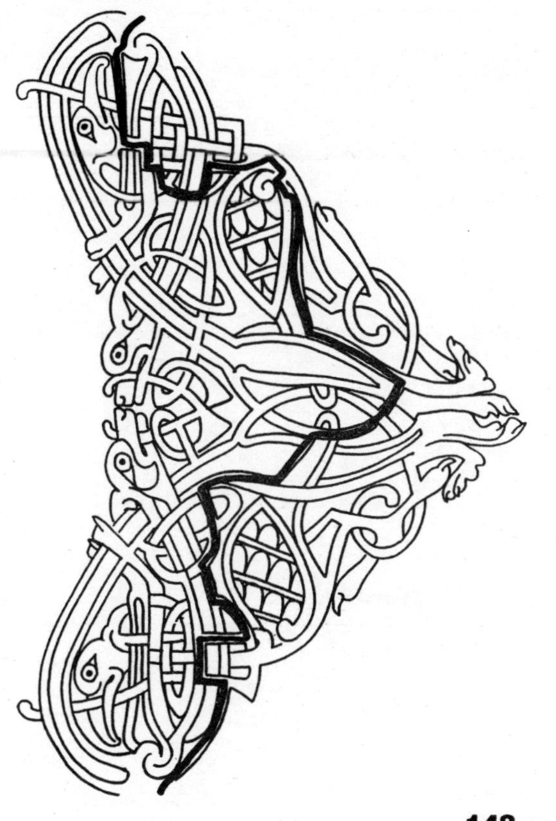

148

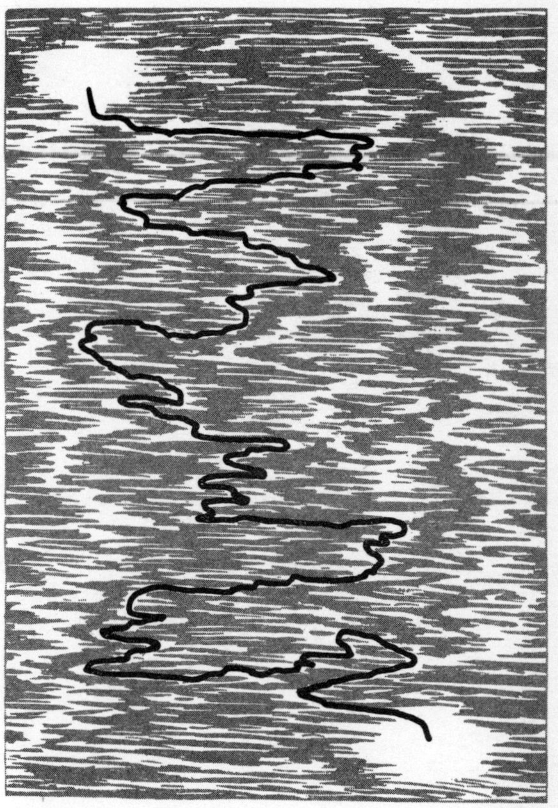

149

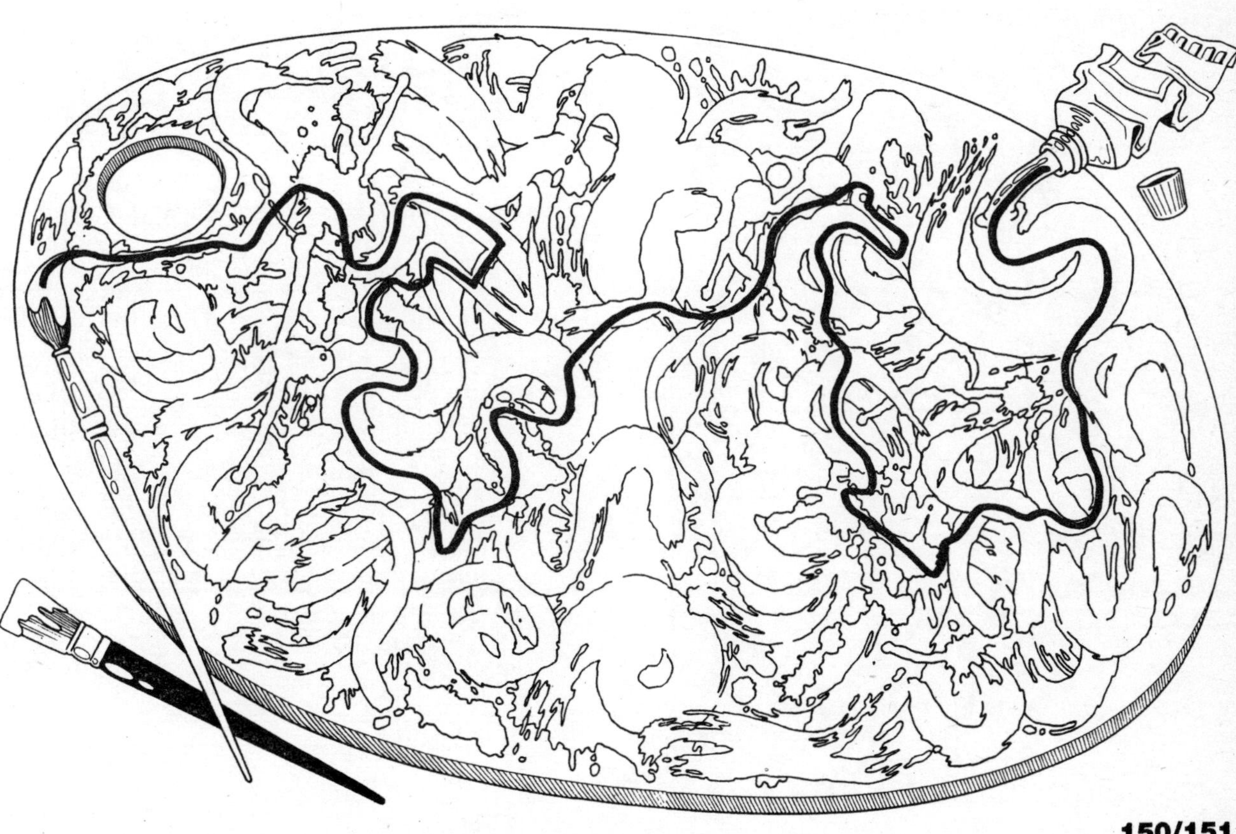

150/151

152

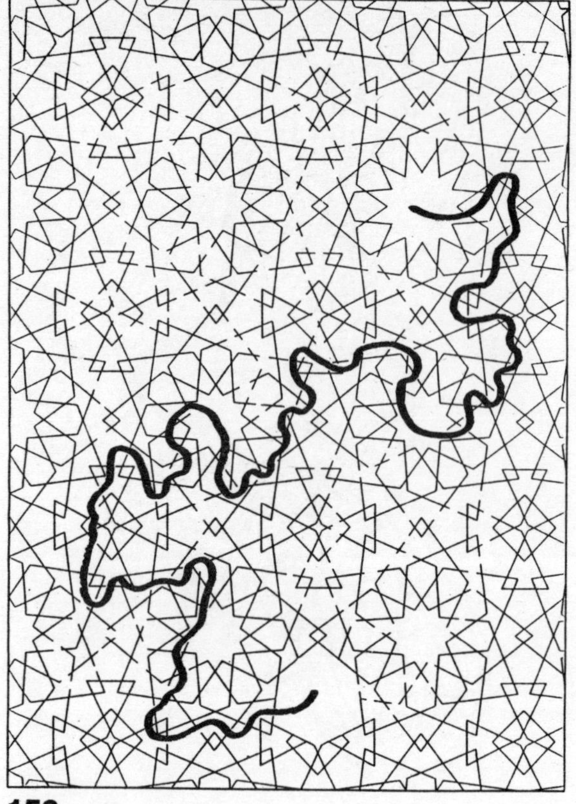
153

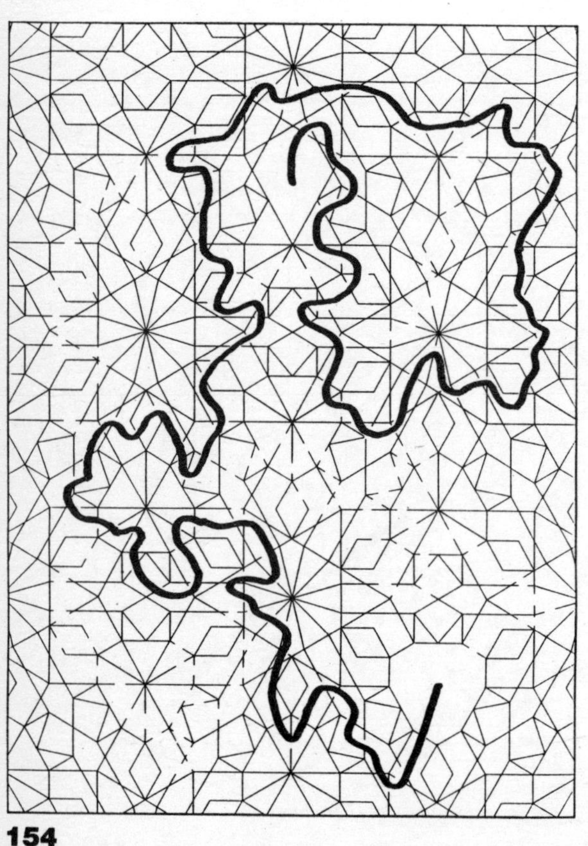
154

155

156

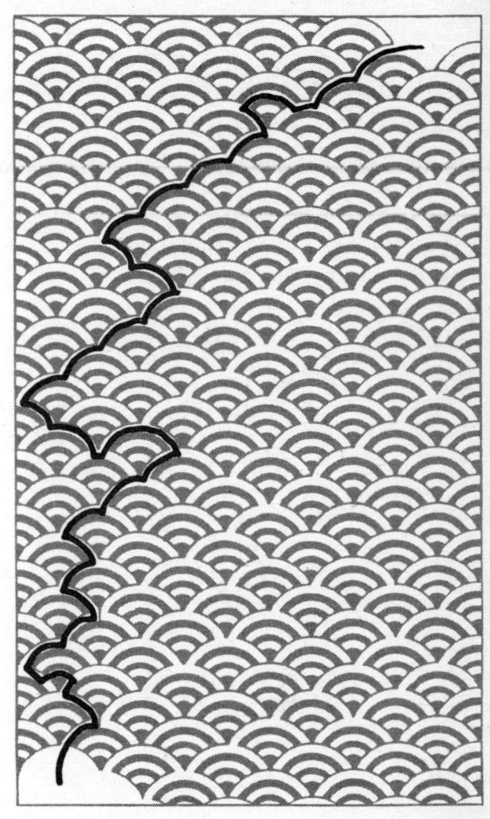
157

158

159

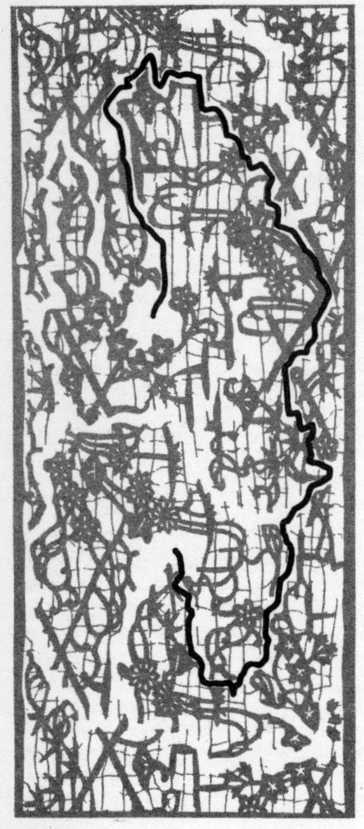

160

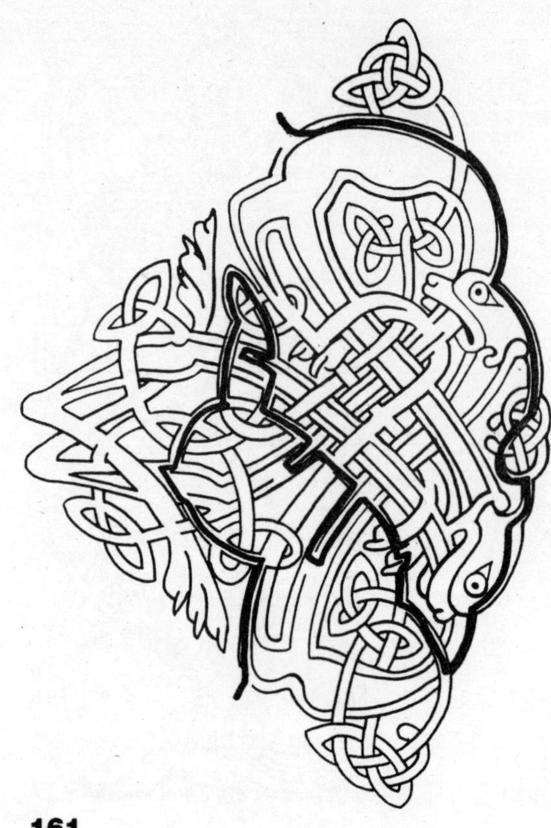

161

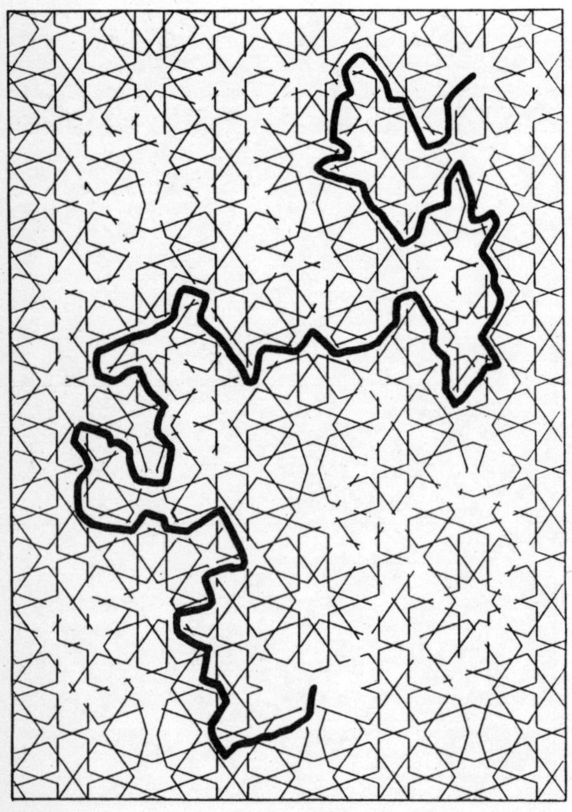

162

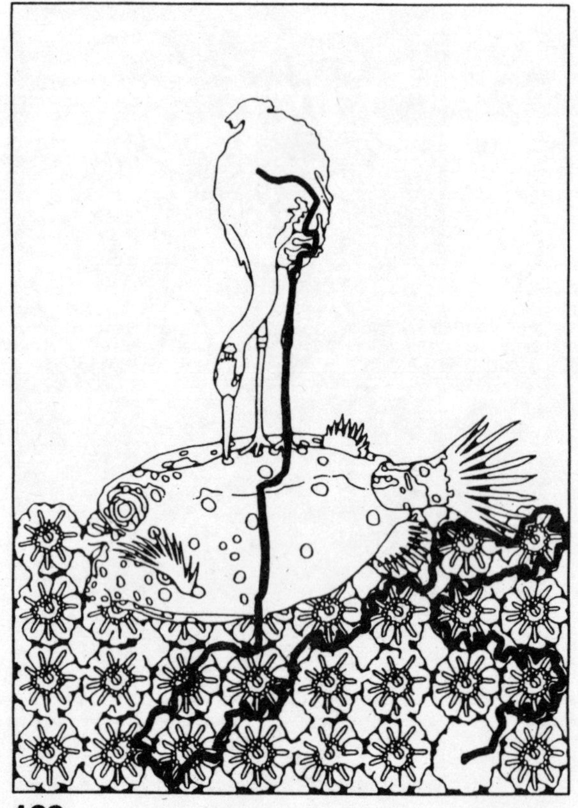

163

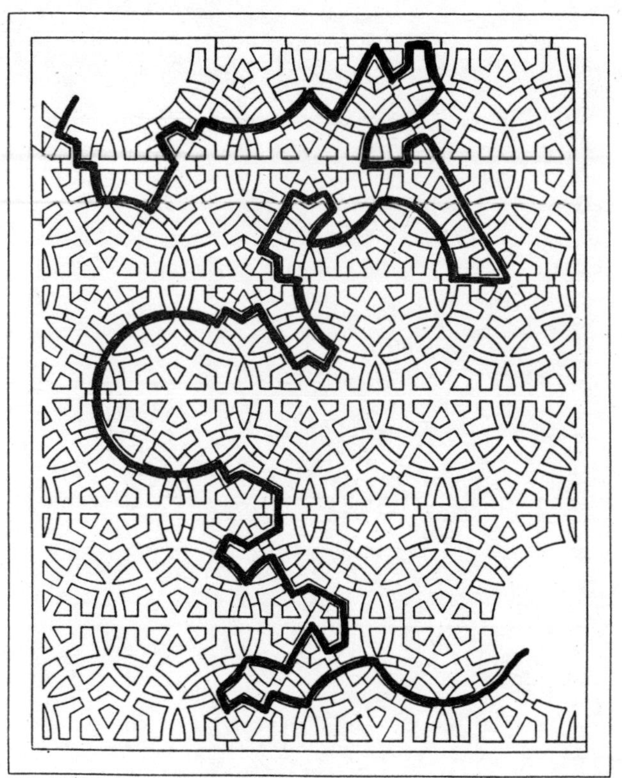

164

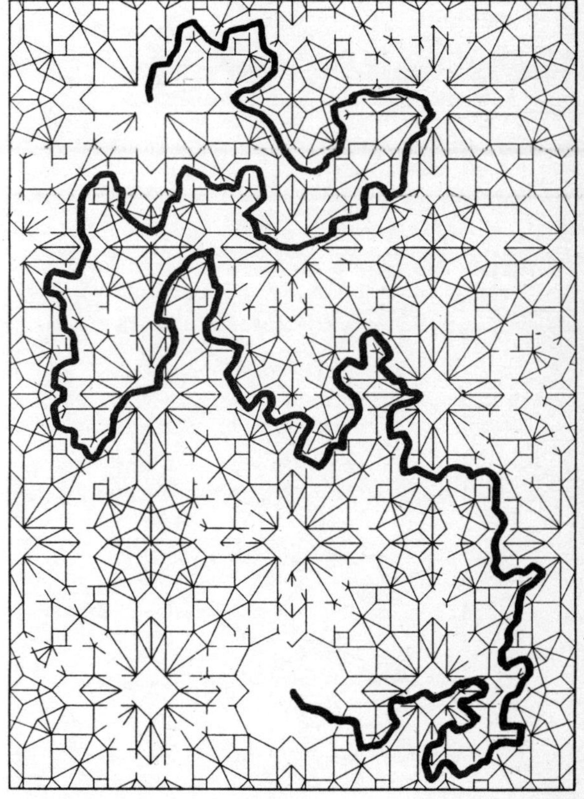

165

166/167

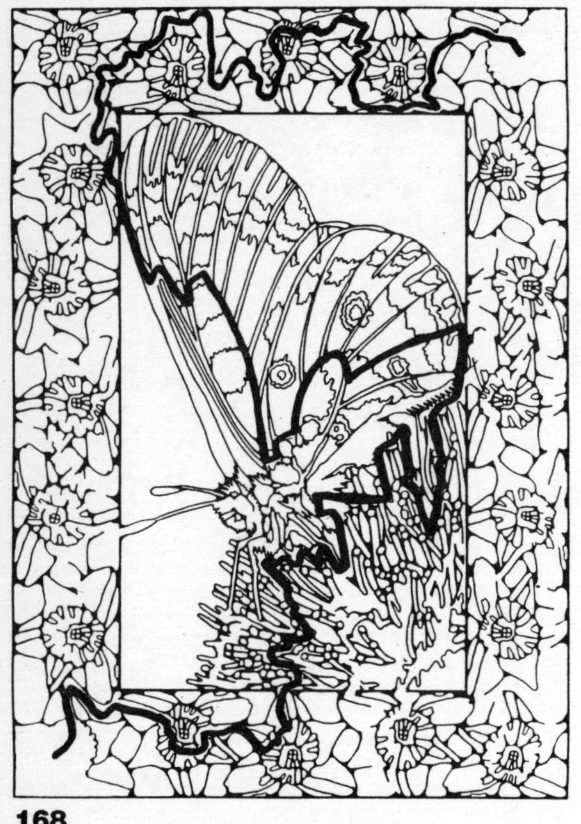

168

169

170

171

172

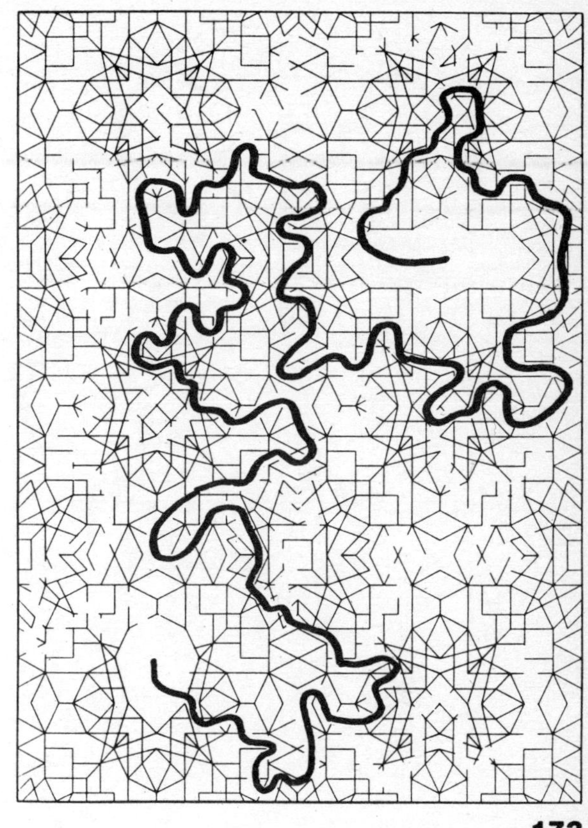

173

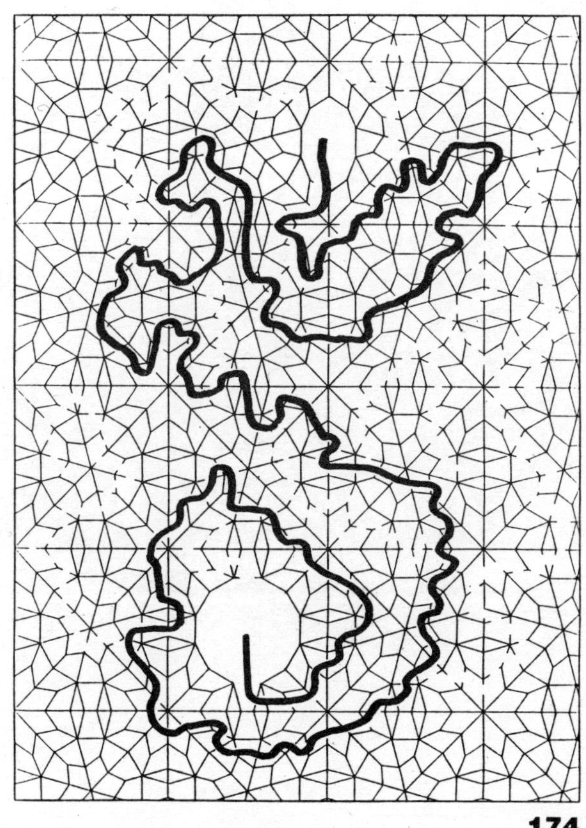

174

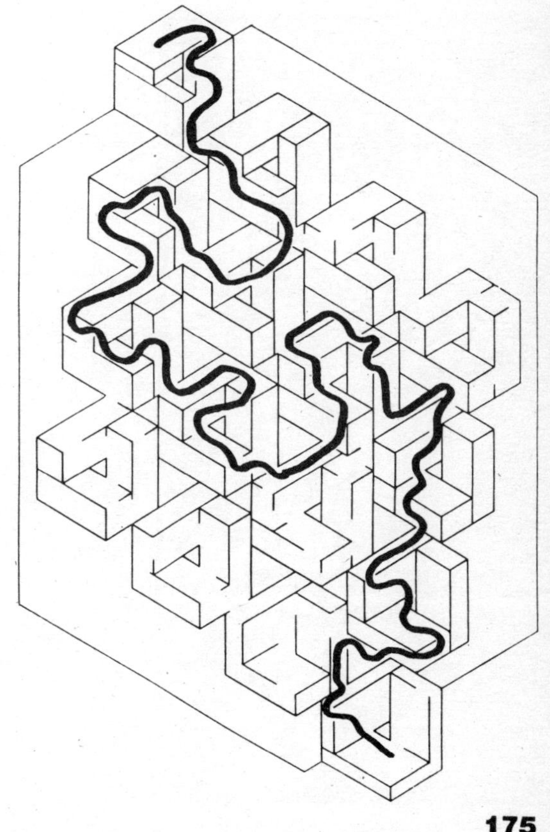

175

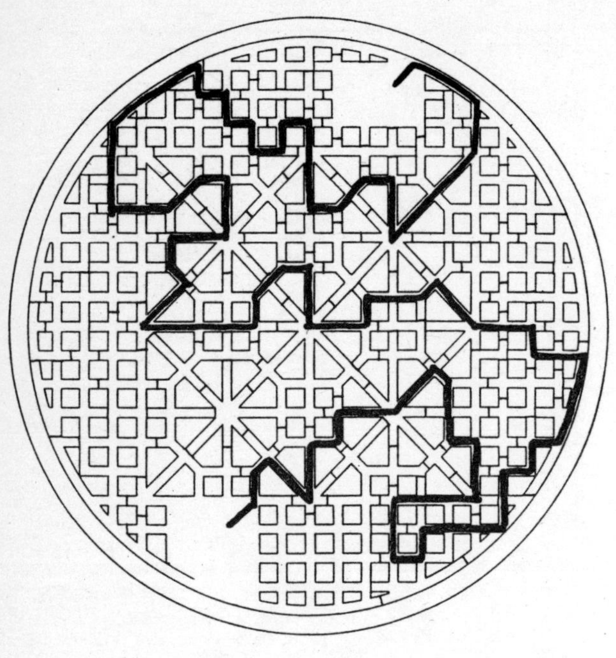

176

177

178

179

180

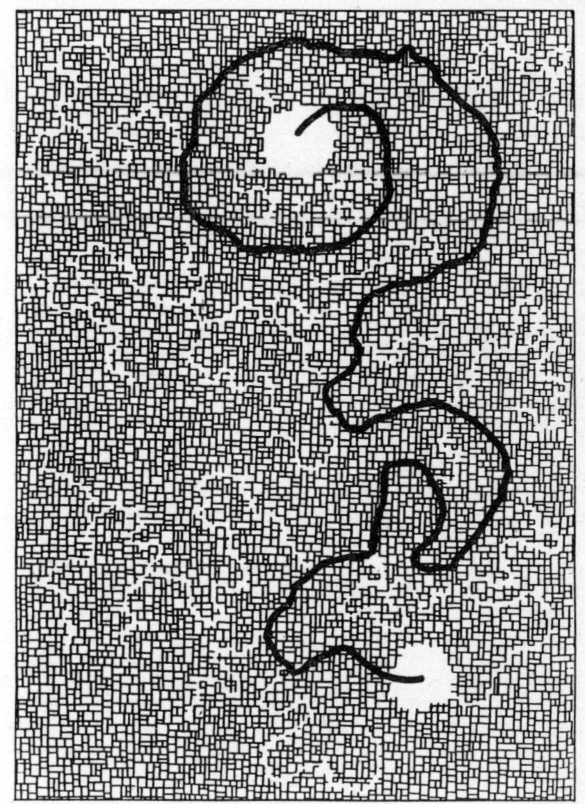

181

182/183

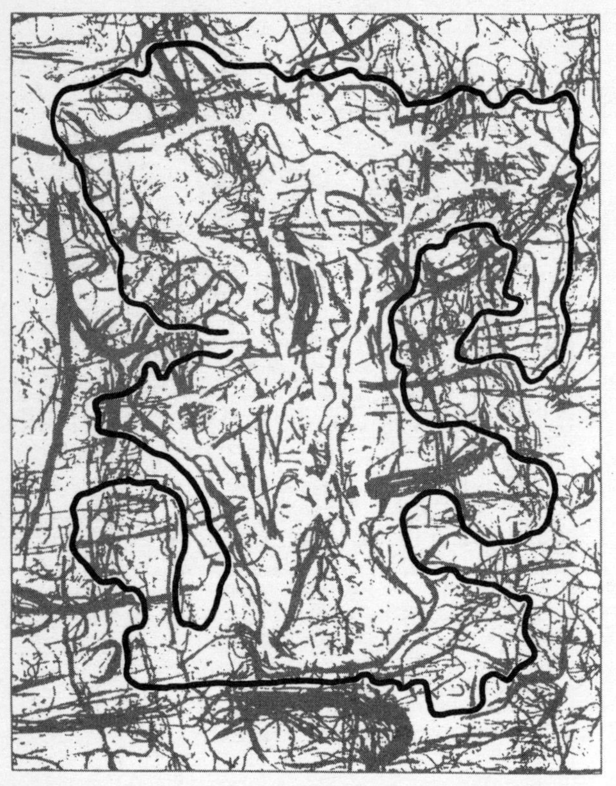

184

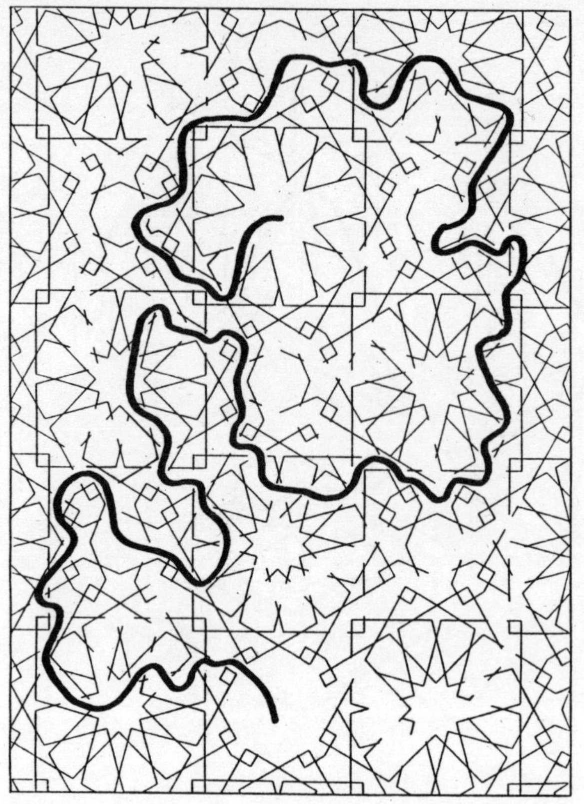

185

186

187

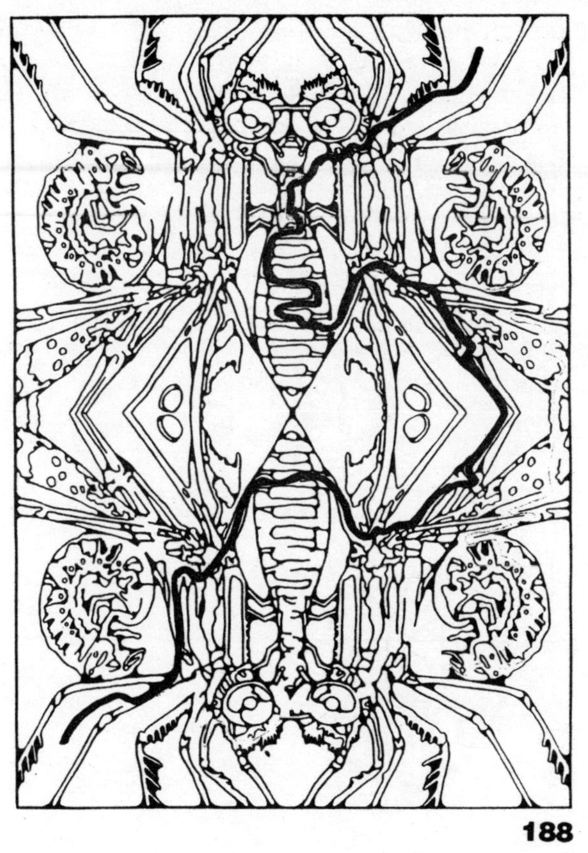

188

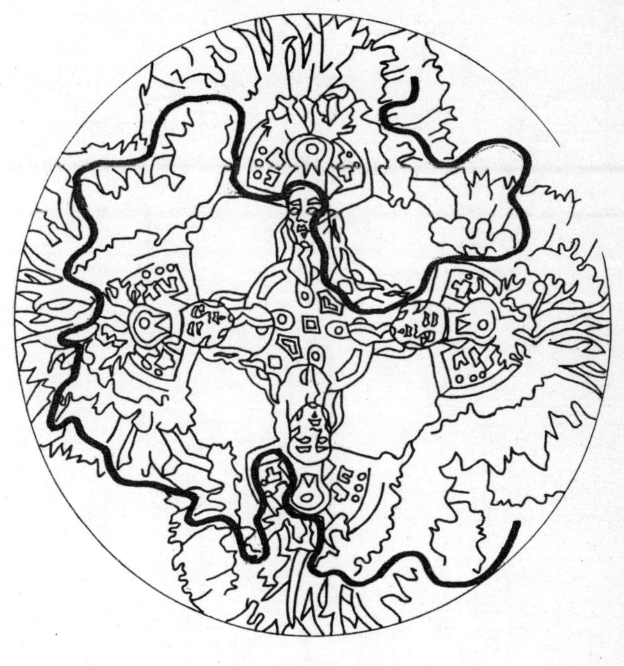

189

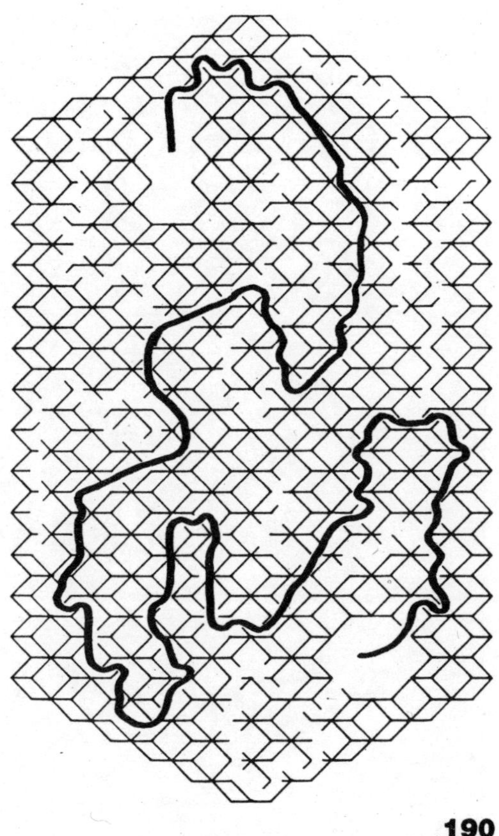

190

191

192

193

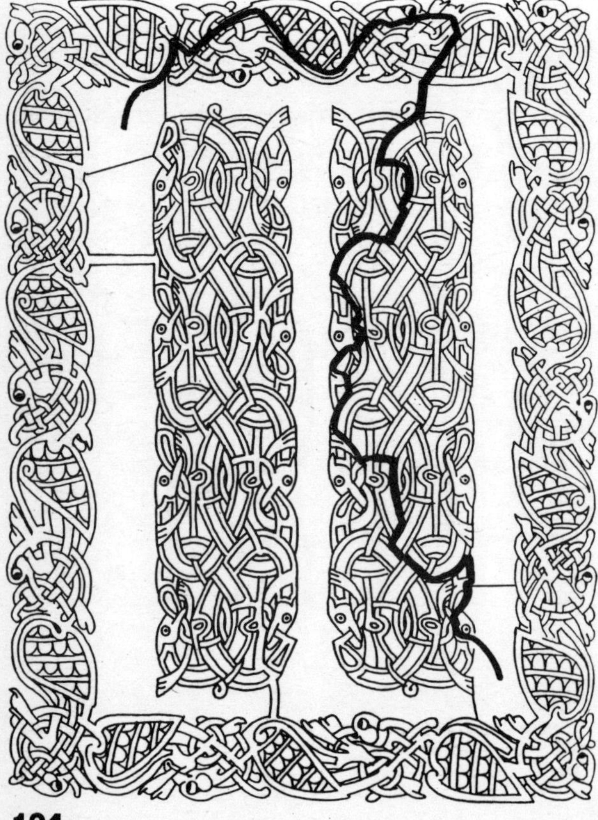
194

195

196

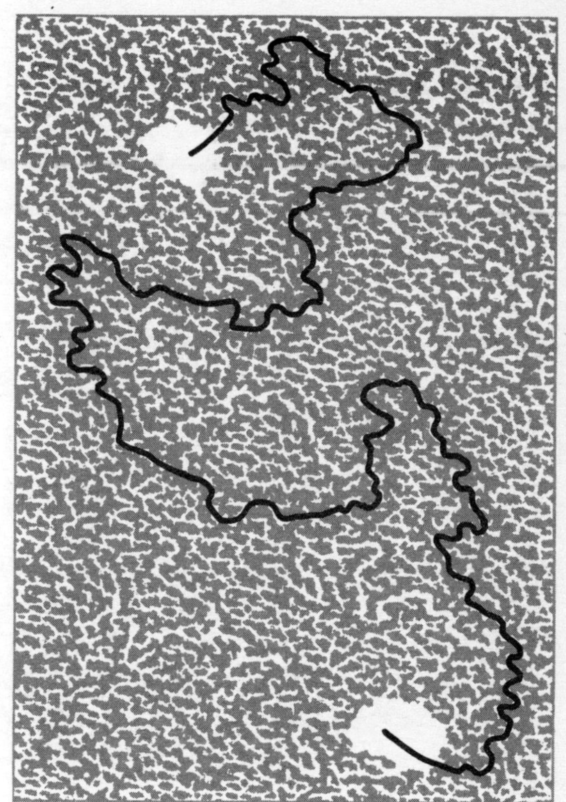

197

198/199

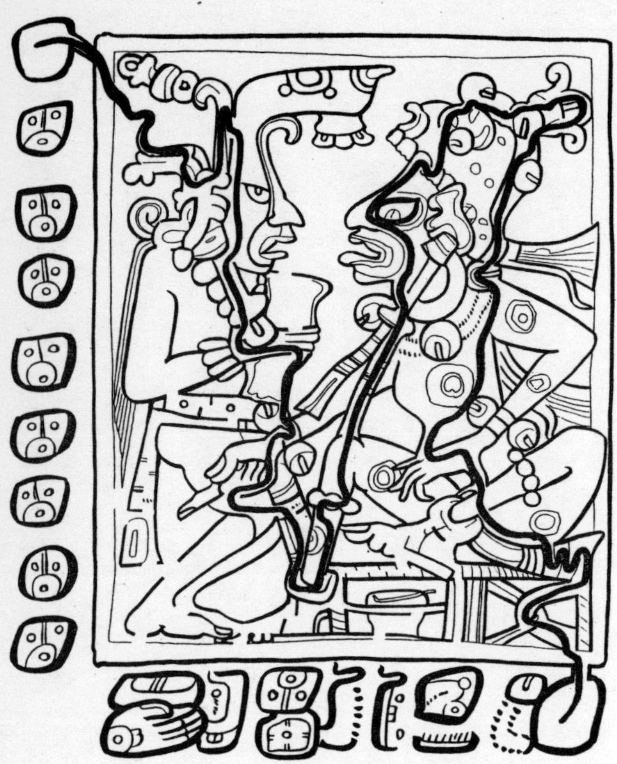

200

YOUR PUZZLE NOTES

Use these pages to jot down notes when working out your answers.